आ नो भद्राः क्रतवो यन्तु विश्वतः ।
Let noble thoughts come to us from every side
—**Rigveda, I-89-i**

BHAVAN'S BOOK UNIVERSITY

GW00759418

RAMAYANA

by

C. RAJAGOPALACHARI

BOOKS BY
C. RAJAGOPALACHARI
PUBLISHED BY THE BHAVAN

Ramayana

Mahabharata

Rajaji's Speeches Vol. I

Rajaji's Speeches Vol. II

Hinduism : Doctrine and Way of Life

Bhagavad Gita

Stories for the Innocent

Kural — The Great Book of Tiru-Valluvar

Upanishads

Our Culture

Bhaja Govindam

Gandhiji's Teachings & Philosophy

Avvaiar (The Great Tamil Poet)

Kathopanishad (Tamil)

Rescue Democracy From Money Power

Bhagavad Gita (Hindi)

Upanishads (Hindi-Cum-English Edition)

Bhajagovind (Kannada)

BHAVAN'S BOOK UNIVERSITY

RAMAYANA

C. RAJAGOPALACHARI

2009

BHARATIYA VIDYA BHAVAN
Kulapati K. M. Munshi Marg
Mumbai - 400 007

1st Edition	-	1951		25th Edition	-	1987
2nd Edition	-	1952		26th Edition	-	1989
3rd Edition	-	1953		27th Edition	-	1990
4th Edition	-	1955		28th Edition	-	1993
5th Edition	-	1958		29th Edition	-	1996
6th Edition	-	1958		30th Edition	-	1996
7th Edition	-	1962		31st Edition	-	1997
8th Edition	-	1966		32nd Edition	-	1997
9th Edition	-	1968		33rd Edition	-	1998
10th Edition	-	1970		34th Edition	-	1998
11th Edition	-	1972		35th Edition	-	1998
12th Edition	-	1973		36th Edition	-	1999
13th Edition	-	1974		37th Edition	-	1999
14th Edition	-	1975		38th Edition	-	1999
15th Edition	-	1975		39th Edition	-	2000
16th Edition	-	1977		40th Edition	-	2000
17th Edition	-	1977		41st Edition	-	2001
18th Edition	-	1978		42nd Edition	-	2005
19th Edition	-	1979		43rd Edition	-	2005
20th Edition	-	1980		44th Edition	-	2006
21st Edition	-	1982		45th Edition	-	2006
22nd Edition	-	1983		46th Edition	-	2007
23rd Edition	-	1985		47th Edition	-	2008
24th Edition	-	1986		48th Edition	-	2009

Price : Rs. 100/-

PRINTED IN INDIA

By Atul Goradia at Siddhi Printers, 13/14, Bhabha Building,
13th Khetwadi Lane, Mumbai - 400 004, and
Published by P. V. Sankarankutty Additional Registrar,
for the Bharatiya Vidya Bhavan,
Kulapati Munshi Marg, Mumbai - 400 007.
E-Mail : bhavan@bhavans.info
Web-site : www.bhavans.info

KULAPATI'S PREFACE

THE Bharatiya Vidya Bhavan—that Institute of Indian Culture in Bombay—needed a Book University, a series of books which, if read, would serve the purpose of providing higher education. Particular emphasis, however, was to be put on such literature as revealed the deeper impulsions of India. As a first step, it was decided to bring out in English 100 books, 50 of which were to be taken in hand almost at once. Each book was to contain from 200 to 250 pages.

It is our intention to publish the books we select, not only in English, but also in the following Indian languages: Hindi, Bengali, Gujarati, Marathi, Tamil, Telugu, Kannada and Malayalam.

This scheme, involving the publication of 900 volumes, requires ample funds and an all-India organisation. The Bhavan is exerting its utmost to supply them.

The objectives for which the Bhavan stands are the reintegration of the Indian culture in the light of modern knowledge and to suit our present-day needs and the resuscitation of its fundamental values in their pristine vigour.

Let me make our goal more explicit:

We seek the dignity of man, which necessarily implies the creation of social conditions which would allow him freedom to evolve along the lines of his own temperament and capacities; we seek the harmony of individual efforts and social relations, not in any makeshift way, but within the frame-work of the Moral Order; we seek the creative art of life, by the alchemy of which human limitations are progressively transmuted, so that man may become the instrument of God and is able to see Him in all and all in Him.

The world, we feel, is too much with us. Nothing would uplift or inspire us so much as the beauty and aspiration which such books can teach. In this series, therefore, the literature of India, ancient and modern, will be published in a form easily accessible to all. Books in other literatures of the world, if they illustrate the principles we stand for, will also be included.

This common pool of literature, it is hoped, will enable the reader, eastern or western, understand and appreciate currents of world thought, as also the movements of the mind in India, which, though they flow through different linguistic channels, have a common urge and aspiration.

Fittingly, the Book University's first venture is the *Mahabharata,* summarised by one of the greatest living Indians. C. Rajagopalachari; the second work is on a section of it, the *Gita*, by H.V. Divatia, an eminent jurist and student of philosophy. Centuries ago, it was proclaimed of the *Mahabharata:* "What is not in it, is nowhere." After twenty-five centuries, we can use the same words about it. He who knows it not, knows not the heights and depths of the soul; he misses the trials and tragedy and the beauty and grandeur of life.

The *Mahabharata* is not a mere epic; it is a romance, telling the tale of heroic men and women, and of some who were divine; it is a whole literature in itself, containing a code of life, a philosophy of social and ethical relations, and speculative thought on human problems that is hard to rival; but, above all, it has for its core the *Gita*, which is, as the world is beginning to find out, the noblest of scriptures and the grandest of sagas in which the climax is reached in the wondrous apocalypse in the Eleventh Canto.

Through such books alone the harmonies underlying true culture, I am convinced, will one day reconcile the disorders of modern life.

I thank all those who have helped to make this new branch of the Bhavan's activity successful.

1, QUEEN VICTORIA ROAD,
NEW DELHI
3rd October, 1951.

KULAPATI'S SUPPLEMENTARY PREFACE

THE publication of *Ramayana*, as summarised by Shri C. Rajagopalachari, is a landmark in the progress of Book University.

During the last five years that the Book University volumes have been in the market, they have commanded an increasingly large audience. Some of the books have in the main revolved round the objects of the Bhavan as stated in my original Preface and have drawn their inspiration from the two immortal epics of India. Nothing more inspiring has been written by man than the *Mahabharata* and the *Ramayana,* which are the Collective Unconscious of India and contain her message to man.

We began the Series with the *Mahabharata* summarised by Shri C. Rajagopalachari. Today, we have the privilege of publishing the *Ramayana* as summarised by him in this Series. Though the works of distinguished authors dealing with this epic have appeared in this Series, Rajaji's work, as always, is striking in its originality and beautiful in expression.

RAJ BHAVAN
NAINITAL   K.M. MUNSHI
12th May, 1957.

AUTHOR'S PREFACE

THE Bharatiya Vidya Bhavan has added to the debt of gratitude I owe it by undertaking the publication of the English version of my Tamil *Ramayana*. They achieved great success in the distribution of my *Mahabharata* book and I trust this book of the story of Rama and Sita will receive similar welcome.

I wrote the Tamil original of this book in a series of weekly chapters in KALKI, in writing which I was greatly encouraged by the warm reception they received in the homes of the Tamil people all over the country. This book is based on the series that appeared contemporaneously in the SUNDAY STANDARD for which Sri Ramnath Goenka of the 'Express' papers was responsible. My friend Sri Navaratna Rama Rao has thoroughly revised the English rendering and if it is found to be good reading it is due to his affectionate labour on this book. The faults such as may be noticed are entirely mine. If readers find pathos and beauty in spite of the defects necessarily involved in translating such matter into a foreign tongue, it is all Valmiki's magic. The chapters were written for Tamil readers and followed a pattern of earnest and intimate talk rather than of written prose.

I must not forget to tender my thanks to Sri. K.V.S. Raghavan who undertook the laborious task of putting the book in clean typescript for the press and completed the work with devotion and care.

Once again, I repeat my confession that in the evening of my busy life during a great and eventful period of Indian history, the writing of these two books wherein I have retold the *Mahabharata* and

Ramayana, is, in my opinion, the best service I have rendered to my people. At any rate, they embody the best joy I have experienced; for in these two books I helped our great sages to speak to our dear men and women again in their own language, elevating their minds through the sorrows borne by Kunti, Kausalya, Draupadi and Sita. The real need of the hour is a re-communion between us and the sages of our land, so that the future may be built on rock and not on sand.

The sophisticated may be inclined to smile where I have often paused in the narration to moralise. To such I must point out that when I wrote the original of these pages I had in mind always my very young readers and that this is but an English rendering of what I wrote in Tamil.

In presenting this English version to a wider circle of readers spread all over the world, I think I am presenting to them the people of Bharat just as they are, with all their virtues and their faults. Our classics really embody our national character in all its aspects and it is well the world sees us as we really are, apart from what we wish to become.

C. Rajagopalachari

Madras
10th May, 1957.

AUTHOR'S PREFACE TO THE SECOND EDITION

Author's Preface to the Second Edition

I AM glad that the Bhavan has so soon found a demand for bringing out a second impression of my *Ramayana*. It fills me not only with pride but with satisfaction. Greece—the Greece we all admire—is gone, but Homer's 'Iliad' and 'Odessey' remain and will remain for ever, not only in Greek but in all the languages of the civilized world. So also will Valmiki's *Ramayana* live in all the tongues of civilized people whatever may happen to India and its politics.

The *Ramayana* is not history or biography. It is a part of Hindu mythology. We cannot understand Greek life and Greek civilisation without knowing all about Zeus, Apollo, Hercules, Venus, Hector, Priam, Achilles, Ulysses and others. So also one cannot understand Hindu *dharma* unless one knows Rama and Seeta, Bharata, Lakshmana, Ravana, Kumbhakarna and Hanuman. Mythology cannot be dispensed with. Philosophy alone or rituals alone or mythology alone cannot be sufficient. These are the three stands of all ancient religions. The attitude towards things spiritual which belongs to a particular people cannot be grasped or preserved or conveyed unless we have all these three. Even an iconoclast like Bernard Shaw has acknowledged the essentiality of myths.

C. Rajagopalachari

Madras
14th October, 1957.

AUTHOR'S PREFACE TO THE THIRD EDITION

I AM grateful to the Bharatiya Vidya Bhavan which has brought out these fresh reprints of my *Ramayana* and *Mahabharata* books. The Bhavan has achieved great work by the very wide distribution organised by it of these two books, which seek to bring Valmiki and Vyasa near to those who have no access to the unrivalled original classics. The characters and incidents of these two *itihasas* have come to be the raw material for the works of numerous poets and saints that came later to write dramas and sing poems and hymns to keep this nation in the straight path. Oral discourses have further played with them in order to entertain and instruct pious audiences and not a few variations and additions have been made to the original. All the languages of India have the *Ramayana* and *Mahabharata* retold by their poets, with additions and variations of their own. It is good to have the narrative written up for young people as told in the original epics, and these two books of mine seek to serve that object.

I appeal particularly to the young men in schools and colleges to read these books. There is not a page in them but after reading you will emerge with greater courage, stronger will and purer mind. They are not just story books, although they are very good in that way too. They are the records of the mind and spirit of our forefathers who cared for the good, ever so much more than for the pleasant and who saw more of the mystery of life than we can do in our interminable pursuit for petty and illusory achievements in the material plane. We should be thankful to those who preserved for us these many-centuries-old epics in spite of all the vicissitudes through which our nation passed since Vyasa and Valmiki's time. Even the poets who wrote these epics in the original did not create but built out of the inherited bricks of national memory prior to their own time. Reading the *Ramayana* and *Mahabharata* even in the form I have given them, we go back to live with our ancient forbears and listen to their grand voices.

Mythology is an integral part of religion. It is as necessary for religion and national culture as the skin and the skeleton that preserve a fruit with its juice and its taste. Form is no less essential than substance. We cannot squeeze religion and hope to bottle and keep the essence by itself. It would neither be very useful nor last very long. Mythology and holy figures are necessary for any great culture to rest on its stable spiritual foundation and function as a life-giving inspiration and guide.

Let us keep ever in our minds the fact that it is the *Ramayana* and the *Mahabharata* that bind our vast numbers together as one people, despite caste, space and language that seemingly divide them.

I wish I were gifted with greater vision and greater ability so that I could have done this work, to which I was called, better than I have done. I am thankful however for what I have been enabled to do. Thorough familiarity with our ancient heritage is necessary if we desire to preserve our individuality as a nation and serve the world through *dharma* which alone can save mankind from error and extinction.

C. Rajagopalachari

Madras
19th October, 1958.

CONTENTS

CHAPTER		PAGE

NOTE FOR PRONUNCIATION

THE vowel sounds in the transliteration of Indian words and names in this book are not on the international scheme with diacritical marks. The scheme followed here is, it is hoped, easy of following, being in consonance with English spelling and pronunciation. The main difficulty in correctly reading romanised Sanskrit is the short and long vowel. It is hoped that the scheme followed in this book, the single 'a' for the short अ and double 'aa' for the long आ tides over much of this difficulty.

अ	—	a
आ	—	aa as in 'war', 'call'
इ	—	i
ई	—	ee as in 'sheep', 'seen'
उ	—	u
ऊ	—	oo as in 'moon', 'cool', 'loop'
ए	—	e as in 'say', 'way', 'made'
ऐ	—	ai
ओ	—	o as in 'code', 'roll'
औ	—	au

e.g., RAAMA, SEETA, SOORPANAKHA

RAAMAAYANA

THE traditional orthodox view is that Vaalmeeki wrote the *Raamaayana* during the life-time of Raamachandra. Judging from normal experience, however, it would appear that the story of Raama had been in existence, though not as a written work, long before Vaalmeeki wrote his epic. It looks as though Vaalmeeki gave form to a story that had been handed down from generation to generation. That probably explains some of the difficult features in the story—e.g., the slaying of Vaali and Seeta's exile under Raama's orders.

In Vaalmeeki's work Raama is portrayed as a great and unique man, not as an incarnation of God. True, in some chapters there are references to him as an *avataar* of God, but in the body of the narrative the Raama pictured by Sage Vaalmeeki is not God himself but a great prince endowed with divine qualities.

Even during Vaalmeeki's days, the idea was prevalent, to some extent, that Raama was an *avataar*. Centuries later, Kamban and Tulsidaas sang the *Raamaayana*, and by that time it had come to be accepted that Sri Raama was an *avataar* of Vishnu. Raama and Krishna were synonyms for Vishnu: and Vishnu, in turn, meant Raama or Krishna. Temples had come into existence with ritual worship of Raama as God. In a situation like that, how could the later poets portray Raama as a mere hero? Any such attempt would have failed. Kamban and Tulsidaas were devotees of the highest order. They were very different from historians and novelists.

The story begins with the visit of the Saint Naarada one morning to Vaalmeeki's *aashrama*. After the usual welcome Vaalmeeki asked him: "O, all-knowing Naarada, tell me, who among the heroes of this world is the highest in virtue and wisdom?"

Knowing through his supernatural power why Vaalmeeki put the question, Naarada answered: "Raama is the Hero that you ask for. Born in the Solar dynasty, he is at present ruling in Ayodhya." Sage Naarada then briefly narrated to Vaalmeeki the story of Raama. So impressed was Vaalmeeki when he heard Raama's story that even long after Naarada had left, his mind was full of it, and he was pondering on it as he went to the river Tamasa for his morning ablutions.

As he was walking along the river-bank he saw in a nearby tree two loving *krauncha* birds sporting and singing in their joy of life and love. Suddenly, the male bird fell down, hit by a hunter's arrow. The female bird, seeing her lover rolling on the ground, lamented in piteous fashion.

Observing this, Vaalmeeki burst into a curse: "O, hunter, as you have killed one of these love-intoxicated birds, you will wander homeless all your long years."

But in a moment the sage recovered himself and was wondering why he lost himself in anger: "What right had I to curse the hunter? Why was I deceived by emotion?"

Recalling the words of his curse, the Rishi marvelled at the rhythm of the words. He discovered that his pity had taken shape in a beautiful *sloka*. He thought that all this was part of the mysterious *leela* of God and went into meditation.

To Vaalmeeki in meditation appeared the four-faced Brahma, and he said: "Be not afraid. These things happened to start you on the story of Raama. From sorrow *(soka)* sprang verse *(sloka)* and in this metre and rhythm the story should be told. I shall give you the vision to see all that happened, aye, even how the characters thought and looked, as clearly as one sees a thing lying on the palm of one's hand. And you shall sing it, with my blessings, for the benefit of the world."

Vaalmeeki and his disciples then repeated the verse again and again and fixed its pattern firmly in their minds. Then Vaalmeeki composed the *Raamaayana* in that metre and taught it to his disciples.

Thus was the holy *Vaalmeeki-Raamaayana* born. The tale of the Lord and His Consort born as mortals, experiencing human sorrow and establishing *dharma* on earth, was sung by the Rishi in words of matchless beauty. And Brahma's words have come true: "As long as the mountains stand and the rivers flow so long shall the *Raamaayana* be cherished among men and save them from sin."

CHAPTER I

THE CONCEPTION

TO the north of the Ganga was the great kingdom of Kosala, made fertile by the river Sarayu. Its capital was Ayodhya, built by Manu, the famous ruler of the Solar dynasty. From Vaalmeeki's description of the capital of Kosala, it is clear that ancient Ayodhya was not inferior to our modern cities. Even in ancient India city civilisation had reached a high level.

King Dasaratha ruled the kingdom from the capital city of Ayodhya. He had fought on the side of the Devas, and his fame spread in the three worlds. He was the equal of Indra and Kubera. The people of Kosala were happy, contented and virtuous. The land was protected by a mighty army, and no enemy could come anywhere near.

It contained forts with moats around them as well as many defensive installations, and true to its name, Ayodhya defied all enemies. (*Ayodhya* means that which cannot be subdued by war).

Dasaratha had eight wise ministers, ever ready to advise him and execute his orders. Great sages like Vasishtha and Vaamadeva and other Braahmanas taught the *dharma* and performed rituals and sacrifices. Taxes were light and punishment of crime was just and inflicted according to the capacity of the wrong-doer. Surrounded by the best counsellors and statesmen, the King's splendour shone as the rising sun.

Many years rolled smoothly by. In the midst of all this prosperity Dasaratha had one regret; he had no son.

One day in early summer he thought of performing a horse-sacrifice for progeny. He consulted his religious masters and, on their advice, got Sage Rishya-Sringa to perform the *yaaga*.

The *yaaga* was a grand affair and the invitees included many of the kings of the day. It was no easy thing to perform *yaagas*. The location and erection of the sacrificial platform had to be attended to in detail strictly according to prescribed rules. There were experts whose guidance was sought in arranging things. It meant the building of a new camp-city, capable of accommodating tens of thousands and providing hospitality and entertainment for the invitees who included the princes and sages of the land. In short, *yaagas* in those days were something like our present-day State-sponsored big scale conferences and exhibitions.

When all arrangements were complete the ceremonies were set in motion strictly as enjoined by the *Shaastras*.

Contemporaneously with the *yaaga* in Ayodhya, there was a conference of the Devas in heaven. The Devas complained to Lord Brahma that Raavana, king of the demons, drunk with the power acquired by the boon granted to him by Brahma, was causing them untold misery and hardship. They represented to Brahma: "It is beyond our capacity to subdue, conquer or kill Raavana. In the security of your boon, he has grown wicked and insolent and ill-treats all, even women. His desire is to dethrone Indra. You are our only refuge and it is for you to devise a method by which Raavana can be slain and his despotism ended."

Brahma knew that he had granted to Raavana the boon prayed for by him that he should be invulnerable and invincible against Devas, Asuras, Gandharvas and other such beings. In his arrogance, Raavana did not care to ask for security against mankind. As Brahma revealed this fateful omission all the Gods rejoiced and turned to Vishnu.

Absolutely surrendering themselves to Hari, the Devas begged him to be born as a man and put an end to Raavana and his atrocities. Hari agreed and assured the Devas that he would be born as four sons of King Dasaratha who was then performing a sacrifice for progeny.

As the *ghee* was poured into the fire and the flames shot up to meet it, from out of the flames came a majestic figure, resplendent like the noonday sun, holding a bowl of gold. Calling King Dasaratha by his name, the figure said: "The Devas are pleased with you and are answering your prayer. Here is *paayasam* sent by the gods for your wives. You will be blessed with sons if they drink this divine beverage."

With joy unbounded, Dasaratha received the bowl as he would receive a child and distributed the *paayasam* to his three wives, Kausalya, Sumitra and Kaikeyi. He asked Kausalya to drink a half of the *paayasam* and he gave a half of what remained to Sumitra. Half of what was then left was drunk by Kaikeyi, and what remained was given to Sumitra again.

Dasaratha's wives were happy, even as a beggar suddenly coming upon buried treasure. And in due course all of them were expectant mothers.

CHAPTER II

SAGE VISWAAMITRA

IN course of time, Dasaratha's sons were born, Raama of Kausalya and Bharata of Kaikeyi. Sumitra gave birth to twins, Lakshmana and Satrughna, she having drunk the divine *paayasam* twice.

In proportion to the quantity of *paayasam* drunk by the respective mothers, the sons are traditionally considered to be parts of Vishnu. Raama was thus half-Vishnu.

But such calculations have no meaning as it is impossible to measure the Infinite arithmetically. *Sruti* tells us that even a fraction of the Supreme Being is whole and complete by itself.

"Om Poornamadah Poornamidam Poornaat Poornamudachyate Poornasya Poornamaadaaya Poornamevaavasishyate."

"What is whole; this is whole; what has come out of the whole is also whole. When the whole is taken out of the whole, the whole still remains whole."

Dasaratha's four sons were given all the training prescribed for princes. Raama and Lakshmana were specially devoted to each other, and so were Bharata and Satrughna. We can imagine that this special attachment arose out of the way the divine *paayasam* was divided among the King's wives. Dasaratha was happy to see his four sons grow up strong, virtuous, brave and lovable and with all other princely qualities.

One day as the King was contemplating his sons' matrimony, ushers rushed in to announce that the great Sage Viswaamitra had arrived to see him.

Viswaamitra was held in awe by all as the most powerful among rishis.

Viswaamitra's arrival at Ayodhya was unexpected; and King Dasaratha stepped down from his throne and advanced a few paces respectfully to receive the sage.

Viswaamitra was a king who attained sainthood through terrible austerities. He had long ago exhibited his spiritual powers by starting to create another Brahma and a rival universe: he had gone as far as the creation of new constellations, but was prevailed upon to stop by the entreaties of the alarmed gods.

Viswaamitra, while he was king once went out with his army and chanced to visit Vasishtha's *aashrama*. The rishi cordially welcomed his royal guest and his huge entourage and extended to them all a hospitality so sumptuous that the King wondered where all the rich abundance came from in a forest hermitage. Questioned by him, Vasishtha called his cow Sabala and explained that she was the fountain of unfailing plenty.

Expressing gratitude to the sage, King Viswaamitra said: "You must give me this cow as she would be more useful with me than with you. Such things of power and wealth by right belong to the King."

Now Vasishtha could not part with the divine cow. He gave many reasons and asked the King not to press his request. But the more unwilling Vasishtha was to give the cow, the more eager the King became to possess her.

Failing in his efforts to tempt or persuade the sage to part with the cow, Viswaamitra became angry and ordered his men to seize the cow by force.

Sabala could not understand why she was being roughly handled and she was unwilling to go away from the sage and his *aashrama*. Shedding tears, she wondered how she had offended Vasishtha that he should stand by and look on while she was being dragged away. The cow easily put to flight the soldiers and sought refuge at the feet of the sage.

Moved by the piteous appeal of his beloved cow, who was like a younger sister to him, the sage said: "Bring forth soldiers to resist Viswaamitra's men."

Sabala instantaneously did so, and the aggressors were soon worsted. Wild with rage, Viswaamitra got into his chariot and, taking up his bow, rained arrows on the soldiers brought forth by the cow, but their strength was inexhaustible, and the royal forces suffered utter defeat. The sons of Viswaamitra now chose Vasishtha himself as their target, only to be reduced to ashes.

Defeated and disgraced, Viswaamitra then and there entrusted his kingdom to one of his sons and proceeded to the Himaalayas to perform *tapas*, directing his devotions to Lord Siva to gain power with which to subdue Vasishtha.

So firm and steadfast was Viswaamitra in his austerities that Lord Siva was pleased and appeared before him. He asked the king what his object was in performing *tapas*.

Viswaamitra replied: "If you, Umaapati, are satisfied with my *tapas* let me be blessed with divine arrows and be master of every weapon."

"So be it," said Siva, and gave Viswaamitra all the weapons available to the Devas, Gandharvas, Rishis, Yakshas and the Demons.

Swelling with pride like the ocean, Viswaamitra considered Vasishtha as already vanquished. He straightway made for the abode of the sage. Frightened at the fearful sight of the onrushing Viswaamitra, Vasishtha's disciples and the animals in his *aashrama* ran helter-skelter.

Hit by the fire-weapon of Viswaamitra, Vasishtha's *aashrama* was reduced to cinders.

Vasishtha regretted the turn of events, but determined to end the haughtiness of the erstwhile king, he faced him calmly with his *Brahmadanda*—holy staff—in hand. Mad with rage, Viswaamitra shot at him all the divine weapons he had acquired, but they were quenched as they approached the rishi's staff and were absorbed by it.

Viswaamitra had but one more weapon in his armoury, and that was the most powerful of all—the *Brahmaastra*. As he hurled it against Vasishtha the world became wrapped in gloom as in some huge eclipse, and the very immortals trembled with fear. But the terrible *astra* itself was merged in the rishi's staff, making both it and the holy man glow with the glory they had absorbed.

Viswaamitra stood dazed. Openly accepting defeat, he said: "Of what use is the Kshatriya's might in arms? With but a staff in his hand, this Vasishtha has nullified all my weapons. Lord Siva has indeed fooled me. There is no alternative for me but to become a *Brahma Rishi* like Vasishtha." So saying, he withdrew from the field of battle and proceeded south for more rigorous *tapas*.

For years and years Viswaamitra went through
terrible austerities. Pleased with his perseverance,
Brahma presented himself before him. Advising
Viswaamitra that, as a result of his *tapas*, he had
risen to the position of a rishi among kings, Brahma
vanished from the scene.

Viswaamitra was disappointed that all his
penance could get him only the status of *Raaja Rishi*.
Not content with anything but the highest—the rank
of a *Brahma Rishi*—he subjected himself to still
more rigorous austerities in order that he might be
acknowledged an equal of Vasishtha.

CHAPTER III

TRISANKU

THAT was the time when the famous king of the Solar dynasty, Trisanku, was reigning, who was so much in love with the beauty of his body that he could not bear the thought of parting with it at death and desired to ascend to heaven in that very body.

Vasishtha, his preceptor, whom he approached for help in realising his wish, advised him to give up attempting the impossible. Dissatisfied with Vasishtha's response, the King approached the sage's sons and sought their help. They were wroth at being asked to do something which their father had pronounced impossible, ridiculed his vanity and curtly bade him begone.

King Trisanku would not give up his aim and told them that, since they and their father were too poor in merit to help him, he would find others who were richer. Vasishtha's sons were provoked beyond endurance, and said: "Be you a *chandaala.*"

The curse began to act and the next morning Trisanku woke up a different person altogether, an untouchable, ugly of form, attired in dirty clothes.

His ministers and his people could not recognise him. Driven out of his kingdom he wandered hungry and weary almost to death, till his destiny took him to Viswaamitra's *aashrama.*

The king's appearance moved the heart of the sage, who enquired: "Aren't you King Trisanku? What has brought you to this plight? Whose curse?"

Recounting all that had happened he fell at the sage's feet and said: "I have been a good king and never swerved from the path of *dharma*. I have committed no sin and wronged none. My preceptor and his sons have deserted me and cursed me and you see me thus before you."

Viswaamitra took pity on the King converted by a curse into a *chandaala*. This was Viswaamitra's great weakness; he was impulsive and easily over-powered by emotions like anger, sympathy and love.

In sweet words, he made the king happy: "O, King, I have heard of your righteous rule. I offer you refuge, be not afraid. I will arrange for the sacrifice which will enable you to enter heaven in your own body. And in this very *chandaala* form you shall reach heaven despite your Guru's curse. Of this you may be sure."

And he made arrangements for a great and unprecedented *yaaga*.

Viswaamitra directed his disciples to invite all the sages and their disciples for the proposed *yaaga*. Afraid of saying "No" to what was more or less a command, all the rishis agreed to be present.

But the sons of Vasishtha declined the invitation and made merry about a *yaaga* at which the officiating priest was a once-upon-a-time Kshatriya and the *yajamaan* a stinking *chandaala*.

This reply, duly conveyed, enraged Viswaamitra who exploded into a curse that Vasishtha's sons do die and be re-born for seven generations in a tribe given to eating dog's flesh.

The sage then began the *yaaga*. Extolling Trisanku's eminent virtues, Vishwaamitra sought the help of the other rishis in effecting the bodily translation of Trisanku to heaven.

Well aware of the sage's mighty powers and fulminous temper, the invitees lent their support, and the *yaaga* went on. It reached the stage when the gods were invoked to descend and accept the offerings. But no god came. It was clear that Viswaamitra's *yaaga* was a failure. And the rishis who had attended the ceremony, laughed within themselves at Viswaamitra's discomfiture.

Wild with rage, Viswaamitra held the ladle of *ghee* over the flames and said: "O Trisanku, here behold my power. I now transfer for your benefit all the merit I have earned. If my austerities have any value, they should lift you to heaven in your physical frame. I care not if the Devas reject my offerings. O King Trisanku! Ascend!"

A miracle followed. To the astonishment of those assembled, Trisanku in his *chandaala* body rose heavenward. The world saw the power of Viswaamitra's *tapas*.

Trisanku reached *Swarga*. But Indra forthwith pushed him down saying, "Who are you, entering heaven with a *chandaala* body? You fool that earned the curse of your preceptor, go down again."

Trisanku fell from heaven, head downwards, screaming, "O Viswaamitra! Save me!"

Visawaamitra, seeing this, was beside himself with rage. Determined to teach the gods a lesson, he shouted to Trisanku, "Stop there! Stop there!" and, to the amazement of all, Trisanku's earthward descent came to an abrupt stop and he stopped in midair, shining like a star. Like a second Brahma, Viswaamitra proceeded to create a new starry horizon to the south as well as a new Indra and new Devas.

Alarmed at their supremacy, the Devas now came to terms and humbly entreated Viswaamitra to desist. They said: "Let Trisanku stay where he is at present. Let the other stars of your creation shine for ever, like your own fame and honour. Control your anger and be friends with us."

Gratified at this submission, and as easily appeased as provoked, Viswaamitra halted his creative process. But his stupendous activities had consumed the whole of the power that he had thus far acquired by his austerities, and he found he had to begin again.

Viswaamitra now proceeded westwards to Pushkara and resumed his austerities. For years the rigorous *tapas* continued, but once again as it was about to bear fruit something happened to rouse his anger and he lost his balance and cursed his own sons. Soon recovering himself, he firmly resolved never again to yield to anger, and resumed his *tapas*.

After many years of austerities, Brahma and the Devas appeared before him and said: "O Kausika! Your *tapas* has borne fruit. You are no longer in the ranks of kings; you have become a real rishi." Having thus blessed Viswaamitra, Brahma returned.

This was again a disappointment. He wanted to become a *Brahma Rishi* and Vasishtha's peer and he had only been acknowledged an ordinary rishi. It was a recognition as futile as the missiles of power which Vasishtha's *Brahmadanda* had swallowed.

He therefore decided to go on with his *tapas*, making it more severe than ever before.

The Devas did not like this. They sent the heavenly damsel Menaka to tempt him with her celestial beauty and allurements. She went to

Pushkara where Viswaamitra was undergoing austerities and played to catch his eye with a hundred wiles of charm and grace. Viswaamitra saw her and was fascinated by her beauty. His vow was broken and he spent ten years in a dream of joy, forgetful of his high resolve.

Awaking at last, he looked at the trembling Menaka sorrowfully and said he would not curse her, for it was his own folly, and not her fault, as in tempting him she was only carrying out the orders of her master. And sadly he wended his way to the Himaalayas to resume his broken *tapas*.

There, for a thousand years, controlling his senses, he performed rigorous *tapas*. At the request of the Devas, Brahma appeared before Viswaamitra, and spoke to him thus sweetly: "I welcome you as a *Maharishi*, my son. Pleased with your soulful *tapas*, I confer on you that title and the sanctity it imports."

Unmoved alike by gratification or disappointment, Viswaamitra folded his hands in adoration and asked the Father of the Universe if the boon meant conquest over the senses.

"By no means", said the Creator, "but strive to subjugate the senses, O tiger among *munis*!"

Resolved on the supreme conquest, Viswaamitra entered on another thousand years of even harder *tapas* which threw the Devas into even greater consternation.

Indra called unto him the celestial damsel Rambha, and enjoined on her as a vital service to the Devas, to employ all her art to bring Viswaamitra under the spell of her charm, and divert him from his purpose. She was sorely afraid, but Indra assured her that she would not be left alone, but be accompanied by the God of Love and the Spirit of Springtime would be with her for support. Unwillingly she went and as she entered the precincts of the hermitage, the forest blossomed into vernal beauty, and the south wind blew gently laden with the scent of flowers, and *kokilas* burst into song. Love and Spring were both there to assist Beauty. Disturbed by stirrings to which he had long been a stranger, Viswaamitra opened his eyes and saw a smiling damsel of surpassing beauty, who seemed the very soul of the spring with its flowers and fragrance and song. At this vision of soft voluptuousness a white heat of anger surged through him as he recognised in it another temptation thrown in his way by the envious gods, and he cursed the temptress: "O Rambha, for seeking to tempt me who am striving to conquer anger and desire, be thou frozen to an image of stone for ten thousand years."

But this explosion of rage made him see how far he was from the fulfilment of his purpose and sadly he quitted the Himaalayan forests, and sought the solitude of the east. There, he restrained his breathing, gave up all thought of the things of the world, and performed austerities so stern that smoke and flames issued from his body and enveloped the universe. Then at the prayer of the panic-stricken gods, Brahma again appeared before him, and hailed him as *Brahma Rishi* — "All hail, *Brahma Rishi*, I am pleased with you. Blessed be your life." Viswaamitra was happy.

But humbly he said: "How can I be happy unless from Vasishtha's lips I hear that I am a *Brahma Rishi*?"

Vasishtha smiled remembering his fight with Viswaamitra, and said to him: "You have achieved the fruit of your great austerities. Indeed you are a *Brahma Rishi*, my brother." There was joy all round.

This was the story of the sage that arrived suddenly at Dasaratha's court.

CHAPTER IV

RAAMA LEAVES HOME

KING Dasaratha received Viswaamitra as Indra would welcome Brahma and touching his feet, the King said: "I am indeed blessed among men. Your coming can only be due to the merit of my ancestors. Like the morning sun that dispels the darkness of night, your face brings joy to my sight. My heart is full. Born a king, you have become through *tapas* a *Brahma Rishi*. And you yourself have come seeking my dwelling. Is there anything in my power that I can do for you? If so, command and I shall obey."

Viswaamitra was rejoiced to hear these words of Dasaratha, and his face brightened. He said: "O King, your words are worthy of you. Born in the Ikshvaaku line, with Vasishtha for your Guru, what else could you say? You have said 'yes' before I asked. This fills my heart with joy." And he straightway explained the purpose of his visit.

Viswaamitra said: "I am engaged in performing a sacrifice. As it nears completion, two powerful *Raakshasas*, Maareecha and Subaahu, defile it. They shower unclean blood and flesh on the sacred fire. Like other rishis we could curse and destroy them. But that would be a waste of all our *tapas*.

"Our troubles will end if you send with me Raama, the eldest of your warlike sons. Under my care, he will grow in princely stature. He will surely defeat these *Raakshasas* and his name will gather lustre.

"Entrust Raama to my care only for a few days. Do not refuse my request. Fulfil the promise you gave me unsought. Of Raama's safety you need have no anxiety. You will earn undying fame in the three worlds. Vasishtha and your ministers will agree with what I say."

Dasaratha trembled with fear and anxiety. He had a hard choice to make; either to give his well-beloved son to be killed by the *Raakshasas* or himself incur the terrible anger of Viswaamitra.

For a few moments, Dasaratha stood speechless, for he was stunned and bewildered. But recovering from the shock, he begged the sage not to press his demand, and said: "Raama is not yet fully sixteen years of age. How can he fight with *Raakshasas*? Of what use is it to send him with you? What does he know of the wiles of *Raakshasas*?

"It is not right that I should send a mere lad to fight them. I am here, and my army is ready to march. How can a lad protect you and your *yaaga*? Tell me all about your foes. I shall go with you at the head of my army and do your bidding and serve your need. Do tell me about these desecrators."

Viswaamitra described Maareecha and Subaahu and Raavana their master. And he demanded again that Raama should be sent along with him.

Dasaratha persisted in refusal. "Parting from Raama will be death to me," he said. "I shall go with you, I and my army. Why, it seems to me the task proposed is pretty hard even for me. How then can my son cope with it? Indeed, I cannot send him. If you please, I am ready with my army."

Dasaratha's attempt to go back on his hasty word, enraged Viswaamitra. The King's pleas and reasons were like oil poured on the fire of his anger.

"This conduct is unworthy of your lineage", the sage said. "Tell me if this is your final word. I shall go back the way I came. Long may you live with your kith and kin, having swerved from the path of Truth!"

The earth quaked and the gods were afraid of the possible consequences of the sage's wrath.

Vasishtha now turned to the King and spoke gently: "It ill becomes you, King, to refuse having promised once. Born in the Ikshvaaku line, you cannot do it. Having once said, 'I will do', you have no option but to do it. Failing, you will lose the merit of all your great gifts and deeds.

"Send Raama with the sage, and send Lakshmana too. You need have no fear for their safety. When they are protected by Viswaamitra, no *Raakshasa* can hurt them.

"As the drink of the gods is shielded by the wheel of fire, so will Raama be by Viswaamitra. You have no idea of Viswaamitra's power; he is *tapas* in human form. Bravest of the brave and wisest of the wise, he is master of every weapon. In the three worlds there is not, and there will never be, any to equal him in martial or spiritual prowess. When he was king, he obtained from the gods mastery of all weapons. He beholds the past, the present and the future. Then why does he want the princes, you may wonder. He can well take care himself of his *yaaga*; but it is for the good of your sons that he has come here and appears to seek your help. Do not hesitate. Send your sons with him."

Listening to the wise Vasishtha, Dasaratha saw things clearly and made up his mind to send Raama and Lakshmana.

The two princes were then brought to the presence of the sage. The King, the Queen-Mothers and Vasishtha blessed them and sent them with Viswaamitra.

A pleasant breeze wafted and flowers were strewn by the denizens of the heavens. Auspicious sounds were heard. Bow in hand, the two lads strode proudly on either side of the Sage.

Vaalmeeki and Kamban revel in this picture of the two handsome princes marching out to their first adventure under the guardianship of a great rishi who had also been a renowned warrior — a teacher who could create a new world; and beside him, head erect, two princely pupils born to end the *Raakshasa* race.

With swords of victory hanging from their waists, bows and quivers mounted on strong shoulders, they moved, each like a three-headed cobra with uplifted hood.

CHAPTER V

RAAMA SLAYS THE MONSTERS

VISWAAMITRA and the two princes spent the night on the bank of the river Sarayu. Before retiring Viswaamitra initiated the princes in two secret *mantras Bala* and *Atibala*, which had the virtue of guarding them from fatigue and harm. They slept on the verdant bank that night and rising at dawn proceeded on their journey. They reached Kaamaashrama in Anga Desa. After presenting the princes to the rishis there, Viswaamitra recounted to them the history of the *aashrama*.

"This," he said, "is the place where the Lord Siva was long engaged in austerities. It was here that the foolish god of love Manmatha aimed his arrow at Siva and was turned to ashes by his wrath. Hence this place is known as Kaamaashrama."

They were the guests of the rishis that night, and the following morning, after performing the usual rites, the sage and his pupils set out on their journey and reached the Ganga. They crossed the river on a raft got ready for them by the rishis.

In midstream, the princes heard a noise and asked Viswaamitra what it could be. He explained to them that it was the sound of the Sarayu flowing into the Ganga. The princes paid silent homage to the confluence of the two holy rivers.

A river or a hill, a tree or a cloud—indeed any object of beauty may raise one to contemplation of the Supreme Being and silent worship of Him. In particular, sacred rivers, temples or images, which have for generations been the objects of devotion and worship, possess this power in a special degree, in virtue of the sacred thoughts they have witnessed and absorbed as garments retain perfumes.

Having crossed the Ganga, Viswaamitra and the princes made their difficult way through a dense forest made dreadful by the reverberating roar of wild beasts.

"This," Viswaamitra said, "is the Dandaka forest. What is now a terrible forest was once a well-peopled country. Once upon a time, Indra was contaminated by sin, having killed Vritra, and had therefore to exile himself from the world of the Devas. The Devas set to themselves the task of cleansing Indra. They brought waters from the sacred rivers and bathed him to the accompaniment of *mantras*. The waters which cleansed Indra flowed into the ground and enriched the earth and the land became tremendously fertile."

All dead things—rotting corpse or stinking garbage—when returned to the earth are transformed into things of beauty such as fruits and flowers and the wholesome things that nourish life. Such is the alchemy of Mother Earth.

Viswaamitra continued: "For long people lived here happily till Taataka (wife of Sunda, a *Yaksha*) and her son Maareecha wrought havoc and changed this into the dreadful wilderness it now is. They are still in this forest. And none dare enter it for fear of Taataka. She is equal in strength to a score of elephants. I have brought you here to rid the forest of this great enemy. There is no doubt that this monster, who is a source of trouble to the rishis, will be destroyed by you."

Raama, who listened to this, asked the sage: "You say she is a *Yaksha*. I have never heard that

Yakshas are particularly strong. What is more, how does a woman happen to possess so much strength?"

Viswaamitra replied: "You are asking a very pertinent question. Her strength comes from a boon granted by Brahma. There lived a *Yaksha* by name Suketu. Having no progeny he performed *tapas* and won a boon from Brahma thus: 'You will have a beautiful daughter of great strength of body, but you will have no son.' Suketu's daughter, Taataka, beautiful and strong, was married to Sunda, a *Yaksha*, and their child is Maareecha.

"Sunda at one time incurred Sage Agastya's curse and died. Provoked by this, Taataka and Maareecha pounced on Agastya who cursed them to be monsters living on the carcasses of men. So Taataka is now an ugly monster.

"Thenceforward, she and Maareecha have been harassing the dwellers in this region of Agastya. Do not hesitate to destroy her on the ground that it is against Kshatriya *dharma* to kill a woman. Her atrocities are intolerable. To punish the wicked, whether male or female, is the duty of kings. It is right to kill her, as to kill a wild animal for the sake of human safety. This is a duty cast on rulers. Many women have been punished with death for their crimes. Hence do not hesitate."

Raama said to Viswaamitra: "Our father's behest is that we should obey you without question. Bidden by you and for the general welfare, we shall kill Taataka."

So saying, he strung his bow and twanged it till the forest echoed to its shrill note and the wild animals scattered in all directions in terror. It reached Taataka in her fastness, filling her with amazement at the audacious intruder who dared enter her domain. Raging with anger, she ran in the direction whence the sound came and sprang on Raama. The battle began.

The prince at first thought of cutting off the limbs of the monster and sparing her life. But Taataka attacked fiercely and, rising in the sky, she rained stones on Raama and Lakshmana. The two princes defended themselves against the attack. The fight continued and Viswaamitra cautioned Raama against delay in dealing the death-blow to the monster.

"She deserves no sympathy," he said. "The sun is about to set and remember that at night *Raakshasas* grow stronger. Do not delay to slay her."

Thus advised, Raama decided on killing Taataka and pierced her chest with a deadly arrow and the huge, ugly monster fell down, lifeless.

The Devas cheered, and Viswaamitra, filled with joy, embraced Raama and blessed him.

With Taataka's end, the forest was freed from the curse and became beautiful to see. The princes spent the night there and next morning they proceeded to Viswaamitra's *aashrama*.

At dawn the next day, Viswaamitra called Raama to his side and blessing him said: "I am very happy indeed. What is it that I can do in return for all that you have done? I shall teach you the use of all the *astras*."

So saying, Viswaamitra gave Raamachandra the divine *astras* which he had obtained through his *tapas*. Viswaamitra taught Raama the use, control and recall of the various divine weapons and Raama in his turn imparted the knowledge to Lakshmana.

As they continued the journey, Raama pointed to a big hill with a lovely forest on its slopes and asked: "Is that the place whereto we have to go? And who are the evil ones who hinder your *yaaga*? And what should I do to destroy them?"

Raamachandra was eager to fight and win the blessings of the sage.

"That is the place we are going to," replied Viswaamitra. "There the Lord Naaraayana performed *tapas* and it was there that he was born as Vaamana. It goes by the name of Siddhaashrama.

"Mahaabali, son of Virochana and grandson of Prahlaada the good *Asura*, was such a powerful ruler that of him even the Devas were afraid. Mahaabali had by his deeds acquired the power of Indra himself.

"Kashyapa and his spouse Aditi, of whom all the gods were off-springs, prayed to Vishnu and begged Him to be born as their son and protect Indra and the Devas from Mahaabali. In answer to the prayers, Vishnu was born of Aditi as Vaamana.

"Vaamana in the form of a young student went to the *yaaga* that was being performed by Mahaabali and whereto all were welcome, to ask for and receive anything they wanted. When Vaamana presented himself as a suitor, Mahaabali's guru, Sukra—the preceptor of all the *Asuras*—knew who he really was and warned Mahaabali against promising to grant the young Braahmana his request—that indeed he was the Lord Hari in disguise come to undo him.

"Mahaabali did not pay heed to this. It was his wont never to turn down a request. Besides, he was at heart a devotee of the Lord, and felt that he would indeed be blessed if the Lord should deign to accept a gift from him. With a smile, Mahaabali bade him ask for what he pleased without hesitation. 'All I have is at your disposal, money, jewels, the wide earth and all it inherits.'

"Vaamana answered that wealth was of no use to him, and all he begged for was three paces of ground, as paced by him.

"The monarch smiled as he looked at the diminutive *brahmachaari's* legs and said, 'So be it; pace and take it.'

"The little Bachelor suddenly grew in size into Trivikrama and with one step measured the earth and with another the entire heavens. And there being no room left for the third step that had been granted, he set his foot on Mahaabali's devoted head. In the eyes of God, the head of a *bhakta* is as wide as the earth or the heavens. And Mahaabali, whose head was blessed by the touch of Naaraayana's foot, became one of the seven immortals of the world."

After narrating the story of Mahaabali, Viswaamitra added: "This is where at first Naaraayana and later Kashyapa performed *tapas*, resulting in the incarnation of God as Vaamana. In this holy place I live. And here the *Raakshasas* come and obstruct our worship and our austerities. Your coming here is to end this evil."

"So be it," said Raama.

The arrival of Viswaamitra and the two princes was a signal for rejoicing at the *aashrama*; the rishis offered water and fruits according to custom. Raama told Viswaamitra that he might begin the preparations for his *yaaga* immediately and Viswaamitra took the vows that very night.

Getting up very early the next morning, the princes went to Viswaamitra and asked when the *Raakshasas* were expected so that they might hold themselves in readiness to receive them.

Viswaamitra was under a vow of silence, and could not answer, but the rishis, his juniors, told the princes that they should be ceaselessly vigilant for six nights and days to safeguard the sacrifice.

The princes, fully armed, kept vigil for six days and nights. On the morning of the sixth day Raama told Lakshmana: "Brother, now is the time for the enemies to come. Let us be wary."

Even as he was saying this, flames shot up from the sacrificial fire, for Agni, the God of Fire, knew that the *Raakshasas* had arrived. As the rites were being performed, there was heard from the sky a great roar.

Raama looked up and saw Maareecha and Subaahu and their followers preparing to shower unclean things on the sacrificial fire. The army of *Raakshasas* covered the sky like a great black cloud.

Raama said, "Look Lakshmana," and let go the *Maanavaastra* at Maareecha. As was intended, it did not kill Maareecha, but wrapping him up in resistless force hurled him a full hundred *yojanas* near the sea.

With the *Aagneyaastra* Raama killed Subaahu; and then the two princes utterly destroyed the entire army of *Raakshasas*.

The sky was bright again.

Viswaamitra was supremely happy at the completion of his *yaaga.* "I am grateful to King Dasaratha," he said. "You have fulfilled the promise, princes. I admire your fortitude. This *aashrama* has through you become again a scene of success, Siddhaashrama." ('Siddha' means success).

The next day, Raama and Lakshmana, after their morning prayers, went to Viswaamitra and asked for further orders.

The purpose of Raama's birth was not unknown to Sage Viswaamitra. And he knew too the powers of the weapons he had given to Raama. Still the actual fact when experienced is something more than expectation. Sage Viswaamitra was happy beyond words, and his face glowed like a flame. He then thought of the service that he still had to do for Raama. This was the prince's marriage with Seeta.

The rishis assembled there said to Raama: "We intend proceeding to the kingdom of Videha where, in the capital city of Mithila, Janaka, the illustrious philosopher king, intends to perform a great sacrifice.

"All of us are going there and it will be good if you and the prince, your brother, accompany us. It is meet and proper that the Prince of Ayodhya should see the marvellous bow in the court of Janaka."

So it was decided, and Raama and Lakshmana went with Viswaamitra to Janaka's city.

CHAPTER VI

SEETA

JANAKA, king of Mithila, was an ideal ruler. He was a much–revered friend of Dasaratha who, when he planned his *yaaga* for progeny, sent not mere messengers but ministers to Mithila to invite King Janaka.

Janaka was not only a brave king but was as well-versed in the *Saastras* and *Vedas* as any rishi and was the beloved pupil of Yaajnavalkya whose exposition of *Brahmajnaana* to him is the substance of the *Brihadaaranyakopanishad*. In the *Bhagavad Gita*, Sri Krishna cites Janaka as an illustrious example of the *Karma yogin*. Janaka was thus worthy to be the father of Seeta who was to be the wife of Vishnu come down on Earth in human form.

Desirous of performing a *yaaga*, Janaka at one time ploughed the chosen site. As usual this was done by his own hand.

As the field was being cleared and levelled, Janaka saw among shrubs a baby divinely beautiful. Janaka was childless and accepted the infant as the goddess Earth's gift to him.

Taking the child in his arms he went to his beloved wife and said: "Here is treasure for us. I found this child on the *yaaga* site and we shall make it our own." And she joyfully consented.

The beauty of the goddess Earth mortal eyes cannot see in its fulness, but we get glimpses of it as we gaze with grateful hearts on the emerald green or golden ripeness of spring-tide or autumn fields, or with awe and adoration on the glories of mountain and valley, rivers and ocean. This loveliness was

Seeta in its entirety. Kamban would have it that
Seeta's beauty threw into the shade Lakshmi herself
who came up with Nectar as the Ocean of Milk was
being churned. This child of divine beauty was
brought up by King Janaka and his dear queen.

When Seeta reached the age of marriage
Janaka was sad that he would have to part with her.
Though he tried hard, he was for long unable to
choose a prince worthy of Seeta. Many kings came to
Mithila, seeking Seeta's hand, but in Janaka's view
none of them was good enough. The King anxiously
thought over the matter and came to a decision.

Long ago, pleased with a *yaaga* performed by
Janaka, Varuna presented to him Rudra's bow and
two quivers. That was an ancient heavenly bow,
which no ordinary man could even move. This was
kept by him as an honoured heir-loom. Since only a
very exceptional man could be considered worthy of
Seeta, Janaka issued this proclamation: "Seeta, my
daughter, will be given in marriage to the prince who
can lift, bend and string the bow of Siva which
Varuna gave me and to none other."

Many princes who had heard of Seeta's beauty,
went to Mithila only to return disappointed. None
could fulfil the condition.

Led by Viswaamitra, the rishis from Siddhaashrama were proceeding to Mithila, with
bullock-carts transporting their luggage. The animals and the birds in the *aashrama* set out to follow
Viswaamitra, but he gently bade them stay behind.

It was evening when they reached the river
Sona. There they rested for the night, Viswaamitra
recounting to Raama and Lakshmana the history of
the place. Getting up in the morning, they continued

their journey and crossed another river, not very deep, and by noon they were at the Ganga.

They bathed in the holy river and the rishis made lustrations to their forbears. They improvised an *aashrama* there, performed their *pujas* and cooked their food. Meal over, they sat round Viswaamitra who, at the request of the two princes, told the story of the Ganga.

Himavaan, king of mountains and his spouse, Manorama, had two daughters, of whom Ganga was the elder. Himavaan sent her to the land of the Devas in response to their request and she dwelt with them. Uma, the younger, won the favour of Siva and became his spouse.

Sagara, a former King of Ayodhya, had no son for long. With his two wives, Kesini and Sumati, he went to Himaalaya and performed *tapas*. Sage Bhrigu, pleased with the king, blessed him and said: "You will get a number of children and will acquire undying fame. One of your wives will give birth to an only son, and through him your lineage will be continued. The other queen will bear sixty thousand strong-armed sons."

Sagara's wives bowed low before the sage and asked which one of them would get an only son and which the sixty thousand children. Sage Bhrigu asked each of them their own desire.

Kesini said she would be satisfied with one son who would continue the line; Sumati chose the other alternative. "Be it so," said the sage.

Satisfied, the king and his wives took leave of the sage and returned to Ayodhya. In course of time, Asamanjas was born to Kesini; Sumati gave birth to a fissiparous mass which divided out into sixty thousand babies. This army of children was well taken care of by nurses.

Years rolled by; and while the sixty thousand grew into strong, handsome princes, Asamanjas turned out to be a cruel lunatic. He indulged in the pastime of throwing little children into the river and laughed merrily as they struggled and died.

Naturally people hated this maniac and banished him from the country. To the great relief of all, Asamanjas' son, Amsumaan, was the opposite of his father and was a brave, virtuous and amiable prince.

King Sagara launched a great horse-sacrifice and prince Amsumaan was in charge of the sacrificial horse, but Indra, in the guise of a *Raakshasa*, managed to carry off the animal. The Devas regarded *yaagas* by mortals as a challenge to their superiority, and lost no opportunity of throwing obstacles in their way. If, however, all obstruction was overcome and the *yaaga* was completed, they accepted offerings made to them. And then he who performed the *yaaga* got due reward.

The king was greatly upset when he heard that the sacrificial horse was stolen. He sent out the sixty thousand sons of Sumati to go in search of the animal all over the earth and to spare no pains to retrieve it.

"The loss of the horse," he impressed on them, "not only means obstruction to the *yaaga*; it casts sin and ignominy on all concerned. You should, therefore, recover the horse, wherever it may be kept hidden."

Eagerly the sons of Sagara proceeded to search the entire earth, but the horse was nowhere to be

found. They even started digging the earth as for
buried treasure, and in their anxiety respected
neither place nor person and only succeeded in
earning the hatred of all they met. The horse was not
to be found; and when they reported their failure to
the King, he bade them ransack the nether world
also.

The princes did as they were told and in
Paataala they saw the horse grazing in a corner of
an *aashrama*, not far from the place where Sage
Kapila who was Vishnu sat in meditation.

The princes at once jumped to the conclusion
that they had not only found the stolen horse but the
thief also, and they rushed on Kapila shouting,
"Here is the thief pretending to be a *yogi*."

Kapila thus disturbed opened his eyes and the
sixty thousand princes were reduced to a heap of
ashes. Indra, the real thief, had artfully left the
horse here with this very intent.

CHAPTER VII

BHAGEERATHA AND
THE STORY OF GANGA

KING Sagara waited in vain for the return of the princes who had gone in search of the sacrificial horse.

After some days he called his grandson, Amsumaan, and said: "I am anxious to know what has happened to the princes who went to *Paataala*. You are brave; go thither, well-armed, find out what has happened and come back crowned with success."

Amsumaan went closely following the path of the princes and reached the nether world where he saw and paid salutations to the mighty elephants standing guard at the four quarters. These guardians of the quarters uttered encouraging words and said he would succeed in his mission.

When in due course Amsumaan entered and went round *Paataala* he was delighted when he found the sacrificial horse grazing contentedly there, but was perplexed and distressed when he saw heaps of ashes all over the place. Could they be all that remained of his valiant uncles?

Garuda, the bird-king, brother of Sumati, Sagara's second wife, who chanced to be there told Amsumaan: "Those ash-heaps are all that is left of the sixty thousand sons of Sagara who were consumed by the wrathful glance of Sage Kapila. Dear child, take the horse and complete the *yaaga*. If these ashes are to be watered according to custom so that the souls of the princes may rest in peace, Ganga should be brought down here from the land of the Devas."

Amsumaan rushed home with the horse and told the king all that he had found and learnt.

Sagara was immersed in sorrow at the fate that had overtaken his sons. However, the horse having been brought back, he completed the *yaaga*. Grieving over his lost sons and despairing of ever bringing Ganga down to the nether world, he died disconsolate.

According to the *Raamaayana*, Sagara lived for 30,000 years. Figures like 30,000 and 60,000 need not confuse us; 'thirty-thousand' may mean either a very large number or just thirty. If we so like, we may take these figures literally.

Amsumaan succeeded Sagara as King of Ayodhya and was, in turn, succeeded by Dileepa. Bhageeratha came after Dileepa.

Amsumaan and Dileepa, though happy and blessed in other respects, died grieving that they were unable to bring Ganga to *Paataala* for the salvation of their forefathers.

Bhageeratha was a valiant king. He was childless. Desiring progeny and hoping to bring Ganga down, he left for Gokarna for performing penance, leaving the kingdom in the hands of his ministers.

Bhageeratha went through severe austerities. With fire on all sides and head exposed to the hot sun, and taking food but once a month, he continued his *tapas*. Bhageeratha's name has come to signify great perseverance in any good cause.

Brahma, pleased with the *tapas*, appeared before Bhageeratha and asked: "What would you have?"

Bhageeratha told him his two wishes: "If you have pity on me, bless me with a child to continue the line of my forebears. Secondly, cursed by Kapilamuni, my ancestors lie a heap of ashes in *Paataala*. The ashes should be washed by the waters of Ganga so that their souls may ascend to heaven. May you be pleased to order Ganga to go down."

Brahma replied: "The Devas are pleased with your *tapas*. Your wishes are granted. But there is one difficulty. The earth cannot withstand the force of Ganga's descent; Siva alone can stand it. Therefore direct your penance and prayers to him."

Bhageeratha renewed his *tapas* and continued long without food or water, and at last won Siva's grace. Siva appeared and said to Bhageeratha: "I shall fulfil your wish. I shall receive Ganga on my head. May her grace be upon you."

When Mahaadeva promised help to Bhageeratha, Ganga began her descent as ordered by Brahma. In her arrogance, she thought she would fall on Mahaadeva's head and sweep him away towards *Paataala*.

The three-eyed God decided to teach Ganga a lesson. And the moment he willed it, the flood of waters that fell on his head were held by his matted hair as in an infinite receptacle. Ganga tried her best but not a drop could emerge from the tangled maze of Siva's matted locks.

This was a lesson to Ganga to be sure, but a heart-breaking disappointment to Bhageeratha. There was nothing for him but to propitiate Siva with *tapas*. This he did to such good purpose that Siva took pity on him and gently let out the waters of

Ganga in *Bindu Saras* from where they flowed down in seven small separate streams.

Three of them flowed west and three east; and the seventh river followed Bhageeratha who was full of joy at the approaching salvation of his ancestors.

Ganga followed Bhageeratha's triumphal chariot; the waters danced and shone like lightning flashes as the river made its course and the Devas and Gandharvas assembled above to witness the grand sight. Sometimes slow and sometimes fast, now sliding down and now jumping up, the river went on dancing behind Bhageeratha's chariot and the folk of heaven enjoyed the sight all the way.

On her course, Ganga damaged the *yaaga* platform of a rishi by name Jahnu. The rishi took the entire flood in his palm and sipped it off. Ganga disappeared again and Bhageeratha was sorely perplexed.

The Devas and other rishis approached Jahnu and begged him to forgive Ganga and allow Bhageeratha to reap the fruit of his great austerities and perseverance. The sage relented and let Ganga out through his right ear. The Devas were glad and blessed Ganga thus: "Coming out of the rishi's body as out of your mother's womb, you are now Jaahnavi, Jahnu's daughter."

There was no further hindrance or mishap and Ganga reached *Paataala* through the ocean. With the holy waters, Bhageeratha performed the funeral rites for his ancestors and secured for them their entry to heaven.

Bhageeratha's efforts having brought Ganga down, she is known as Bhaageerathi.

After concluding this narrative, Viswaamitra blessed the princes. "The sun is setting," he said. "Let us say our evening prayers in the waters of Ganga whom your ancestor brought down to this world."

Those who bathe in the holy waters of Ganga or read or listen to this divine story with devotion, will be cleansed of sin and endowed with virtue, strength and unflagging zeal.

CHAPTER VIII

AHALYA

AFTER a day's stay in the City of Visaala, Viswaamitra and his party left for Mithila. On the way, not far from Mithila, they saw a beautiful *aashrama* which seemed untenanted. Raama asked Viswaamitra: "Whose is this *aashrama* with ancient trees? Why does such a beautiful abode stand deserted?"

Viswaamitra replied:

"This *aashrama* is subject to a curse. Sage Gautama lived here with his wife Ahalya, spending his days in peace and holy meditation. One day during the sage's absence from the *aashrama*, Indra, filled with unholy desire for the beautiful Ahalya, entered it disguised as Gautama and approached the lady with urgent solicitation. She was not deceived by the impersonation, but vain of her beauty and proud that it had won her the love of the lord of the celestials, she lost her judgment and yielded to his desire.

"When the sin had been sinned, realising its heinousness and the fierce spiritual energy of her betrayed husband, she warned Indra of his terrible peril and begged him to be gone in the instant.

"Indra was fleeing in guilty panic; but unfortunately for him he almost bumped into the rishi who was just returning from his ablutions, clad in wet garments and radiating spiritual lustre. Pretence was hopeless before that all-seeing wisdom and Indra bowed in abject supplication, and threw himself on the mercy of the rishi. The sage looked at him with wrath and loathing and cursed him:

'Lustful beast as you are, dead to all truth and righteousness, may your manhood fall away from you.'

"Indra at once became an eunuch and went back to the Devas in ignominious shame.

"Then the sage turned to his erring wife and prescribed a long penance for her. He said: 'Living on air, you shall stay here, unseen by anyone. After a long time, Dasaratha's son will pass this way. When he sets foot in this *aashrama*, you will be freed from the curse. Welcome him as a guest. You will then recover your lost virtue and get back your own beauty.'

"The sage then left his violated *aashrama* for Himaalaya to engage himself in austerities there."

Viswaamitra said to Raama: "Let us enter the *aashrama*. You will bring redemption to Ahalya and re-kindle the light in her as the sage promised."

And they went into the *aashrama*. As Raama set foot in the *aashrama*, the curse was lifted and Ahalya stood before them in all her beauty. Having lain concealed behind leaves and creepers and kept her vow for many years, she now shone, says the poet, in Raama's presence, like the moon emerging from the clouds, like a flame issuing from smoke and like the sun's reflection in rippling water.

Raama and Lakshmana touched the feet of the sage's wife made pure by penance. She welcomed the divine princes with all the customary rites of hospitality. A shower of flowers descended from the heavens as Ahalya cleansed of sin, shone like a goddess; simultaneously the sage Gautama returned to the *aashrama* and received his repentant and purified wife back to his affection.

That is Ahalya's story as told by Vaalmeeki.
There are in other Puraanas and popular stories
slightly varying versions, but the differences need
not trouble us.

Now, a word to those of our times who read
Raamaayana and *Bhaarata* and other Puraanas. In
these works, there are frequent references to Devas
and *Raakshasas*. The latter were wicked, had no
regard for *dharma*, and revelled in evil deeds.
Asuras were also like *Raakshasas*. But even among
Raakshasas there were a few wise and virtuous
people. There spring up bad men even in the best of
races and vice versa. On the whole, *Asuras* and
Raakshasas were those who rejoiced in doing wicked
deeds. It is a pity that some people in their ignorance
identify the *Asuras* and *Raakshasas* with ancient
Indian tribes and races—a view not supported by
any literary work or tradition or recorded history.

The conjecture of foreigners that the *Raaksha-*
sas were the Dravidian race, is not borne out by any
authority in Tamil or other literature. The Tamil
people are not descendants of the *Asuras* or
Raakshasas.

The Devas were generally upholders of *dharma*
and took on themselves the task of putting down the
Raakshasas. According to the Puraanas, they had at
times to deviate from *dharma* in dealing with the
Raakshasas, some of whom had attained great
power through *tapas*.

The Devas were generally good; and those
among them who swerved from the path of
righteousness paid the price for it. There was no
separate code of conduct for the Devas; the law of
karma admits of no distinction between the Devas

and others. The law dealt with the Devas as with others.

Wedded to virtue as the Devas generally were, lapses on their part appear big to us, like stains on white cloth. The *Raakshasas'* evil deeds are taken for granted and do not attract much attention, like stains on black cloth.

The honest, when they happen to go astray, should evoke our sympathy. It is however the way of the world—but it is not right—to condemn in strong terms casual lapses of the virtuous, while tolerating habitual wrong-doers.

It should be noted that in the Puraanas we see the gods getting entangled in dilemmas of *dharma*. Indra and other Devas are shown often as committing serious sins. Why did the sages who told the Puraanas involve themselves in such difficulties? Their aim was to awaken people to a sense of the dangers of *adharma*. Else, the sages need not have deliberately attributed sinful acts to their own heroes and created difficulties for themselves.

Some persons take pleasure in jumping to wrong conclusions from the incidents in the Puraanas. They argue: "Raavana was a very good king. Vaalmeeki has falsely accused him of wicked deeds." They ask: "Did not Raama act unjustly on a certain occasion? Did not Seeta utter a lie?" and the like.

Vaalmeeki could well have omitted incidents which are not edifying. Both Raama and Raavana were first presented to us by the poet Vaalmeeki. There was no earlier work referring to Raavana that can be quoted to contradict Vaalmeeki and stamp him as being partial to Raama, Seeta and the Devas,

and twisting facts to deceive people. Vaalmeeki's
Raamaayana is the fountain source of the story of
Raama; in it, one comes across seemingly wrong
deeds.

Calm consideration of such situations would
show that they are just portrayals of similar
difficulties in our day-to-day life. It is for us to
benefit from the moral trials contained in them. The
lesson of the Ahalya episode is that, however deadly
one's sin, one may hope to be freed from its
consequence by penitence and punishment. Instead
of condemning others for their sins, we should look
within our own hearts and try to purify them of
every evil thought. The best of us have need for
eternal vigilance, if we would escape sin. This is the
moral of Ahalya's error.

CHAPTER IX

RAAMA WINS SEETA'S HAND

ALL arrangements for Janaka's *yaaga* had been completed and to Mithila had come many rishis and Braahmanas from various kingdoms. Viswaamitra and the princes were duly welcomed. Janaka's preceptor, Sataananda, was the first to pay honour to Viswaamitra, Janaka followed him.

The King said to the sage: "I am indeed blessed that you should attend my *yaaga*."

Pointing to Raama and Lakshmana, Janaka asked Viswaamitra: "Who are these god-like youths who resemble each other, and carry their weapons with the proud ease of seasoned warriors? Who is the happy father of such sons?"

Viswaamitra told Janaka that they were the sons of King Dasaratha. He narrated how they had protected his own *yaaga* and destroyed the *Raakshasas*. "They have come here," the sage went on, "to see, if they may, the great bow of Rudra in your palace." Janaka understood the meaning of Viswaamitra's words and rejoiced.

The King said: "The Prince is welcome to see the bow. If he can string it, he will win the hand of my daughter. Many were the princes who saw this bow and went back, unable even to move it. I shall indeed be happy if this prince succeeds where so many have failed and I am thereby enabled to give Seeta to him."

Janaka then ordered his men to bring the bow which was kept safe and sacred in an iron box. It was brought on an eight-wheeled carriage and dragged like a temple chariot during a festival.

"Here", said Janaka, "is Rudra's bow wor-
shipped by me and my ancestors. Let Raama see this
bow."

After obtaining permission from Viswaamitra
and the King, Raama stepped out to the iron
bow-case, while all eyes were fixed on him in wishful
expectation. Opening the box, he lifted the bow
effortlessly, as if it were a garland of flowers, and
resting one end of it against his toe, he bent and
strung it and drew the string back with such
irresistible force that the mighty bow snapped with a
crash like a clap of thunder. And there fell from
heaven a shower of flowers.

Janaka proclaimed: "My beloved daughter shall
be wedded to this Prince."

Viswaamitra said to Janaka: "Send your
swiftest messengers to Ayodhya to give the news to
Dasaratha and invite him."

Janaka's messengers reached Ayodhya in three
days. They met King Dasaratha who was seated, like
Indra, on his throne and said to him: "Sage
Viswaamitra and King Janaka have sent you happy
news. Your son who came to Mithila has won our
princess Seeta by fulfilling the condition set for her
hand. He not only strung Rudra's bow which none
before could so much as lift, but bent its tough pride
till it broke. King Janaka eagerly awaits your
gracious consent for the marriage, and your presence
and blessing at the festivities. May it please you to
start for Mithila with your retinue."

Dasaratha, who had sent Raama with Viswaamitra with a heart not altogether free from
anxiety even after the sage's assurance, was thrilled
with joy on hearing this good news. He told his

ministers to prepare for the journey and left the very next day for Janaka's capital.

Dasaratha and his following reached Mithila and were received with enthusiastic welcome. Exchange of courtesies over, Janaka said to Dasaratha: "My *yaaga* will soon be over. I think it best to have the marriage as soon as the *yaaga* is over," and sought his approval. Dasaratha replied: "You are the bride's father and it is for you to order things as you wish."

At the appointed day and hour, giving away the bride, King Janaka said to Raama: "Here is my daughter, Seeta, who will ever tread with you the path of *dharma*. Take her hand in yours. Blessed and devoted, she will ever walk with you like your own shadow:

> *"Iyam Seetaa mama sutaa*
> *(sahadharmacharee tava)*
> *prateechchha chainaam bhadram te*
> *paanim grihneeshwa paaninaa*
> *pativrataa mahaabhaagaa*
> *chhaayevaanugataa sadaa."*

This *sloka* is uttered in every wedding in upper India when the bride is given away.

Thus was Seeta given by Janaka to Raama. Were they not Eternal Lovers re-united? And so they rejoiced like lovers come together after separation.

CHAPTER X

PARASURAAMA'S DISCOMFITURE

HAVING thus safely handed back to Dasaratha at Mithila the princes entrusted to him in Ayodhya, and after attending the wedding celebrations, Viswaamitra took leave of the two kings and went to Himaalaya. In the story of Raama, Viswaamitra has no further part.

Viswaamitra may be said to be the foundation of the grand temple of Raama's story. After Raama's wedding in Mithila, we do not see him again. It should be noted that characters who play a leading role in one canto of Vaalmeeki almost fade out in subsequent cantos. Viswaamitra who dominates the Baala Kaanda does not appear again. Similarly, Kaikeyi and Guha are prominent only in Ayodhya Kaanda. The same thing can be said of Bharata whom we do not come across in the chapters intervening between the Chitrakoota meeting and Raama's return to Ayodhya. The poet hardly brings Bharata before our eyes during the period of Raama's distress. The characters in Vaalmeeki *Raamaayana* (unlike those in the *Mahaabhaarata* and in ordinary plays and novels) do not present themselves off and on. Critics should bear this general characteristic of Vaalmeeki's epic in mind.

King Dasaratha returned to Ayodhya, accompanied by his retinue. On the way, there were bad omens and anxious Dasaratha asked Vasishtha what they portended. Vasishtha replied that there was no need to be alarmed, for though the birds in the air indicated approaching trouble, the animals on the land promised a happy consummation.

As Dasaratha and Vasishtha were thus conversing, there broke out a great storm; trees were uprooted; the earth quaked and clouds of dust went up and hid the sun and there was an all-enveloping darkness. Everyone was terror-struck. Soon they knew the reason for the strange phenomenon. There stood before them the awe-inspiring figure Parasuraama, the sworn enemy of Kshatriyas, with a bow on one shoulder and a battle-axe on the other, and with an arrow shining like lightning in his hand. Terrible in appearance, with his matted locks gathered overhead, he looked like Rudra exulting in the destruction of Tripura. His face emitted flame-like radiance. The son of Sage Jamadagni struck terror among Kshatriyas, many generations of whom he had annihilated. Wherever he went he was preceded by storm and earth-quake. And the Kshatriya race trembled in fear.

The Braahmanas in Dasaratha's retinue said to one another: "Because his father was killed by a king, Parasuraama took a vow to destroy the Kshatriya race. We dared to hope that his vengeful wrath had been quenched in the blood of the innumerable kings he has slain. Has he again started his cruel campaign?" However, they honoured him with the customary offering of water. After receiving it, Parasuraama addressed himself to Raama: "Son of Dasaratha, I have heard of your prowess. I was somewhat surprised to learn that you strung the bow in King Janaka's court and that you drew the string till the bow broke. Here is my bow, equal in all respects to the one that you broke. This is the bow of Vishnu which was entrusted to my father. If you are able to string this bow, you will be worthy of my battle."

Dasaratha was perturbed at this turn of events and he begged that his son Raama should be spared the trial. He said to Parasuraama: "You are a Braahmana. We have heard that, satiated with your revenge, you have gone back to *tapas* as becomes your order, in pursuance of your plighted word to Indra, after giving away the earth you had conquered to Kaashyapa. Is it proper that you should break your vow, and seek to injure a prince of tender years who has done you no wrong, and who is dearer to us than life?"

Parasuraama heard him unmoved without so much as looking at him, and addressed himself solely to Raama, as though the others did not exist: "Viswakarma originally made two exactly similar bows. One of them was given to Rudra and the other to Vishnu. This is the one given to Vishnu. What you are said to have strung and bent to breaking point was Siva's bow. See if you can string this bow of Vishnu; and if you do, it will be proof of your skill and strength and I will then honour you by fighting with you."

Parasuraama spoke in a loud and arrogant tone. To him Raama replied in courteous manner, yet in firm tones: "Son of Jamadagni! You have been vengeful because your father was killed by a king. I do not blame you for that. But you cannot put me down as you have humbled others. Please give me your bow."

So saying, he took the bow and arrow from Parasuraama. He strung the bow and setting the arrow to it, drew the string. Addressing Parasuraama, he said with a smile: "This mighty Vaishnava arrow placed on the string cannot be put back idly. It must destroy something. Tell me, shall it destroy your powers of locomotion, or would you rather that it consumes the fruits of your *tapas*?"

As the son of Dasaratha strung the bow of Vishnu, the glory on Parasuraama's face faded, and he stood, no longer the warlike conqueror, but a self-subdued rishi, for the purpose of the Parasuraama *avataar* was over.

Parasuraama said mildly to the Prince of Ayodhya: "I realise who you are. I am not sorry that you have quenched my arrogance. Let all my *tapas* go to you. But because of my promise to Kaashyapa, I cannot remain in his domains and have therefore to hurry back to the Mahendra mountains before the sun sets. Let me use my power of locomotion for this single thing. Subject to this, let the arrow which you have set to the bow consume all my power earned through *tapas*."

So saying, Parasuraama went in reverent circumambulation round the Prince and departed.

Ayodhya's citizens were over-joyed to hear that Dasaratha and the royal princes were returning to the capital. The city was festive with flowers and shone like the *deva-loka*.

Raama and Seeta lived happily in Ayodhya for twelve years. Raama had surrendered his heart to Seeta. It was difficult for one to say whether their love grew because of their virtues or it was planted in their beauty of form. Their hearts communed even without speech. Seeta, rejoicing in Raama's love, shone like Lakshmi in heaven.

Long afterwards, when their forest-life began, Anasooya, the great sage Atri's holy wife, extolled Seeta's love for Raama. And Seeta answered: "How else could it be? Raama is a perfect being. His love for me equals mine for him. His affection is unchanging. Pure of heart, he has mastered the senses."

CHAPTER XI

FESTIVE PREPARATIONS

RAAMA and Seeta spent twelve happy years in Ayodhya. But now the Lord and his consort in human form had to experience the hardships, sorrows and conflicts of life on earth.

As Bhagavaan himself explains: "Whatever *avataar* I assume, my play must go through the feelings and experiences appropriate to that incarnation."

Who was the Prince of Ayodhya who through his body, life and experience, suffered the sorrows of mankind and saved the gods? The ever-present, all-pervasive Being who rules the world from within and without.

Kamban, the Tamil poet, begins the Ayodhya Kaanda referring to this marvel of how the King of Kings allowed himself to suffer the cruel machinations of the hunchback maid-servant and of a step-mother which deprived him of the sceptre and banished him to the forest and beyond the sea.

Dasaratha loved all his four sons and yet he had a special affection for Raama. And the latter deserved it by his royal qualities and adherence to *dharma*. Queen Kausalya—like Aditi, the mother of the gods—was proud that she had such a son as Raama.

Vaalmeeki has filled pages with the tale of Raama's virtues. The *muni* is never satiated drinking from the ocean of Raama's qualities. He describes Raama's gifts and graces sometimes directly, sometimes as seen and admired by others;

thus and in many other ways he dwells on the qualities that made Raama the ideal man.

Raama's graceful frame and virile beauty, his strength, his courage, the purity of his heart, his perfect life, his compassion, sweetness of speech, his serenity, his deep wisdom and his statesmanship were admired by the people and made them eagerly look forward to his becoming king.

And Dasaratha knew and rejoiced in this expectation. Hence, considering his old age, he wished to crown Raama as *Yuvaraaja* and entrust him with the *de facto* rule of the kingdom. Informing his ministers of his desire, he had the *Raaja Sabha* convened. Rishis and wise men, leaders of the city and kings from neighbouring lands, attended the *Raaja Sabha*. When all were seated, each in his appropriate place, Dasaratha rose and addressed them.

His deep manly voice, like the sound of a trumpet or the roar of rain-bearing clouds, filled the great hall. A royal radiance shone from his face. His words were full of meaning and charmed all ears.

"Like my ancestors, I have tended this kingdom as a mother cares for her child. I have worked unremittingly for the people. Now my body is old and infirm. I wish therefore to appoint my eldest son as *Yuvaraaja* and transfer to him the burden of responsibility. Following the holy custom of my forefathers, I hope to spend the rest of my life in austerities in the forest. Raama is fully equal to the task of kingship. He is expert in administration and statecraft and he is unequalled in valour. I can transfer this trust of sovereignty to him without any anxiety and I hope that this honoured assembly will permit me to do so."

Shouts of joyous acclaim rose from the great assembly and with one voice the gathered princes and notables exclaimed: "So be it."

The King spoke again: "You agree with my proposal but give no reason. This will not do. Let the wise men explain why they agree."

Then several speakers rose and explained Raama's virtues and fitness to rule. The King's heart was filled with joy to hear these praises of Raama.

At last the whole assembly rose and said with one voice: "Let there be no delay. Let Raama be anointed *Yuvaraaja*."

The King answered that he was happy and would forthwith carry out their wishes. Then turning to Vasishtha, Vaamadeva and the other holy men and guardians of the sacred rites, he said: "This is the auspicious month of Chaitra, the season when the trees in the forest are covered with flowers. Revered elders, make all preparations for the anointing of Raama."

The assembly was glad to hear these prompt orders. As bidden by the King, Sumantra, the minister in charge of the household, went to fetch Raama. Raama, ignorant of all these happenings, came and stood before his father.

Hearing of the decision to anoint him *Yuvaraaja*, he humbly bowed acceptance, saying "I am in duty bound to carry out your orders, whatever they be."

Dasaratha blessed Raama and said: "You are a good prince beloved of the people. Let not your courtesy and your consideration flag but increase with your opportunities of doing good, and earn you enduring glory." And Raama returned to his dwelling.

Hardly had Raama returned home when Sumantra called in haste and told him that his father wished to see him. Asked for the reason, Sumantra could not tell; he only knew he had been enjoined to fetch the prince at once.

Raama thought: "The King must have taken counsel over the coronation ceremony and perhaps met with some difficulty. But whatever happens is for the best." Raama was not eager to assume authority, but looked on it as only a duty to be done. If the King wanted him to take it up, he was ready to do so. But if the King wanted him to give it up, he was equally willing. In this mood, Raama went to his father.

CHAPTER XII

MANTHARA'S EVIL COUNSEL

THE King embraced Raama, seated him beside him on the throne and said: "I am old; I have enjoyed my life as a man and a king. I have discharged all my duties to my ancestors. There is nothing left for me to do.

"My only desire is to install you on the throne of our fathers. Last night I had bad dreams. Those who read the future advise me that a great sorrow, even death, may overtake me very soon. Hence I wish to have the coronation performed tomorrow. Tomorrow, the readers of the stars say, is auspicious. Something within me says, 'Do this at once.' You and Seeta should prepare for tomorrow's anointment by fasting tonight. Lie down on a bed of *darbha* grass and have trusty and vigilant friends to look after your safety. It seems to me that the present time when Bharata is away is particularly opportune for your installation. Not that I do not know that Bharata is the soul of righteousness in thought and conduct alike, and that he is devoted to you, but the minds of men are changeful and open to unexpected influences."

And so the King decided that the coronation should be performed on the very next day and told Vasishtha of his decision. Bad dreams added to the reasons for fixing the day for the coronation at once.

Taking leave of his father, Raama went to Kausalya's apartment to give her the news and seek her blessing. But the Queen had heard the news already. Sumitra, Seeta and Lakshmana were all there with Kausalya, who, clad in ceremonial white, sat offering prayers for the son.

Raama reported to his mother the King's latest command. She answered: "This I have heard. May you live long. Be a good ruler. Conquer your foes and protect your subjects and kinsfolk. You have pleased your father and you have made me happy."

Then bidding farewell to his mother and step-mother, Raama went to his own apartment. As directed by the King, Vasishtha came to Raama's place. He was welcomed by him at the entrance. Vasishtha initiated Raama with due *mantras* in his pre-coronation fast.

As Vasishtha returned to the King, he saw groups of people on the royal road, cheerfully discussing the great festival of the morrow. Houses were being decorated with flowers, festoons and flags. It was with difficulty that Vasishtha could make his way through the crowds to the King's palace. The King was pleased to hear that the fast had begun duly and all was being got ready for the ceremony.

But in his heart of hearts there was a fear that some mishap might come between him and his one wish.

The city was in a joyous commotion of expectancy. In every house, in every street, men, women and children looked on the coronation as a great and auspicious occasion in their own lives and awaited it with enthusiasm.

Raama and Seeta in their dwelling meditated long on Naaraayana, fed with *ghee* the sacrificial fire, and reverently sipped what remained of the *ghee*, and slept on grass spread on the floor.

Early the following morning, they were roused from slumber by music and held themselves in readiness to proceed to the palace and in expectation of the auspicious call.

But the summons that came was of an entirely opposite nature.

In accordance with the practice in royal households, Queen Kaikeyi had a woman companion and confidential servant. She was a hunch-back named Manthara. Being a distant relation of the Queen, she claimed great intimacy with her.

Manthara is one of the best known characters in the *Raamayana*. Every man, woman and child in our land knows and detests her, as the cause of Raama's exile, Dasaratha's death and all the sorrows which befell the royal family.

On the day on which Dasaratha summoned the Assembly and decided to anoint Raama as *Yuvaraaja*, Manthara happened to climb up to the terrace of the women's apartments and stood surveying the town below. She saw the streets were sprinkled with water and gaily decorated. Flags flew from the house-tops. Wearing new clothes and bright jewels, smeared with sandal paste and decked in flowers, people moved about in crowds, engrossed in happy talk. Musical instruments played in the temples.

Manthara could not understand the reason for all this, for she did not know what the King had decided. Some celebration was on, she guessed.

Manthara turned to a servant and asked her: "Why are you wearing this silk dress? What is on in the City? Kausalya seems to be distributing gifts to Braahmanas. She is a thrifty lady and would not be doing this for nothing. There are festive sights and sounds everywhere. Do you know what all this is about?"

The little servant girl answered, dancing with joy: "Why, do you not know that our Raamachandra is going to be anointed *Yuvaraaja* tomorrow morning?"

This was news! Manthara was overpowered with sudden anger. Quickly she hobbled downstairs. Straight she entered Kaikeyi's room. Kaikeyi was resting on her bed.

"Rise, rise, foolish woman! A flood of misfortune is rising to drown and swallow you! You are betrayed and ruined. Your sun is setting. Foolish girl, is this the time to sleep?"

Kaikeyi, fearing that some calamity had overtaken Manthara, asked her gently: "What is troubling you? Why are you thus upset?"

And the clever Manthara began: "Destruction has come upon both you and me, my girl. Dasaratha has decided to make Raama *Yuvaraaja*— the real ruler of this land. What greater cause for sorrow need I have? When grief comes to you, how can I remain unconcerned? I have come running to you. You were born and bred in a royal family. You were married into a royal family. Now, alas, all is over.

"Like the simple woman you are, you have been deceived. Your husband has cheated you with sweet words. It is a deep plot, as any one can see. He put Bharata out of the way by sending him to the distant place of his uncle, and is taking advantage of his absence by hurriedly crowning Raama. By tomorrow it will all be over. And you watch all this, lying in bed and doing nothing, while you and all who depend on you are being destroyed."

And so, Manthara went on talking. Kaikeyi's ears heard the words without quite heeding their drift. Like the rest of the royal household her mind was overwhelmed now with the joyous expectation of Raama's coronation, for she loved and esteemed Raama like everybody else.

"Manthara, you have brought me good news," she said. "Is my son Raama to be crowned tomorrow? What greater joy can come to me? Here, take this. Ask me for anything else." So saying, Kaikeyi took the necklace off her neck and gave it to Manthara. It was a royal custom at once to reward with a rich gift the bringer of any important good news.

Kaikeyi thought Manthara, like any other officious personal attendant, was ingratiatingly jealous in her mistress's interests. How could this woman understand the goodness of Raama, or affairs of State? And so she thought her foolish fears would be banished if she saw that her mistress was happy at the event. Kaikeyi's mind was still uncorrupted. She had the culture of her noble lineage and was not easily amenable to low thoughts.

This but increased Manthara's grief. She flung away the necklace and said: "Woe to you, stupid woman. All is lost and stupidly you laugh with joy. How can you be blind to the misfortune that is coming to you? Am I to laugh or cry at this folly? Your rival, Raama's mother, has conspired to making him King. And you jump with joy. Insane woman! What would be Bharata's state when Raama reigns? Would not Raama fear and ever look upon Bharata as a dangerous enemy? Raama knows human nature. He knows that Bharata alive would be a constant threat to his power and therefore must be killed. Does not one kill a cobra out of fear? Hereafter there is no security for Bharata's life. Tomorrow morning Kausalya will be a happy woman and you will bend before her as a well-dressed slave. You will stand before her, hands clasped in obedience. From tomorrow your son too will be a subject and a slave. In these apartments there will be no more honour or joy."

And she stopped, unable for grief to continue. Kaikeyi heard all this and wondered "Why should Manthara have such fears? Does she not know Raama? Is he not *dharma* embodied in human form?"

She said: "Manthara, have you not known and rejoiced in Raama's truthfulness, right conduct and humility? He is the elder prince and he gets the kingdom. Bharata will get it one day after him. What is wrong with all this? Why, dear friend, do you feel such grief? After Raama, Bharata will reign for a hundred years. Do not cry. You know how affectionate Raama is to me. Indeed he cares for me more than for his own mother. Does not Raama hold his brothers as dear as life? It is not right that you should fear any harm from Raama."

"Alas, Alas!" said Manthara. "Why are you so foolish? Once Raama is crowned king, what chance has Bharata? Do you not know the rule of succession? When Raama ascends the throne all prospects of royalty for Bharata and his line are at an end. After Raama, Raama's son will be king, and after him that son's son will be king, and so the succession will go on. Eldest son succeeds eldest son. There is no chance for a younger brother, no matter how good or manly he is. My dear, you know not even this. What is one to do?"

"Once Raama is crowned," she continued, "he will not leave Bharata alone. There will be danger to Bharata's life. If you want Bharata to live, advise him to remain away, an exile from home; for if he returns he will be coming to his death. It would be safest for him to leave even his uncle's house, and hide his head in obscurity in some more distant land.

"And Kausalya is no friend of yours. She bears you a grudge because you are the King's favourite and have often slighted her. And now she is sure to wreak vengeance on you. You know the wrath of a rival wife is a raging fire when it finds its chance. You may take it that, if Raama is king, Bharata is as good as dead. Therefore, think hard. Be firm. Decide something and stick to it. Somehow Bharata must be crowned. Raama must be banished from the kingdom."

Fear now entered the heart of the Queen. Manthara won. Kaikeyi's face was flushed; her breath became hot. Helpless she clung to Manthara for comfort and safety.

Because his first two wives had borne no children, Dasaratha, following the royal custom, married Kaikeyi. At that time Kaikeyi's father secured from Dasaratha the promise that the child of her womb should become king after him. In such a promise given by a childless king there was nothing surprising and nothing wrong. At that time, his then queens had long been childless. The King took a third wife for the sake of progeny. Even then his wish for a son to be born was not fulfilled. Many years passed.

After the great sacrifice was performed, all three wives bore children. The son of the Queen Eminent, Raama, was the eldest among four sons. He was also great in virtue, fully equal to the burden of Kingship, acceptable to ministers, citizens and vassal princes. How could Dasaratha violate the royal custom and ignoring Raama's claim anoint Bharata?

Moreover, neither Bharata nor Kaikeyi had ever thought of or wished for the fulfilment of this old and forgotten promise. During all the intervening years, no word had been spoken on this subject. Hence the King thought there could be no difficulty in installing Raama as *Yuvaraaja* in accordance with the custom of the dynasty and public expectation. And there was no cloud in Kaikeyi's mind. This is clear from Kaikeyi's behaviour. And Bharata was too good and noble to raise a question.

And, yet, as Dasaratha told Raama, even the purest of minds is mutable. When fate conspires with bad counsel, any one of us might be corrupted. And this happened to Kaikeyi. The gods in Heaven had received an assurance, and the sages had performed *tapas* for the destruction of Raavana. What we call destiny, therefore, ordained that Kaikeyi's pure heart should be changed by Manthara's evil counsel. So says Kamban in the Tamil *Raamaayana* in his own inimitable style.

Fearing that delay might bring some unpredictable obstacles, Dasaratha had ordered the coronation to be done without waiting for Bharata's return to the capital. This same fear and hurry were used by Manthara to persuade Kaikeyi to take the wrong path. "Think, my Queen. Why this haste? Why does your husband rush through the ceremony when your son is absent? Is it not to cheat him of his right? Is not the motive plain? The King pretends to be enamoured of you. But this is only his hypocritical shrewdness."

Thus tempted, Kaikeyi thought over Manthara's advice. Kaikeyi was weak like any other woman. She had good feeling and good culture, besides a keen intellect. But she had little knowledge of the world. She was also terribly obstinate. Easily deceived, she did not have the power to foresee the full consequences of her action. Thus began the chapter of grief in the *Raamaayana*.

CHAPTER XIII

KAIKEYI SUCCUMBS

KAIKEYI, who had looked upon Raama as her own son, was enmeshed in Manthara's arguments and became helpless.

"Indeed, I am afraid," she said. "Tell me what we should do. Am I to be a servant to Kausalya? Never, Bharata must be crowned. You are quite right. And Raama must be sent to forest. But how shall we get all this done? Tell me. You are clever and know the way."

And she clung to Manthara. In Kaikeyi's eyes at that time Manthara's crooked frame appeared handsome. This is not a joke; it is a subtle psychological phenomenon.

"This is indeed strange, Kaikeyi," said Manthara. "Is it for me to tell you how this could be brought about? Have you really forgotten? Or, are you only pretending? But if you want me to say it, I shall do so. Listen."

And then she paused. Kaikeyi, all impatient, cried: "Tell me, tell me. Somehow Bharata must be crowned and Raama's coronation must be stopped."

"Very well," said Manthara, "I shall tell you. Do not be impatient. You remember how your husband Dasaratha, long ago, fought against Sambara in the South? And you were with him, were you not? Your husband went, did he not, to help Indra? Sambara of Vaijayanti was too powerful for Indra, who sought Dasaratha's help. Did not Dasaratha get wounded in battle and lose consciousness? Then, you drove his chariot skilfully out of the battle-field, gently removed the arrows from his body and revived him and saved his life. Have you forgotten all this?

"And what did he tell you then? He told you in gratitude: 'Ask me for two boons. I shall give you anything you want.' Then you answered: 'I shall ask for my boons later. I want nothing now.' Then he promised, did he not, 'You will have your two gifts whenever you want them'? You told me all this long ago yourself. You may have forgotten it, but I have not. The time has arrived to get him to redeem his promise.

"Demand that he should crown Bharata instead of Raama. This will be the first of two gifts he promised. For the second gift, ask that Raama be sent to the forest for fourteen years.

"Do not be frightened. Do not fear to ask. Do not think it sinful to demand this. Do what I tell you. It is only if Raama is sent into the forest that his hold on the people will relax and disappear in course of time and your son's position will be secure.

"Go now and lie down in the sulking room. Throw away your fine dress and your jewels, wear an old saree and stretch yourself on the floor. When the King enters the room, do not speak to him. Do not even look at him. I am sure he cannot endure your sorrow. You will then have your way with him.

"The King will try to get round you. Do not yield. He will offer many alternatives. Accept none of them. Insist on the two boons. Be firm.

"Bound by his promise the King will finally come round. I know how passionately he loves you. He would give up his life for your sake. To please you he would jump into fire. Do what I tell you. Do not be afraid.

"Unless Raama is sent to the forest, your wish will not be fulfilled. Raama must be sent away. Only then the position you get for Bharata will be real and lasting. Remember this. Mind you do not weaken."

Listening to this exhortation, Kaikeyi's face shone with hope. "What a brain you have, Manthara," exclaimed Kaikeyi. "You have been the saving of me." And she jumped about in joy like a filly.

Manthara repeated again and again that Raama must be sent to the forest. "Do not delay. What needs to be done, do at once. It is no good strengthening the tank-bund after the waters have flown out. Remember what I have told you. Everything depends on your firmness. Victory is your's if you do not yield."

Kaikeyi assured Manthara of her firmness and forthwith entered the sulking room, removed her jewels and scattered them on the floor, changed her clothes and stretched herself on the floor. Then, assuming a broken voice, she said:

"Manthara, you will yourself carry the news to my father Kekaya. You will yourself tell him one of two things: either that Bharata is to be crowned or that Kaikeyi is dead. My dear, dear Manthara!"

Kaikeyi in her anger believed that Dasaratha had really been treacherous to her. Even then, stretched on the ground divesting herself of all ornaments and putting on a face of grief and anger, she looked inexpressibly beautiful. So great was her beauty.

The sinful thought had found lodgment in her mind and her whole nature was transformed. The fear that she would lead a slave's life, and that even

Bharata's life was in peril, had got hold of her. For the first time in her life she cast aside the sense of shame and sin and hardened her heart. Heaving heavy sighs, perspiring, and with eyes closed, Kaikeyi, beautiful like a Naga goddess, unbraided her hair and lay on the floor with dishevelled tresses and sprawling like a bird shot down by a hunter. The flowers and shining jewels, which once adorned her person, lay scattered in the dark room like stars in the midnight sky.

Having dismissed the Assembly and given orders for the due celebration of the coronation ceremony, Dasaratha, relieved of care and wishing to relax, sought the apartments of his favourite consort. He had decided on the coronation of Raama after receiving the approval of all those who had a right to be consulted and he felt happy and free, as after laying down a heavy burden.

He entered Kaikeyi's chamber to tell her the happy news and spend in pleasant talk the night before the coronation. The junior queen's residence was a beautiful palace with lovely gardens and tanks, birds playing in the water and peacocks dancing with tails spread out and trees resplendent with bright flowers. In Dasaratha's happy mood it appeared unusually beautiful that night.

Like the full moon rising brightly before an eclipse, without knowing of the eclipse that lies in wait for her, the poor old King entered Kaikeyi's dwelling with a beaming face.

The incense pots and drinks were in their usual places but he did not see the Queen whom he was eager to meet. Of all his consorts Kaikeyi was the one whose company he sought for joyous relaxation from all cares of state, for she never interfered in public affairs, and always waited for him at the entrance and welcomed him with a warm embrace. But, today, she was nowhere to be found.

The King was perplexed. He went round and looked in vain for her in all her favourite haunts thinking that she was playing a sweet game of hide and seek. He did not find her.

This sort of thing had never happened before! He asked a maidservant where the Queen was. Folding her hands in reverence, the girl said: "Lord, the Queen is angry. She is in the inner chamber."

The surprised King entered the room. And he saw a sight which amazed and distressed him, for there she lay on the bare floor, with draggled robes and dishevelled hair, like one in mortal pain. She seemed too full of anguish even to look at him as he entered.

The poor guileless King, all unconscious of having given any cause for offence, behaved with the doting fondness of an old husband and seating himself by her on the floor stroked her hair and strove to console her with loving words and caresses:

"What has come over you? Are you ill? Do you feel any pain? Have I not the best doctors in the land? I shall send for them at once. They can cure any malady. Do not be afraid."

Kaikeyi sighed heavily, but would not speak.

The King proceeded: "Was anyone in the palace guilty of discourteous behaviour? Tell me and I shall punish him. Did anyone slight you or was there anything you wanted which I neglected to give you? Tell me."

In this way, he mentioned faults that might have occurred in the running of a big house and asked her what the matter was and why she was upset. Kaikeyi paid no attention to his questions and was mute like one possessed.

The King begged her more importunately: "State your wish. It shall be done. Do you want anyone punished? I shall punish him. Do you want anyone freed from punishment? I shall free him, even if he be a murderer."

"You know my absolute authority. I can give and I can take, as I please. Anywhere, to anyone, I can do what I wish. Ask me anything and it shall be done at once."

Kaikeyi sat up. The King was pleased. And she began: "No one slighted or dishonoured me. But there is something which you can do and you must do it for my sake. Give me your word that you will fulfil my desire. Then I shall tell you what it is."

Hearing this, the unsuspecting old man was filled with joy. Possessing absolute powers, he had no doubt that he could fulfil her wishes whatever they were, and so boldly and joyously he said: "Well, Kaikeyi, tell me your wish. It shall be done. I swear it. I swear it on all I love most— on you, the dearest among women, and on Raama, dearest to me among men! I swear in the name of Raama: Whatever you desire, I shall do, I promise, I swear."

Guileful wickedness and trustful misfortune were reaching the climax in their unequal encounter. The King's swearing in the name of Raama filled Kaikeyi with supreme delight. She was now sure that she had won, for the King would never break a promise coupled with that beloved name.

"Do you promise? Very well!" she exclaimed. "Swear again in the name of Raama that you will do what I wish without fail. Swear it!"

The King said: "My beloved queen, I promise. I swear it on Raama. Whatever you wish I shall do. This is my sworn word."

At this stage, as she thought of the tremendousness of her intended request, Kaikeyi's heart misgave her and she feared that on hearing it her horror-stricken husband would exclaim—God forbid! No oath or promise is strong enough to justify so heinous a sin! — and recoil from her with abhorrence.

She stood erect and with folded hands, turning in the four directions, invoked in a solemn voice the heavenly powers to witness and confirm the oath: "Oh, Ye Gods! You have heard and witnessed the promise given to me by my husband. Sun, Moon and Planets, you are my holy witnesses. Ye, Five Elements! You have heard the promise. He who has never broken his word, my husband, has sworn to do my wish. Bear witness to this."

Dasaratha was looking at her with hungry, joyous eyes. She knew her man and she began boldly: "Do you remember, King, how, when long ago in the field of battle you were about to lose your life, I drove your chariot in the dark night, took you out of the battle-field, removed the arrows from your body and comforted and revived you? When you came out of your faint, you said something, did you not?

"You said: 'You have restored to me the life which my foes had taken from me. I shall give you any two gifts you ask.' Then I said: 'I want nothing now. It is joy enough now for me that you are alive. I shall ask for my gifts later.' Do you remember this ?"

The King answered: "Yes, I do remember this. Ask for your two gifts. You shall have them now."

Kaikeyi said: "Remember you have made a vow. You have given a pledge. You have sworn in the name of Raama. The gods and the five elements have witnessed your promise. I shall state my wishes. Your ancestors never broke their word. Prove yourself their worthy descendant by being true to the word you have given. With the preparations now afoot for the coronation, crown my son Bharata. This is my first wish. The second boon that I demand is, send your son Raama to live in the Dandaka forest for fourteen years. Remember your solemn vow which you cannot break. The good name of your great dynasty is in your hands."

CHAPTER XIV

WIFE OR DEMON?

DASARATHA was thunder-struck.

When his mind resumed its function, he doubted the reality of what had happened. "Could it be other than a hideous dream? Or the phantasmagoria of a disordered brain? Or the sudden materialisation of the sins of some past birth called up for my chastisement? I am certainly the victim of an illusion. I cannot believe this to be reality."

Unable to stand the confused agony of shapeless terrors, he closed his eyes and became unconscious. Opening his eyes a little later, they fell on Kaikeyi and he trembled like a stag at the sight of a tiger. He sat up on the floor and moaned, swaying helplessly this side and that like a cobra held by the spell of a potent charm. Again he swooned.

After a long interval, he recovered his senses and, with eyes turned to his tormentor and inflamed with helpless anger, cried out: "O wicked ogress! Destroyer of my dynasty! What harm has Raama done to you? Has he not looked upon you as his own mother? I thought you were a woman. I now see you are a venomous serpent brought from far away and cherished in my bosom only to sting me to death!"

Kaikeyi was unmoved and spoke not a word.

The King went on: "On what pretext can I banish Raama, whom all the people love and praise? I may lose Kausalya and survive. I may lose the pure-minded Sumitra and survive. But if I lose Raama, I cannot live thereafter. Without water, without sunlight, I may live for a while, but never without Raama. Expel from your mind this sinful thought. With my head bowed at your feet, I beg of you. Have you not said many a time, "Two dear sons I have. And of them Raama, the elder, is dearer to me"? In deciding to crown Raama, what have I done but carry out in action your unspoken wish? Why then do you demand these cruel boons? No, no, it cannot be really that you mean this. You are only testing me to find out if I indeed love your son Bharata. Do not, through a great sin, destroy our famous line of Kings."

Even then Kaikeyi spoke no word, but her eyes blazed scornful anger.

The King continued: "Till this day you have done nothing to cause me sorrow, never spoken an unworthy word. Who has corrupted you now? I cannot believe that this evil thought is your own. How often have you told me, my dear, that, noble as Bharata is, Raama is nobler still? Is it the same Raama that you now want to be sent to the forest? How can he dwell in the forest? How can you even entertain the thought of his going away into the wilderness infested by ferocious beasts? How lovingly has Raama treated you and served you! How can you forget all this and steel your heart and utter the words, 'Send him to the forest'? What fault has he committed? Of the hundreds of women in the palace, has anyone ever uttered a word against his honour or virtue? The whole world loves him for his great and good qualities. How did you alone among so many find cause to dislike him? Is not Raama like Indra himself? Is not his face radiant with goodness and spiritual light like a rishi's? The whole world praises his truthfulness and friendliness, his learning and wisdom, his heroism and humility. No one has heard a harsh word from his lips. How can I, his father, say to him 'Son, go to the forest'? This can never be. Have mercy on me, an old man nearing the end of his days. Kaikeyi, ask for anything else in this kingdom, ask for everything else, and I will give. With folded hands, I beg you, do not send me to Yama. Clinging to your feet I beg you, I beg you humbly, save Raama! Save me from sin!"

To the King thus struggling in a sea of grief, pitiless Kaikeyi spoke cruel words:

"King, if having promised the boons you regret it and will be forsworn, what sort of king would you be and what right would you have to speak of *satya* and *dharma*? How can you face other kings? Will you shamelessly confess to them, 'Yes, Kaikeyi saved me from death and I gave her a promise. Later, I was sorry I gave it and I broke it'? What else could you tell them? All monarchs will shun you as a disgrace to their order! And common people will laugh in scorn at their rulers and say, 'Kings break promises even when given to their queens. Do not expect kings to keep their word.' Do you not know that Saibya, to redeem the pledge he gave to a bird, cut the very flesh off his bones and gave it away? Have you not heard of Alarka who plucked his eyes out to keep his word? The sea stays within its limits and does not overflow the land, because it feels bound by its agreement. Do not violate your solemn pledge. Follow the path of your royal ancestors. O, I fear that you, their unworthy descendant, will forsake *dharma*; you will crown Raama and you will dally with Kausalya. What do you care what happens to *dharma*? What do you care what happens to *satya*? If you deny me the gifts you promised on oath, I shall this very night drink poison and end my life. You may anoint and install Raama, but before your eyes,

O, promise-breaker, I shall be dead. This is certain. And I swear it in the name of Bharata. It will be well and good if you fulfil your promise and banish Raama to the forest. Else, I shall end my life."

With this firm declaration, Kaikeyi stopped. Dasaratha stood speechless, staring at his pitiless wife. Was this lovely creation really Kaikeyi or a demon? Then, like a huge tree felled by a forester with his axe, the King shook and toppled down and lay stretched unconscious on the floor in pitiful ruin.

Regaining his senses after a while, he spoke in a low voice: "Kaikeyi, who has corrupted your mind to see me dead and our race destroyed? What evil spirit has possessed you and makes you dance in this shameless fashion? Do you really think that Bharata will agree to be king after sending Raama to the forest? He never will, and you know it. Can I possibly bear to tell Raama to go to the forest? Will not the kings of the world despise me, saying, 'This uxorious old dotard has banished his eldest son, the best of men'? Don't you see that they would laugh at me? It is easy enough for you to say 'Send Raama away to the forest,' but can Kausalya or I survive his departure? And have you thought of Janaka's daughter? Would it not kill her to hear that Raama is to go away to the Dandaka forest?

"Cheated by your face I thought you a woman and took you for my wife. Like a deluded man, tempted by the flavour of poisoned wine, I was lured by your beauty into marrying you. Like a deer ensnared by a hunter, I am caught in your net and perish. Like a drunken Braahmana in the streets I shall be universally despised. What boons have you demanded? Boons that for ever will taint the fame of our dynasty with the ignominy of lustful dotage that drove an old fool to the banishment of a beloved and peerless son.

"If I tell Raama to go to the forest, yes, he will cheerfully obey and go to the forest. Myself and then Kausalya and Sumitra will die. How will you enjoy the kingdom thus secured, O sinful, foolish woman?

"And will Bharata agree to your plans? If he does agree, he shall not perform my obsequies. O shameless woman, my life's enemy, kill your husband and attain widowhood to enjoy the kingdom with your son. O, how sinful are women and how pitiless! No, no. Only this woman is cruel. Why should I insult other women? What a pity that my Bharata should have this monster for a mother! No, I can never do this. Kaikeyi, I fall at your feet and beg you. Have some pity on me!"

The King rolled on the ground and writhed in agony. What shall we say of this scene? A great emperor, famous for his long and glorious reign, crying and rolling on the ground, clasping his wife's feet and begging for mercy. It was like Yayaati, thrown back to earth when, his accumulated merit exhausted, he was ejected from *Swarga*.

No matter how humbly he begged, Kaikeyi was obstinate and said firmly: "You have yourself boasted that you are a truth-speaker. But now having sworn before the gods that you have granted a boon, you attempt to retract your promise. If you break your word, I shall surely kill myself and that will not add greatly to the glory of your dynasty, of which you are so proud!"

"Very well, then," said Dasaratha. "Let Raama go to the forest and let me die. Having destroyed me and my race, a jubilant widow, you will gain your wish and seek joy in your life!"

Again, after a while, the old King cried: "What good you will gain by sending Raama to the forest, I fail to see. The only result will be that the whole world will despise you. After many years of prayer and penance, I had Raama by the grace of God. And him I now banish into the forest, I, most wretched of men!"

Lifting his eyes to the sky, he said: "Oh night! Stay on. For when you pass and day dawns, what shall I do? What shall I say to those eager crowds, who, full of love for Raama, will be awaiting the coronation festivities? O heavens! Stay still for my sake with your stars! No, no. Stay not, for then I must keep looking at this sinful woman. Depart at once, O night, so that I may escape this face."

Thus delirious and conscious by turns, the poor old man suffered agony—a king who had reigned for sixty-thousand years.

"Pity me, Kaikeyi," he said. "Forget the harsh things I uttered in anger. I beg you in the name of the love you bore me. You may take it that I have given the kingdom to you. It is yours. And you can give it with your own hands to Raama and see that the coronation goes through. The *Raaja Sabha* has decided and I have announced to the elders and to Raama that his coronation is to take place tomorrow. Let not this announcement become false. Have pity on me. Give the kingdom as your own to Raama. The fame of this magnanimous gift will last as long as the world endures. My wish, the people's wish, the Elders' wish, Bharata's wish —they are all that Raama should be crowned. Do this, my love, my life." Again the king clung to the feet of Kaikeyi.

But she answered: "Have done with this foolery, see that you do not break your word and drive me to keep mine, and kill myself. It is useless for you to try to evade."

The King said: "With due rites and in the presence of Fire, I took your hand and called you wife. Here and now I renounce you, and with you the son you bore. Night is gone; the dawn is near and the morning will see not Raama's coronation, but my funeral."

Kaikeyi cut him short: "You are prattling vainly. Send at once for Raama. Let him come here. Tell him the kingdom is Bharata's and he should go to the forest. Keep your promise. Do not waste time."

Dasaratha groaned: "Very well. Let me at last set eyes on Raama's face. My death is near. Let Raama come. Let me see his face before I die. Tied down by *dharma* this old fool is helpless."

And again he fell unconscious.

CHAPTER XV

BEHOLD A WONDER!

POOR Dasaratha was in extreme agony, pulled by natural affection on one side and by the moral obligation to fulfil a pledge on the other. He had fondly hoped that Kaikeyi would relent and that somehow the conflict of duties would be resolved. But now he saw that this was not to be.

He had still one faint hope: "Raama is in no way bound by my promises and pledges. Strong as he is in people's love and in his peerless prowess, he may disregard my promise, and stand on his own rights—but I cannot conceive his doing so, for my slightest wish has always been sacred to him. Yet, if by some chance he did so, it would save the situation."

In the confusion and anguish of his heart, the old King consoled himself with such false hopes, forgetting that Raama would never think of disregarding his father's promise and that filial obedience was a fundamental rule of his life.

But the false hopes did not persist long. He felt that his death was near. In this agonising conflict of duties, death would be a relief, and save him from the disruption and sorrows to come.

As death drew near, his mind recalled past events. He remembered a great sin committed by him in youth. He felt that he was now reaping what he then sowed: "I killed the Rishi's son and brought grief to his aged parents. How could this sin be wiped off except by my suffering the anguish of losing a dear son?" Thus Dasaratha resigned himself to his fate as a just retribution for the wrong he had once done.

He concluded that he had no alternative but to fulfil his word to his cruel wife and left the ordering of things entirely to Kaikeyi.

Day dawned. The hour fixed for the coronation was approaching. The procession of Vasishtha and his disciples carrying the golden vessels containing the waters of holy rivers was coming towards the palace. The great street was decorated and was crowded with eager men and women. They rejoiced to see Vasishtha and his disciples march to the palace with the holy waters, and the paraphernalia of installation. As they saw the honey, curds, clarified butter, fried rice, sacred grass, flowers, maidens, elephants, horses and chariots, the white umbrella, the bull, the horse and the tiger-skin seat moving to the accompaniment of music from many instruments, the people made loud and jubilant acclamations which filled the air.

Vasishtha, approaching the palace gate, saw Sumantra and said to him: "Pray, go in at once and inform the King that the people are waiting and all preparations are complete."

Sumantra approached the King's bed-chamber and chanting the morning hymn, conveyed Vasishtha's message. "Oh King," he said, "arise from slumber to the hymn of your charioteer as the king of the gods does to Maatali's waking songs. May all the gods be gracious unto you. The elders, generals, and chief citizens are waiting for your *darshan*. The goddess of night has withdrawn. The day's work awaits your ordering. Oh King of kings, be pleased to rise. Holy Vasishtha and his men are waiting."

At that moment the King was speechless with agony, but Kaikeyi boldly answered for him and told Sumantra: "The King spent the night talking of Raama's coronation and had no sleep. So now he is in a slumber. Go at once and bring Raama."

Thus the clever woman sent Sumantra to fetch Raama to convey the King's command. She knew that Dasaratha had agreed but had not the strength to do what had to be done. Hence Kaikeyi resolved that she would herself do what needed to be done.

Sumantra went to Raama's palace. Seeta and Raama were getting ready for coronation. Then Sumantra gave to Raama the message that the King and Queen Kaikeyi wanted his presence. Raama hastened to obey.

The unexpected delay and these strange goings and comings roused doubts, but no one dared to talk of them. The men concerned hoped that somehow things would turn out right and went on with their allotted work.

The streets were brightly decorated; the great hour was approaching as in the Queen's chamber strange and sinister events were developing.

"Why this long delay?" the people wondered. "Perhaps the preliminary rites are more elaborate than we had thought."

The crowds in the streets grew bigger and bigger and more impatient.

Sumantra accompanied Raama to Kaikeyi's palace, threading the way with difficulty through the throng. Raama entered the Queen's apartment. As he stepped over the threshold, he started as if he had set his foot upon a snake, for he saw with awe-struck amazement his father lying on the bare floor in anguish. The King evidently had been struck down with some great sorrow. His face was like a *paarijaata* blossom wilted in the sun.

He touched his father's feet and paid the same filial worship to Kaikeyi.

Dasaratha uttered in a low voice the name of Raama and stopped. He could speak no more. He could not look straight into the face of Raama.

Raama was perplexed and filled with apprehension at the sight of his father, lying there unable to speak, in the grip of some great agony—what it could be Raama could not even guess. He turned to Kaikeyi and said: "Mother, this is indeed strange. No matter how angry he was, my father would speak sweetly to me. Have I without knowing it offended him in any matter? Has some sudden sickness struck him down? Has someone spoken rudely to him? Do tell me what has happened. I can bear this suspense no longer."

Bold Kaikeyi seized the chance and said: "The King is angry with no one. There is nothing wrong with his health. But there is something in his mind which he is afraid to tell you. That is all. He is afraid to say it to you, lest you should feel hurt. That is why he is silent. Once upon a time, pleased with me he offered, and I accepted, the gift to two boons. Now, like an uncultured person, the King regrets he did so. Is this worthy of him? Is it not unbecoming of a King to pledge his word and then regret it? You have the power to fulfil his promise, but he fears even to tell you of it and is thinking of violating it. Would it be right? If you assure him that he need not be anxious about your attitude and that he should keep his word at all costs, you will give him the needed strength to behave righteously. You must give him the help he needs. The thing is in your hands. I shall tell you what it is, but after you promise me that you will help the King to fulfil his pledge."

Raama, saddened at the thought that he should in any way be the occasion of distress to his father, said to Kaikeyi: "Mother, am I indeed the cause of all this trouble? I do not deserve that you should have any doubts about me. If my father asks me to jump into the fire, I shall not hesitate to do it. If he asks me to drink poison, I shall drink it without hesitation. You know this. You know well enough that at his bidding I would drown myself in the sea. Here mother, I give you my solemn promise that I shall fulfil the King's promise to you, and I never break my word."

When Raam uttered these words, Kaikeyi exulted, for she knew she had conquered. The King for his part was in despair, seeing that all escape was barred.

Thereupon the pitiless Kaikeyi uttered these terrible words: "Raama, your words are worthy of you. What higher duty has a son than helping fulfilment of the word his father has given? Now I shall let you know your father's promise to me. When in the battle with Sambara your father was wounded, I rescued and revived him. Your father in gratitude for having been rescued by me when grievously wounded gave me two boons to be claimed and specified when I choose. I have claimed and specified them now. They are that Bharata should be anointed *Yuvaraaja* and that you should be sent away this very day to the Dandaka forest, to remain in exile for fourteen years. You have sworn solemnly to carry out his promise to me, and now it is your duty to prove true to your pledged word. If you find right conduct as hard as your father did, that is another matter. Otherwise, listen to what I say. It is for you now to relinquish the installation and to go out into exile with matted locks and hermit weeds, leaving the preparations now ready to serve for Bharata's installation."

When she uttered these cruel words the King writhed in agony, but Raama heard her untroubled. Kaikeyi beheld a miracle. There was not the slightest sign of disappointment or sorrow in Raama's face. Smiling, the Prince said: "Is that all, mother? Surely, the King's promise must be fulfilled. My hair shall be twisted and I shall wear the bark and I shall go this very day to the forest."

Kaikeyi spoke prophetic words when she said Raama's dutifulness would bring him glory undying. That glory will continue as long as the Himaalaya stands and the waters of Ganga flow and as long as the ocean-waves beat on the solid earth.

Raama said to Kaikeyi, in unperturbed tones: "I am not in the least annoyed. Would I not be happy to give anything to Bharata? Even if no one asked me, I would cheerfully give him my all. And how can I hold back a moment when my father commands it? What pains me a little is that father should have entertained any doubt about my willingness. Why should he have hesitated to tell me what he wanted and left it to you to say it to me? Am I not his son, bound to do his behest? What glory or what joy can I look for except to make good his word? How did I deserve it that my father should avert his face from me and refrain from speaking loving words to me? My grievance, if at all, is that he did not send for me straight and give me his command. I shall go to the forest this very day, with no regret. Send swift messengers at once to fetch Bharata home."

The Prince's face glowed like a sacrificial fire bursting into flame as the *ghee* is poured into it. Kaikeyi felt glad at her apparent success. She could not look into the future and its sorrow, for what greater grief can come to a woman than the scorn of her own son? Greed deceived her into folly. It prevented her from understanding aright the mind of her own son Bharata.

Like a captive elephant hemmed in on all sides, Dasaratha lay in anguish. With needless harshness, Kaikeyi hurried Raama saying, "Do not wait for the King to speak and prolong the affair."

At this Raama said: "Mother, you have not, it seems, known me. I value no pleasure higher than to honour my father's pledge. Let Bharata carry the burden of kingship, and look after our aged father. It will indeed give me the greatest joy."

Dasaratha, silent till now though listening intently, moaned aloud. Raama touched the feet of his father and Kaikeyi and hurried out of the chamber.

Lakshmana had been standing outside. He knew what had happened and with eyes red with anger he followed Raama. On the way Raama saw the vessels holding the consecrated water for the coronation. He walked round them in worship. With calm majesty he left behind the white umbrella and other royal insignia and advised the crowds to disperse. The Prince, in whom desire had been vanquished, went to the house of Queen Kausalya to give her the news and take her blessings before departing to the forest.

Readers should exercise their imagination and
build up in their own hearts the passions and
sorrows of the persons figuring in this epic.
Dasaratha's anguish, Raama's cheerful renunciation
and the greedy passion of Kaikeyi which smothered
all noble impulses—these are familiar phases in our
daily lives. Vaalmeeki and Kamban saw with the
vision of genius and made the events in Raama's
story live again in song. We too should see them
through imagination. This is the meaning of the
tradition that, wherever Raama's tale is told
Hanumaan himself joins the gathering and reverently stands with tear-filled eyes, listening.

May everyone that reads this chapter receive by
Raama's Grace strength to bear the sorrows that
have to be faced in life.

CHAPTER XVI

STORM AND CALM

RAAMA went to Queen Kausalya's dwelling. Many visitors were assembled there, eagerly awaiting the coronation. In the innermost apartment, the Queen, clad in white silk, was before the sacrificial fire invoking blessings on her son.

As soon as Raama entered, she embraced him and showed him, who she thought was to become the *Yuvaraaja*, to a specially raised seat.

"Mother, this seat is now too high for me," said Raama. "I am a hermit and should sit on grass spread on the floor. I have brought you news which may sadden you. Listen, and give me your blessings."

And he told her briefly what had happened: "The King wishes to give the crown to Bharata. His command is that I should spend fourteen years in the Dandaka forest. I must leave today, mother, and I come for your blessings before I go."

When Kausalya heard this, she fell on the ground like a plantain tree suddenly cut down. Lakshmana and Raama gently raised her.

She clung to Raama and cried: "Is my heart made of stone or iron that I still live?"

Lakshmana could not bear the sight of the Queen's grief. Angrily he spoke: "This old King has pronounced on Raama a doom that is reserved for the most wicked evil-doers. What sin or crime has Raama committed? Not even his worst enemy could find any fault in Raama. The doting old man has lost his senses over his young wife and is not fit to be king any more.

"How can a king listen to a woman and violate *dharma*? Even your enemies, O! Raama, when they look at you begin to love you, but this dotard of a father sends you to the forest. Look here, brother, let us together throw out this King and take charge of the kingdom ourselves. Who dare oppose us? I shall make an end of any one who dares. Only give me leave and I shall do this single-handed.

"A young brother to become King and you to go to the forest! The world would laugh at this absurdity. Don't consent to this. I at any rate won't stand this. I shall put down all opposition and see that you rule the kingdom without let or hindrance. Never doubt but I have strength to do it. Instead of the sun rising, a great darkness has descended upon the land this morning, for when we were expecting your coronation the King sentences you to banishment! In the face of such injustice there is no use being nice and polite. I cannot stand this. I must do my duty. Mother, now you will see the strength of my arm and so you, brother."

Lakshmana's words were some solace to Kausalya, but yet this strange talk of ousting the King and seizing the throne frightened her.

She said: "Raama, consider well what Lakshmana says. Don't go to the forest. If you go away, how can I stay here all alone among enemies? I too shall go with you."

Raama had listened in silence to Lakshmana's outburst, for it was wise to let the pent up passion find outlet in words. Then, turning to Kausalya he said: "Mother, let there be no talk of anyone going with me to the forest. It is your duty to stay here serving the King and sharing the sorrow that has come to him in his old age. How can the crowned

Queen of an Emperor wander with me like a widow in the forest? This cannot be. I shall return after my term of forest life.

"It is my duty to fulfil my father's word. It is all the same to me, whether it is just or unjust, spontaneous or extorted by force or fraud. If I fail in this primary duty, I can gain no satisfaction or good name through any amount of wealth or power. Lakshmana, your proposals are quite wrong. I know your great strength and I have no doubt that you can vanquish and destroy all opponents and secure for me the kingdom. I know also your affection for me.

"But the way in which you propose to use it is not worthy of the dynasty to which we belong. Our highest duty is to fulfil our father's word. If we fail in that, no other achievement can make up for it."

Raama tried to console both his mother and his brother, but Lakshmana's anger could not be easily put down. Perhaps it could have been, if he himself—not Raama— were the sufferer. But it was Raama who was the victim of this cruel injustice. And so Lakshmana writhed in anger like a wounded cobra. Raama took him apart, made him sit down and tried to calm him:

"Lakshmana, are you not my other self, my very soul in another body? Listen to me. You are courageous and strong. Control your anger and grief on my account. Don't allow these evil spirits to possess you. Holding fast to *dharma*, let us convert our present disgrace into a great joy. Let us forget all about the coronation, and think worthily as becomes our race.

"Consider our father's condition. Our hearts should go out to him in sympathy, for he is stricken with a great sorrow. Whatever be the reason, he gave a promise and if he should break it, he would be committing a shameful sin which would besmirch and blot out all his great and glorious deeds. He is heart-broken at the wrong he feels he has done me; but I do not feel it a wrong at all, for a king must keep his word and a son must obey his father. You should show that you too are free from any sense of injury. Only so can we bring him mental relief.

"He gave us the life that we hold and we should give him peace of mind. He is afraid about the other world. We should free him from this fear. So far, we have never given him cause for sorrow or dissatisfaction. Now we have become the cause of a great fear in his mind about what is to happen to him in the other world. We can easily relieve him. Instead of doing this, are we to add to his troubles? For this reason my mind has altogether turned away from the coronation and is intent on the journey to the forest.

"My sole desire now is to go to the forest and see that Bharata is crowned. This would please me best. If I delay, Kaikeyi will grow suspicious. Hence I should go to the forest this very day and bring peace to her mind. Rid of the fear of the sin of breaking a promise and assured of my willing and cheerful acceptance of his command, our father will be happy.

"And we should not be angry with Kaikeyi either. Has she not been kind to us all these years? That she should suddenly conceive this idea is surely the working of fate. We should not blame her for it. One proposes something and fate decides otherwise. In this, Kaikeyi is but a passive instrument in the hand of fate.

"Our little mother will have to bear the grievous burden of the world's blame, but our love for her should remain the same as ever. If, before this, there had been evil in her thought, her conduct would have shown it. There is no dobut that some higher force has made her say suddenly and harshly, 'Raama, go to the forest.' Otherwise how could a high-minded woman who so far looked upon us as her own children now behave so brazenly before her husband? Who can oppose destiny? Even steadfast sages have swerved suddenly from their *tapas*. How can poor Kaikeyi hope to resist fate?

"Let us resolve firmly to change this sorrow into joy. That would be a proof of our nobility and courage, Lakshmana. With the blessings of my mothers and elders, I shall go to the forest. Bring here the water, the water from the Ganga for the coronation. I shall use it for ablution before departing for the forest. No, no, that water belongs to the State and is intended for the coronation. How can we touch it? We shall go to holy Ganga ourselves and fetch the water for my ablution. Brother, be not sad thinking of kingdom or wealth; life in the forest will be my highest joy."

So Raama revealed to his brother his inmost thoughts. In these passages Vaalmeeki uses the word *daiva*. In Sanskrit literature, *daivam* means fate. *Daivam*, *dishtam*, *bhaagyam*, *niyati* and *vidhi* are all words conveying the idea of something unexpected and inexplicable. Because of the belief in God as the Prime Cause, a natural confusion arises between fate and God's will. What Raama said to Lakshmana on the present occasion does not mean that he thought that the gods contrived Kaikeyi's action for their own benefit. Raama offered no more than the usual consolation: "It is the work of fate. Do not grieve. No one is to blame for this."

In *Kamba Raamaayana* also, addressing his brother 'raging like the fire of Dissolution', Raama says: "It is not the river's fault that the bed is dry. Even so, my going hence is not the King's fault, nor Queen Kaikeyi's nor her son's. The wrong is the work of fate. Why should one be angry then?"

This explanation calmed Lakshmana for a while. But soon his anger boiled up again. He said: "Very well, then. This is the work of fate. Fate, I grant, is the cause of our step-mother's sudden folly. And I am not angry with her. But are we, on that account, to sit still and do nothing? It is *Kshatriya dharma* to overcome evil and establish justice.

"A hero does not bow down before fate. Having announced Raama's coronation by beat of drum to the town and country, the treacherous King invokes some old forgotten boon and orders you to go to the forest. Is it manly to call this fate and obey it meekly? Only cowards go down under fate. Heroes should oppose and vanquish it. I am no weakling to yield to fate. You will see today the might of a hero matched against fate. I shall tame the mad elephant fate and make it serve me.

"I shall banish to the forest those who conspired to banish you. If you wish to visit the forest for a change, you can do so later. The proper time for it will be when you have reigned as king for many years and then entrusted the crown to your sons. That was the way of our ancestors. If anyone questions your kingship now, I stand here to annihilate him.

"Are these two shoulders merely for beauty? This bow, these arrows and this sword hanging on my side, are they mere decorations? Or do you think they are theatrical equipment put on for show? I await your orders. Give me the word and test my prowess."

Raama gently pacified Lakshmana's rage which was flaming up into a conflagration. "As long as our parents are alive," said Raama, "it is our duty to obey them. I cannot dream of disobeying my father. It is our prime duty to do his bidding and enable him to fulfil his pledge. What joy is there in getting a kingship after insulting our parents and slaying Bharata, the embodiment of *dharma*?"

And he wiped with his hand the tears from Lakshmana's eyes. When Raama did this, Lakshmana grew calm. For the affectionate magic of Raama's hand could work wonders.

CHAPTER XVII

SEETA'S RESOLVE

WHAT took place in the inner apartments of the palace was not yet known to the town-people. But Raama for his part lost no time in preparing for forest life.

He went to Queen Kausalya to receive her blessings before leaving the city. Kausalya said to him again: "How can I stay in Ayodhya after you are gone? It is best that I go with you to the forest." Of course, she knew that her duty was to serve her husband in his old age and share his sorrow in Ayodhya. And yet her mind was now so confused by grief that she did not see things clearly.

But Raama would not hear of it and put her in mind of her duty to be with the heart-stricken old King in his sad solitude.

She recognised the justice of this counsel. She gave him her benedictions in sweet words 'diluted with the salt of broken tears.' "Do as your father has decreed and return in glory." Raama put heart in her with a smile saying: "The fourteen years will pass quickly and you will see me back."

The poet says that, as Raama received his mother's benedictions, his bright face glowed with added effulgence. How truly he pictures the sublime loveliness that comes of a great renunciation that illumines one's being as with an inner light!

We saw that Raama left Seeta and went to the King in answer to the message brought by Sumantra. Seeta was expecting Raama to return in a chariot with the royal umbrella, followed by a great retinue. But now she saw Raama return alone, unattended, with none of the royal insignia. And she noted on his face the glow of some fixed resolve. Raama was thinking as he came how he could break to his beloved the news that his father had decreed that he was to go to the forest.

"Something troubles the mind of my lord," thought Seeta, "but what can anything matter so long as there is our love?" And she asked him: "What is the matter? Why do you look so strangely?"

Raama told the story briefly and then added: "Princess, my love, I can well imagine your sorrow at having to part from me and stay here. Janaka's daughter requires not my guidance to her duty. Be thoughtful of the comfort of the King and the three Queens—your mothers. Do not expect any better treatment than that given to the other princesses in the palace. Be respectful to Bharata who will be Ruler and guard against any offence to his feelings. Your love for me, I trust, will not grow any less during this absence. I shall return from forest after these fourteen years. Till then do not neglect customary rites and ceremonies. Mother Kausalya in her sorrow will need your attentive care. Bharata and Satrughna are dear to me. You will look upon them as your brothers. Conduct yourself as befits your royal race and your own nature. Avoid extolling me so as to give possible offence to other good men. I must go to the forest today. Keep your mind steady and calm."

When Seeta heard this unexpected speech, her love for Raama manifested itself as anger that he should for a moment conceive that she could consent to part from him and live in comfort in the palace while he was a homeless wanderer in pathless forests.

"A fine speech you have made, O Knower of *dharma*. It is to me a strange doctrine that a wife is diverse from her husband and that his duty is not hers, and that she has no right to share in it. I can never accept it. I hold that your fortunes are mine, and if Raama has to go to the forest, the command includes Seeta also, who is a part of him. I shall walk in front of you in the forest ways and tread the thorns and the hard ground to make them smooth for your feet. Do not think me obstinate. My father and mother have instructed me in *dharma*. What you tell me is totally opposed to what they have taught me. To go with you wherever you go—that is my only course. If you must go to the forest today, then today I go with you. There is no room here for any discussion. Do not think that I cannot bear forest life. With you by my side it will be a joyous holiday. I shall not be a source of trouble to you. I shall eat fruit and roots like you and I shall not lag behind as we walk.

"I have long wished to go to the woods with you and rejoice in the sight of great mountains and rivers. I shall spend the time most happily among the birds and flowers, bathing in the rivers and doing the daily rites. Away from you, I do not care for Heaven itself. I shall surely die if you leave me behind. I implore you to take me with you. Have pity on me. Do not forsake me now."

Beginning in anger, her speech ended in sobs. Raama explained to Seeta that life in the forest was not as easy as she thought and set out at great length the difficulties and dangers and again insisted that she should not think of accompanying him.

Seeta's eyes filled with tears. "Tigers, lions, bears, snakes—none of them will come near me. They will flee from us at the sight of you. The sun, rain, wind and hunger and the spikes and thorny shrubs you speak of—I shall endure them all cheerfully.

"I am not in the least afraid, and on the other hand you may be certain life will depart from this body if you leave me here and go.

"When I was in Mithila," she said, "the Braahmanas and astrologers told my mother that I was destined to live in the forest for a while. Can I fulfil this prediction alone in the forest? Here is the opportunity for me to fulfil it in your company which will make the forest a garden of delight. For whom is forest life unpleasant? Only to those men and women who have not controlled their senses. You and I can be masters of our senses and miss nothing. I implore you, put me not away from you, for parting from you is more cruel than death."

There is a strength in supreme love which defies reason and laughs at death itself, and Raama suffered himself to be persuaded—partly because his love was great as hers and every passionate word she spoke found ready lodgment in his heart, and partly because he was confident of his ability to protect her. It was settled that Seeta should accompany Raama to the forest.

She sent for the poor and gave away all her belongings and prepared herself for life in the forest. Lakshmana also decided to go with his brother and be of service to him in the forest, and Raama had to agree. The three went to take leave of the aged King.

In the streets and on the balconies were crowds of people looking on. Through the windows and from the terraces of mansions, men and women saw Raama and Lakshmana and the princess proceeding on foot, like the poorest in the land.

Filled with boundless grief and indignation, the people said to one another: "What kind of a King is this who sends so noble a prince to the forest? And there Seeta walks, a princess that should command the service of the royal chariot. Can she bear the heat and the rain of the forest? This is monstrous!

"We shall go then to the forest too. Let us gather up all we have and get away to the forest with these princes. The forest where Raama dwells shall be our Ayodhya.

"Let these houses here henceforth deserted be, infested with snakes and rats. Let Kaikeyi rule over the ruins of Ayodhya. Wild beasts and vultures of the forest will come to stay here. This will become a forest, and the forest will become Ayodhya."

Raama heard people talking thus, but took no notice. At the entrance to Kaikeyi's palace, Raama saw Sumantra seated sorrowfully aside in a corner. Raama tenderly spoke to him: "The three of us have come to meet the King. Sumantra, crave leave for us to enter his presence."

Sumantra went in accordingly to announce them to the King. What a sight met him there! Like the sun in eclipse, like an oven filled all over with ash, like a tank gone dry, the King was stretched flat on the floor, his glory gone and his face shrunken and distorted with anguish.

Sumantra, his voice trembling with grief and his hands clasped together, said: "The Prince waits at the entrance and seeks audience to take your blessings before he gives away all he has to the Braahmanas and starts for the Dandaka forest."

The King bade Sumantra let the Prince in.

Raama came and bowed to the King from a distance. As soon as he saw Raama, the King suddenly rose and rushed with out – stretched arms to embrace him, but dropped in a swoon before reaching his son.

Raama and Lakshmana tenderly lifted him up and put him on the couch. "My Lord," said Raama, "we have come to seek your leave to go to the forest. Vaidehi and Lakshmana too are going with me in spite of all I could do to make them desist. Pray give us your benedictions and leave to depart."

Dasaratha then said: "Raama, I am bound by the boons that I have given to Kaikeyi. But you are not so bound. Why do you not brush me aside and seize the kingdom by force?"

That had long been in the King's mind as the best and only solution of this cruel problem and came out now clearly in words.

But Raama said: "I have no desire for kingdom or power, father. May you reign for a thousand years more. My heart is now set on going to the forest and I am even now in readiness to start after receiving your blessing. When the fourteen years have passed I shall return and tender obeisance."

The King's faint hope, it was now clear, must be abandoned. "My son! Bring glory to our line of kings. Go, but come back unscathed. May danger flee from your path. Cling to *dharma*. You are unshakable in resolution. Firm and unchangeable is your will. But do not go away today. Spend but this night here with me.

"Let me fill my eyes with the sight of you. You can go away at dawn. Like one handling a live coal deceptively covered with ash, I gave the promise to Kaikeyi not knowing what was in her mind. I am now helpless and caught in her net. And you say, 'I shall fulfil my father's promise. I shall not let dishonour blot the name of my father. I shall give up the kingdom and go to the forest.' Where in the world can one find a son like unto you? I swear to you, I did not intend this great wrong."

Thus piteously spoke the King. It was Dasaratha's wish to die without losing—even in his last moments—the respect of Raama.

"Father, send for Bharata at once and fulfil the promise you have given to mother Kaikeyi. Do not be troubled by the thought that you are doing me a wrong, for I had no desire for the throne, and do not feel it a deprivation to be denied it. Untroubled by grief or doubt, have Bharata crowned and give him your blessings. Cast all grief aside. Shed no tears. Can the ocean dry up? So may you too not lose your balance ever, great father.

"My sole wish is to make good the word you gave. If I got all the wealth of the world, but falsify your word, what joy would that be to me? I shall spend my time happily in the forest. Where but in the forests can one find beauty or joy? Father, you are my God. I take it that it is God that sends me to the forest. When the fourteen years are over, you will see me again. Do not grieve.

"What profits it that I stay here a night longer and go tomorrow? Time is made up of a succession of tomorrows and one day is just like another. Inevitable sorrows do not become joys by postponement."

"Well then, send for the commanders," said the King to Sumantra, "and order them to get ready the chariots, elephants, horses and foot soldiers, to go with Raama to the forest. And along with the army send all the necessary stores for Raama to live with the Rishis of the forest. Let there be nothing wanting in men, money or things."

Poor Dasaratha imagined that he could make Raama's exile to the forest something like a royal tour affording a pleasant change from routine, and enlivened by exchange of gracious hospitalities with the sylvan population.

As he spoke Kaikeyi's face paled with anger. She glowered at the King, and in a voice tremulous with scornful wrath she said: "A good and generous monarch surely! You will give Bharata this kingdom after squeezing out of it all the good it holds, as one might offer in mockery an empty tankard to a man dying of thirst! What pleasure or glory will my son have in ruling a deserted state?"

Dasaratha groaned in helpless chagrin and marvelled at a cruelty that could stab a man already crushed under an intolerable burden. Angry words rose from the mouths of those around, for even the courtiers found this open heartlessness more than they could suffer in silence. Raama put an end to all recriminations by saying he would not agree to take paraphernalia incongruous with what was intended in forest life.

"Honoured Lord," he said, "what use have I, who am departing to the forest to live on what sylvan nature yields, for an army or the glittering equipage of a royal pageant? After gladly renouncing the throne, what use have I for its trammels? Would it not be covetous folly, after having parted with the elephant, to burden oneself with the ponderous chain? Father, I have cheerfully relinquished my claim to the kingdom in favour of Bharata and his mother, and with it all the incidents of royalty. For my fourteen years of forest life I require nothing but bark garments such as Rishis wear and simple necessaries of forest life such as spades and baskets."

Hardly had Raama spoken these words when the unabashed Kaikeyi hastened to produce the forest dress she had kept ready and gave it herself without a blush to Raama. Then and there Raama dressed himself in bark. And in these garments he shone like a Rishi. Lakshmana too changed into bark dress, while Dasaratha watched all this in helpless anguish.

Then Kaikeyi brought a bark dress for Seeta too. She received it and stood bewildered, for she had never worn such garments before and did not know how to change into them.

Approaching Raama, who stood there resplendent with divine effulgence, Seeta said shyly: "Pray tell me, how does one put this thing on?" As Raama took up the bark dress and, wrapping it over Seeta's silk, made a knot over her shoulder, the ladies-in-waiting wailed aloud and Dasaratha fell into a swoon.

When he regained consciousness, he loudly reviled Kaikeyi, but she only smiled scornfully. She surely was not responsible for Seeta going in the forest. The princess sought her own pleasure by going to the forest with her husband and would not be dissuaded.

Lowering his eyes as he was leaving, Raama said: "Father, I leave behind my mother Kausalya, blameless and tender-hearted lady, bereft of her son in her old age. This sudden fate is bitter to her as death, but she consents to live only for your sake, to share your sorrow and console you. She is incapable of harbouring an unkind thought towards any one, and she has never before felt the pang of such poignant parting. Be kind to her when I am no longer here and, when I return after my long exile in the hope of putting my head on her feet, let me not hear that she has died of sorrow."

Thus Raama spoke, unable to bear the thought of his mother's grief. As Raama went out speaking thus, Dasaratha could not endure the sight and covered his face with his hands.

CHAPTER XVIII

TO THE FOREST

AFTER Raama left his father's presence with these words, the stricken King lay prostrated in speechless sorrow, and it was some time before he could muster his faculties sufficiently even to think.

When he recovered some strength, he muttered half unconsciously: "Surely I must in a previous birth have inflicted hideous suffering to loving hearts. I must have torn calves from their mothers, children from their parents, husbands from their wives. How else could I suffer thus? And death does not come when we want it. And I have to endure the torture of always having before my mind's eye my godlike son deprived of his birthright and forced into the bark-garments of a hermit. O life, how bitterly you cling to those who would be rid of you! Raama has gone into exile and yet I do not die! Raama...........Raama.............Have you gone?............."

A little later, his mind clearer, the King said: "Sumantra, get ready the chariot and take my sons and Jaanaki to the frontier of the kingdom."

Lakshmana touched the feet of his mother Sumitra and uttered the single word "Mother." She embraced him, kissed his head and said: "Your devotion to your brother has filled your mother's heart with pride and joy. It is your duty, child, to guard and serve Raama. Always stand in vigilant watch by Raama's side in the forest. Your elder brother is to you both preceptor and king. This is the *dharma* of our race.

"Go with my blessing, Lakshmana. In the forest, regard Raama as your father and look upon

Jaanaki as myself and the forest will be to you as Ayodhya. Go cheerfully, my dear son,—and God bless you."

In the *Raamaayana*, Sumitra is a woman of few words and mature wisdom and great tact and infinite courage, full of faith, in whom 'hope shines like a flame when it has gone out in all others.' The tradition is that Sumitra knew Raama's divinity and the purpose of his incarnation and that this enabled her not only to comfort Kausalya but to see a holy ministration in Lakshmana's sharing Raama's exile.

Sumantra said: "Ascend the chariot, O Prince – God bless you. Tell me where I am to drive, for the fourteen-year period has begun, my Prince."

Seeta got up the chariot, cheerfully. Kausalya had made up for her a packet of personal requirements. The shields, bows and arrows and other weapons of the two brothers together with pickaxes and baskets were placed in the chariot. Pickaxes and baskets are essential in the forest. Raama and Lakshmana ascended the chariot. Sumantra drove it forward.

Let us pause a while at this stage when Raama's forest life begins, and pray that we may be purified of our sins. Truth, courage and love is the gospel of the *Raamaayana* to us. To give it to us was Raama born. We shall gain these gifts if we meditate on the Princes and Jaanaki in the bark habiliments as they left the city.

The crowds in the street cried to the charioteer: "Go slow, go slow. Let us have a look at Raama's face."

"Alas, Alas, who could send such children to the forest? How could their mothers endure this sorrow and survive? Look at Vaidehi's face. She is indeed blessed. And Lakshmana is happy to have such a brother to whom he can give devoted service. He is indeed a hero and a knower of *dharma*." So the people of the city talked among themselves as they followed the chariot. And their grief swelled like a flood.

Raama was saying to the good charioteer, "Faster, faster." The people were saying, "slow, slow". And the crowd became bigger and bigger. Sumantra managed somehow to take the chariot out of the press of the mourning town where, in addition to the loud sorrow of the crowded streets, the houses were full of mourning women and children.

The King stepped out of Kaikeyi's apartment and looked at the departing chariot. A long time he stood there watching the cloud of dust as though he saw in it the beloved form of Raama. When even this went out of sight, he fell down moaning. Kausalya and Kaikeyi sat on either side.

"Do not touch me," said Dasaratha to Kaikeyi. "I hate the sight of you, sinful woman! Everything is at an end between you and me. I renounce you here and now."

"If Bharata agrees to your arrangements and accepts the kingdom," he said again, "he need not perform my obsequies, and even if he did, my departed spirit would reject his offering of waters."

"How can Raama live in the forest? Will he sleep on the bare ground with a stone or a log for a pillow? Will he eat fruits and berries?"

Thus the king went on lamenting helplessly.

Sometimes he would turn to Kaikeyi and say, "May you be happy in your success! Long may you live a happy widow."

Heart-broken and empty like one returning home from the cremation ground, he entered Kaikeyi's apartment by force of habit; then suddenly he said, 'Not here. Take me to the dwelling of Kausalya."

And so they did, and there he lay waiting for his end.

At midnight, he said. "Kausalya, are you there? Touch me with your hand. My sight is gone with Raama."

Poor Kausalya did her best to comfort the King, but what comfort was there in her wounded heart to give? For as the slow sorrow-laden hours crawled from watch to watch, the cold night seemed to her a devouring flame, and the gentle moon fierce as the noonday sun.

To her thus sorrowing Sumitra said: "Sister, you have heard the *Shaastras* and know *dharma.* Why should you grieve like this? It is your office to put courage in others, you should not lose heart yourself. Raama has gone to the forest for guarding the King's honour. You are indeed blessed among women, for you are the mother of a hero who has scorned a kingdom and preferred to uphold his father's honour. Why should you grieve for a son who fulfils a difficult duty to perfection? We should not feel sorry for one who walks in the path of his ancestors and wins undying fame. I am proud that Lakshmana has accompained Raama. Jaanaki, though knowing well the hardships she has to face, has also gone with her husband. Raama's glory will shine like an undying lamp. This is no occasion for grief. His purity, his virtue shall be a shield and armour to them.

"He is so great and holy that the sun's rays falling on him will not burn him and the wind that blows will caress him with its coolness. His pure frame, as he sleeps at night, will be embraced and protected by the moon-beams as an infant is by its loving mother. Shed all anxiety over your heroic son. No foe can encounter him and escape with life. Our Raama is endowed with all auspicious qualities. Your hero-son will surely return to Ayodhya and ascend the throne. The Lord of the world, and no other, is Raama.

"Seeta is with him, and Seeta is no other than the Goddess Lakshmi. Raama will return and ascending the thorne will fill with delight the kingdom which now laments his exile. You saw the grief of the citizens as they watched his departure. My heroic son, the devoted Lakshmana, armed with bow and sword, has gone with him to guard his person. No harm, no danger can approach Raama. You will see with your own eyes Raama returning after fulfilment of his vow.

"Believe me, Raama will return, beautiful like the full moon, and touch your feet with joy and devotion. You will then shed tears not of grief but of joy. Dear, dear Kausalya, give up your grief. You will see the three of them returning. You should console and encourage the other women in the palace and not stand broken-hearted yourself. Who else in this world stands firm by *dharma* like Raama? Is this a cause for grief? No, be proud of your son, Kausalya!"

Listening to Sumitra's words, Kausalya was somewhat consoled.

The people of the city followed Raama's chariot in a huge crowd. They tried to stop the chariot, shouting, "Do not go to the forest. Return to the city."

"I am going to the forest to uphold my father's word," Raama said. "There is no theme for sorrow here and you should not seek to hinder me."

But the people would not listen to him, and went in crowds after him shouting wildly: "Do not go to the forest, do not go to the forest!" Raama stopped the chariot and addressed them with his eyes full of love for them: "Citizens of Ayodhya, I know the love you bear for me. You will show it best by transferring it on my behalf, and at my behest, to my beloved brother Bharata. Nothing else will please me more. Bharata is good and noble, has all royal qualities and is fully worthy of love. So conduct yourselves as to please him. Young in years, he is old in wisdom and his heart is at once heroic and tender. He has the strength to protect you. He is your king, and you owe him loyalty and affection.

"I am going to the forest to fulfil my father's word and the King has appointed Bharata as *Yuvaraja*. He is in every way fitted for that position. You and I alike should obey the King's commands. You should go back and try to mitigate the sorrow of my father at parting from me."

Thus Raama spoke to them in kindly tones. But they loved him all the more because of this and would not be consoled. Some Braahmanas, old in years and excellent in virtue, looking at the chariot wept and cried: "Why, O horses, do you carry our Raama into the forest? We have heard it said that horses are sharp of hearing. Listen to us then and bring back our Raama."

Hearing these words of yearning from old Braahmanas, Raama stopped the chariot. The three descended from it and went forward walking.

The common people, leading citizens and wise elders, men of penance — why, even the birds on wings — tried to prevent Raama from going to the forest. The river Tamasa, says the poet, seemed to conspire with them, for now it flowed across his path. The chariot stopped on the river bank. Sumantra unyoked and watered the horses and let them loose to graze.

Raama said: "Lakshmana, this is the first night of our forest life. Let us spend it on the bank of this holy river. Life in the forest holds no hardship, as you and I know. Look, the birds, the animals and even the trees seem to sympathise with us. The only pain is when we think of the grief of our parents in Ayodhya, though I feel re-assured as I think of Bharata's nobility and goodness. He will assuredly tend our parents with true affection. Sumantra, go, look after the horses."

Then, Raama offered the evening prayers by the river and said: "Let us fast on this first night of our forest life, Lakshmana. Your presence by my side rids me of all care."

Lakshmana spread some grass on the ground for Raama and Seeta to sleep on but he himself spent the night in vigil talking with Sumantra.

Long before dawn Raama rose from sleep and told Sumantra: "The citizens who have followed us, fatigued by their long journey, are fast asleep. I am deeply moved by their affection; but I cannot permit their love to force me to go back. Let us, therefore, move on even now, while they are yet asleep."

The horses were harnessed and the chariot slowly crossed the river. Standing on the southern bank, Raama told Sumantra: "If you take the chariot to the other shore, where the people are asleep, and drive it for a little distance towards Ayodhya and then bring it back to this side, we can proceed on our journey before they wake up. They will see the track of the chariot going towards the city, and thinking that we have returned home, may themselves go back. Unless you do this the crowd will go on following us."

Sumantra did this and, when the chariot returned, the three got into it again and proceeded southwards.

CHAPTER XIX

ALONE BY THEMSELVES

THE citizens who had slept on the bank of the Tamasa woke up in the morning and looked round. They were surprised to see that Raama and the chariot had disappeared. They followed the track of the chariot-wheels but were disappointed to find that it was lost in the main road to the capital.

They returned home to their own houses and sought satisfaction in reviling Kaikeyi. Without Raama, the city was bereft of beauty and wrapt in gloom.

Sumantra and the princes had crossed the Tamasa long before dawn and travelled far into the forest. Crossing several streams they approached the southern boundary of the Kosala country. As they journeyed on, Raama said to Sumantra: "I wonder when I shall hunt again in the forest of Sarayu. Is hunting good for princes? Perhaps, it is — in moderation."

Thus conversing on many matters, they went forward. When they reached the southern boundary of the kingdom, Raama stopped the chariot and facing north towards Ayodhya, bent his head in a prayer, saying: "O, jewel among cities! O ancient capital of the Ikshvaakus! Shall I, finishing my penance in the forest, live to see my father and mother and you? Grant me that supreme joy."

The chariot reached the bank of the Ganga. They proceeded along the bank, admiring the beauty of the river. Finding a spot of surpassing charm, Raama said: "We shall spend the night here."

Untying the horses, they sat under a tree. Guha, the chief of the region, having learnt already from his men that Raama would be coming there, came forward with his retinue to greet Raama and Lakshmana.

He had unbounded love for the Royal family and for Raama. Being the chieftain of the tribes who dwelt on the banks of Ganga, he was a man of great prestige and power. Raama and Lakshmana rose to greet Guha, even while the latter was still at some distance from them. Guha welcomed them with a hearty embrace, saying: "Regard this land as your own. This place is as much yours as is Ayodhya. Who can hope to have a guest like you? It is indeed my good fortune."

Guha had prepared a lavish entertainment. He said "Feel perfectly at home and happy in my kingdom. You may spend all the fourteen years with us here. You will not lack anything, I assure you. Looking after you will be a pleasure and privilege to me. Be gracious enough to accept my hospitality."

Warmly embracing Guha again, Raama said: "Brother, I know how deep is your love for me. Your wish is itself as good as hospitality rendered. I am bound by my vows and must refuse anything more. I have come to dwell in the forest and not to enjoy life as a chieftain's guest. These horses are my dear father's favourites. Pray feed them well. We shall be content with simple food and rest for the night."

They lay under the tree for the night. Guha and Lakshmana kept awake, conversing with Sumantra.

Said Guha to Lakshmana: "Brother, do go and rest. There is a bed made ready for you. My men will keep careful watch. None dare do anything in the forest unknown to me. Have no anxiety regarding Raama. Do sleep."

Lakshmana replied: "How can I find sleep, Guha? Here, lying on the bare ground, is Seeta, daughter of the great Janaka and daughter-in-law of the great Dasaratha. The great Purushottama himself who could subdue the three worlds lies stretched on the grass. How can I sleep who sees this?

"I wonder how Ayodhya is bearing it. The queens' apartments must be loud with wailing. I even doubt if at this moment Kausalya and my mother are alive. My father indeed found strength somehow to say to Raama, 'Go to the forest,' but I doubt if he has strength enough left to survive Raama's actual departure. And if he has passed away, our mothers too will have given up their lives. And here we are, deprived even of the privilege of doing the last offices to the dead.

"In any case it is hardly possible that our father and mothers will be alive to greet us, when we return to Ayodhya after our term in the forest."

Thus spoke Lakshmana in sorrow. Guha was in tears. The night was spent in such sad conversation.

Early next morning, Raama told Lakshmana: "We must now cross the river. Ask Guha to make ready a boat big enough for crossing this broad river." Guha ordered his men to get this done and informed Raama.

Sumantra bowed low and stood before Raama seeking his further commands.

Raama understood Sumantra's unuttered grief and, laying his hand on Sumantra's shoulders, said: "Sumantra, return to Ayodhya with all speed and be at the side of the King. Your duty is now to look after him."

"O Raama," exclaimed Sumantra, "rectitude, learning and culture seem to be of no value. You and your brother and Vaidehi are going to live in the forest. What is going to be our lot? How are we going to fare under Kaikeyi's rule?" He now wept like a child.

Wiping the tears from Sumantra's eyes, Raama said: "Our family has known no nobler friend than you. It will be your task to console my father. His heart is riven by grief. Whatever his commands, carry them out dutifully. Do not ask yourself whether he wants a thing for himself or with a view to pleasing Kaikeyi. Avoid giving him any pain of mind. Have no anxiety about us.

"You should say this on my behalf to my aged father who is stricken with a grief he never knew before. Clasp his feet as you have seen me do, and assure him from me that none of us — not I nor Lakshmana, nor Seeta — feel injured or sorry at having been sent away from Ayodhya. We look forward to fourteen years of forest life which will speed on happy wings, and then surely we shall return to his feet for blessings. Give our love to my mother Kausalya, and tell her that protected by her blessings we are well and give a like message to my stepmothers, specially to Kaikeyi, lest she should think we have parted in anger. Tell the Mahaaraaja that it is my earnest prayer that he should hasten with the installation of Bharata, so that he may be a comfort to him in our absence."

But Sumantra, unable to restrain his grief, burst out: "How am I to return and with what words can I give comfort?" And when he looked at the empty chariot, he wept and said: "How shall I drive this chariot that stands desolate without you?"

Once again Raama, spoke words of comfort and courage to Sumantra and urged on him the duty of patience, and sent him home. "Guha", said Rama, "I could indeed spend fourteen years in your kingdom as you desire. But would that be fulfilling my vow? I have left Ayodhya to fulfil my father's pledge. I must therefore lead the life of a *tapasvi*. I must not touch dishes daintily cooked and served. We have to live only on fruits, roots and permissible kinds of meat such as we offer in the sacrificial fire."

Comforting Guha thus, the brothers got their locks matted with the milk of the banyan. They helped Seeta into the boat and then got into it themselves. Guha bade the boatmen to row it across.

The boatmen took them quickly across the river. At midstream Seeta offered a prayer to the goddess of the river: "Devi, help us fulfil our vow and return safe to our homeland."

They talked as they went on. They reached the farther bank of Ganga. And there, for the first time, the three stood alone, unattended by friends!

"Lakshmana, you are my sole armed guard now," said Raama. "You will go first. Seeta will follow. And I shall walk behind you both. We must save Seeta as far as possible from the hardships of forest life. Hereafter there will be none to keep us company and no fun or amusement."

Raama's thoughts went to his mother Kausalya.

"Lakshmana," he said, "should you not go back to Ayodhya and look after mother Kausalya and

Sumitra Devi? I shall manage my forest stay somehow."

Lakshmana replied: "Forgive me, brother; I am not going back to Ayodhya." Raama indeed expected no other answer.

Thus now and again we shall see the human element come up and the divine Prince grieve and talk as common people do. This is the fascination of the *Raamaayana*. If Almightly God remains almighty and does everything Himself, then where is room or need for an *avataar* and how could the *dharma* of common men be established?

This is the difference between the earlier *avataars* and the later. In the Raama-*avataar,* the course of human conduct and the *dharma* governing it come linked together. This has been made explicit by Vaalmeeki:

On the occasion of Seeta's ordeal by fire at the end of the battle, Raama says to Brahma who appeared then among others and deprecated the idea of putting Seeta to proof:-

"I regard myself only as Raama, son of Dasaratha, an ordinary human being. Who I am in reality, where I belong, why I took birth, are matters on which *you* must enlighten me, and I do not know."

While Raama was plunged in thinking of the mothers left behind, Lakshmana ministered to him with loving words of courage and hope.

They spent that night under a banyan tree and left early next morning for Bharadwaaja's *aashrama* which they reached at sunset.

Partaking of the hospitality of the sage, they besought him to tell where they could spend the

years quietly in the forest and on his advice and with
his blessings left for Chitrakoota.

CHAPTER XX

CHITRAKOOTA

RAAMA spent the night in Bharadwaaja's *aashrama*. Getting up in the morning, they paid their respects to the *Maharishi* and, taking leave of him, set out for the Chitrakoota hill. The *muni* treated them affectionately as if they were his own children and sent them forth with his blessings after explaining to them the way they should take through the forest.

The three followed his topographical instructions closely and in due course came upon the river Kaalindi. They constructed a raft with logs and bamboos and creepers of the forest and on it Lakshmana made a seat for Seeta with little twigs and leaves on which she sat. The passage of the river was accomplished in safety.

In midstream Seeta offered salutations to the river goddess and prayed that Raama might fulfil his vow and the three be enabled safely to return home.

After crossing a few more streams, they came to a big banyan tree which had been described by Bharadwaaja. And under this tree Seeta again offered prayers saying: "Grant, O holy tree, that my husband may complete his vow and that I may see again the queens Kausalya and Sumitra."

Raama asked Lakshmana to walk in front with Seeta behind him while he himself followed in rear. "Whatever flower or fruit she asks for on the way," he said, "get if for her and keep her spirits up."

As Seeta went she showed an eager curiosity, asking about forest trees and creepers and was lost in admiration at the many-sided beauty of forest life.

They greatly enjoyed the journey and rested for the night on the bank of a river.

Here and in other places, Vaalmeeki describes how Raama and Lakshmana secured food by hunting. He makes it quite plain that they had to subsist largely on meat. Some good men are troubled by this. But meat was not prohibited for Kshatriyas. Indeed, it has always been the rule in India to permit any food legitimately obtained and consecrated as a sacrifice. Raama was a Kshatriya and he lived in the forest in the Kshatriya way, though abstemiously.

The following morning Raama woke up Lakshmana and said: "Listen, the birds are singing to the morning sun. It is time for us to start."

The popular story that Lakshmana spent the whole period of forest life without food or sleep is not found in Vaalmeeki. Sometimes, even, through fatigue Lakshmana did not get up quite early in the morning and Raama had to rouse him from slumber!

They performed their ablutions and worship and resumed their journey in the path indicated by Bharadwaaja. The season was summer and the trees and plants were ablaze with multicoloured flowers. The branches bowed under the weight of fruits and blossoms.

Raama pointed out the beauty of the forest to Seeta from time to time, saying as they walked: "How beautiful is the forest unspoilt by human interference! Look at the beehives hanging there! Look at the ground entirely covered with fallen flowers! Listen to the birds! How beautifully they sing to one another and live in joy! Life would indeed be pleasant if we could always enjoy such sights and sounds."

Then they saw at a distance the Chitrakoota hill. They were glad and began to walk briskly towards it. "How beautiful this region is!" exclaimed Raama. "The forest here has fine edible roots and fruits. The water is clear and sweet. Rishis dwell in *aashramas* in this forest and we may most certainly live happily here in their holy company."

They proceeded to put up an *aashrama* there for themselves. Lakshmana was a clever workman. He soon constructed a strong hut, which was weather-proof and made it comfortable and convenient. Single-handed, he completed the mud hut with windows and doors all made of bamboos and jungle material.

Kamban and Vaalmeeki vie with each other in their accounts of this episode. Kamban says that when Lakshmana had completed the structure, Raama embraced him weeping and asked him: "When and how did you learn all this?" One can imagine the scene.

Raama, his eyes filled with tears of joy, said, according to Kamban: "The flower-soft feet of the Princess of Mithila have traversed the hard forest floor. If her feet have done a wonder, why, Lakshmana, your hands too have wrought a miracle of house-building! I have seen today the gain that is in misfortune."

Here, beside the lovely Chitrakoota hill, on the bank of the river Maalyavati, in that cottage the three young people lived, free from care, performing their daily devotional routine. They forgot that they were in exile and spent the time happily, like Indra in Heaven surrounded by the gods.

The happy life in Chitrakoota is a wonderful background to set off the later sufferings and sorrows of the three.

CHAPTER XXI

A MOTHER'S GRIEF

SUMANTRA and Guha stood watching the three figures as long as they could. When they disappeared from sight, they were plunged in sorrow and went back to Guha's town. After a while Sumantra returned to Ayodhya.

As the charioteer approached the city, he found it desolate and devoid of the usual cheerful bustle of urban life. As soon as he crossed the fortress-gate and entered the city, his chariot was surrounded by a crowd eagerly asking: "Where did you leave Raama? How was he when you left him?"

"Dear people of Ayodhya," said Sumantra, "Raama and Lakshmana have crossed the Ganga. Ordering me to return home, they entered the forest on foot.

A great cry of grief rose from the multitude and many cursed themselves and attributed the catastrophe to their own sins. On both sides of the streets women stood as the chariot passed and cried: "Look at the car which departed with the princes and Seeta and has come back empty."

Sumantra drove forward covering his face with the end of his upper garment, ashamed of himself. He stopped the chariot in front of Dasaratha's palace and alighted.

There in front of the palace a great crowd had gathered. Women were saying, "How is Sumantra going to meet Kausalya and tell her that he left her son in the forest? How will she survive the report?"

With increasing sorrow and confusion, Sumantra entered the Queen's apartment. There he saw the

King more dead than alive. In low tones, he spoke of Raama's message to the King who heard it in heart-broken silence.

Then Kausalya, unable to control her wrath, addressed the King: "Here stands your minister who has returned from the forest after leaving my child to fulfil your command. Why are you silent? It was easy and pleasant to give boons to Kaikeyi. Why are you ashamed of it now? Did you not know that this would be the result of what you did? You have honoured your word. You may be happy over that. But who can share my sorrow with me? I have to bear it all. My grief cannot be reduced by your pain.

"No convention binds you to feel or appear to be grieved for what you have deliberately done. Why are you silent? You need not refrain from giving expression to sorrow for fear of offending Kaikeyi, for she is not here. Surely you should enquire of Sumantra about Raama. Have you no humanity? Why do you try to suppress even natural feelings?"

Her grief and love for Raama blinded her to the state of her husband's body and mind. Instead of lightening, she aggravated his suffering.

Dasaratha opened his eyes and Sumantra reported duly Raama's message in his own words.

Sumantra tried his best to console Kausalya. But she went on repeating: "Take me and leave me where Raama is. Young Seeta is there with him facing the hardships of the forest. I cannot bear this agony. Let me go to Dandaka and be with Seeta."

Sumantra answered: "Queen, be brave. Banish this grief. Raama spends his time even more happily in the forest than he did in Ayodhya. He feels no sorrow. Lakshmana finds joy in the supreme job of

dutiful service to the brother he loves. He is very
happy. As for Seeta, there in the forest, as here in the
palace, she lives for Raama with every breath and
knows neither fear nor sorrow. She spends her time
as though she were a sylvan goddess and is as happy
there as she was here playing in the groves and
gardens of Ayodhya. The beauty of her face is still
like the rising moon's. Like a forest fawn she lives
there with care-free grace, spending the golden
hours with Raama by her side. Every sight and
sound is a new source of joy to her and the theme of
talk with Raama and Lakshmana.

"Walking barefoot, her feet are red like the
lotus, and need no painting with henna. She walks in
the forest as if she were dancing; she only lacks the
tinkling anklets to make it complete. All that I say is
true. There is no need for you to grive.

"The three of them are fulfilling their sacred
duty and offering an object lesson to the world. They
are making the King's word good. Their life will be
remembered and praised for ever. Why, then, should
we grive for them?"

With such talk, Kausalya would be consoled for
a while. But soon she would break down again and
cry: "Alas, alas, Raama, my child." Her grief seemed
redoubled when she saw Sumantra come back,
leaving Raama in the forest.

CHAPTER XXII

IDLE SPORT AND TERRIBLE RESULT

DASARATHA had been driven ruthlessly by circumstances to an action which not only broke his heart but made him hate himself and deprived him even of self-pity. The only way out of the dilemma of either breaking his plighted word or doing a great wrong to Raama would have been for the latter to disobey him and insist on his rights; but Raama placed his duty to his father high above all other things, and Raama was all the world to Seeta and Lakshmana. So they had all gone together.

To Dasaratha, agonising on his bed of pain in desolation and remorse, Kausalya spoke reproachful words.

The stinging words in which Kausalya's sorrow found expression caused excruciating pain to Dasaratha, but she seemed to find some relief in giving vent to her feelings in this way.

"Proud of having kept your word and happy in young Kaikeyi's approval and gratification, have you any thought for others? You have been my world and my god, my joy in this world and my hope for the next and you have forsaken me. My son, the light of my life, has been wrenched away from me and banished. I live here alone, old, helpless woman, without the love of my lord or the sight of my only son. Was ever a woman left more desolate? But you — are you not delighted with what you have done?

"It is enough for you that Kaikeyi and Bharata are happy. You need not entertain any fear that Raama will mar that happiness, even if he returned from the forest after fourteen years. He will not touch the kingdom once ruled by Bharata. The tiger does not touch the leavings of another animal's kill. Like a fish eating its offspring, you have killed your own child."

Touched to the quick, the King even in the intensity of his anguish turned to his wife with a humble prayer for forgiveness with clasped hands.

"Have pity on me, Kausalya," he moaned. "You have been kind and forgiving even to strangers. Do have some compassion on your husband who has always loved and honoured you and whose heart is broken by a sorrow which knows no remedy!"

These piteous words and the sight of her husband in supplication and the memory of happier hours pierced the noble queen to the heart and she fell at his feet imploring forgiveness for unbecoming words forced out of her by grief.

As the leaden hours crept slowly on, Dasaratha remembered something that had happened long ago and it aggravated the anguish of his heart. The King turned to Kausalya and said:

"Are you still here, my dear? The fruit of one's action can never be escaped. I now endure the result of a great sin that I committed in the days that are gone. Men in their ignorance sometimes do great evils for the sake of some slight momentary pleasure. Then when the time comes the price has to be paid.

"When I was young, I had the skill to use my bow against unseen targets aiming by sound only. For the pleasure of exercising this skill, I once killed an innocent man and committed a great sin. Listen, I shall relate to you that sad adventure.

"It was before you came to me. One night I went out in my chariot to hunt on the banks of the Sarayu. It had been raining heavily and, from the mountain sides, the streams were running dyed with the rich colours of minerals and fresh soil. The birds were silent. The forest seemed asleep.

"I could take the aim by the ear and shoot, without seeing, a tiger or bear or other wild beast that might come to slake its thirst in the stream. I wanted to test this skill of mine. It was dense darkness. I waited for some wild animal to come.

"Then I heard a gurgling sound as of an elephant drinking. At once I aimed an arrow in the direction whence the sound came. Like a venomous serpent, swish went my dart and hit the object. But I was shocked to hear a human voice exclaim: 'Alas! I am dead!'

"I heard the man cry again piteously, 'Who can be my enemy? Never have I done any harm to anyone. Who then could want to kill me thus as I was filling my pitcher with water? What could he gain by this? Why should anyone bear hate against one living his innocent hermit life in the forest? What is to happen to my old blind parents now, with none to look after them? O misery!'

"Horror-struck, I stood trembling in every limb. My bow and arrow slipped from my hands. I approached the place from where the voice came and I found a young ascetic lying on the ground with dishevelled hair, covered all over with blood and earth. Beside him lay an upturned pitcher. The look of his eyes was as fire. When he saw me, he cried, 'O, sinner that has killed me! Why did you aim your arrow at me that was taking water from the stream? My old blind parents are thirsty and are waiting for me in the *aashrama*, thinking that I would return with my pitcher filled. Why did you kill me? O God, my penances and my devotions have all gone to naught. My parents do not know that I lie here stricken and helpless. They will go on waiting for me and even if they knew it, what could they do, blind and helpless? Who are you? What! Are you not the King of Kosala? And so, you, the King, who should by right protect me, have slain me. Very well, O King, go yourself and tell them what you have done. Fall at their feet and beg for forgiveness. Else, their anger will reduce you to ashes. Go straight to the *aashrama*. Take that path there. Go at once and save yourself. But this arrow is a torture. Pull it out and relieve me of the pain before you go.'

"I knew that if I pulled out the arrow from his body, his pain would end indeed, but so would his life in a gush of blood. My hand refused to do the deed. For a while I stood, not knowing what to do.

"Then, the young ascetic said: 'Do not hesitate. Do end my pain. My mind is now clear and I have calmed myself. Boldly pull out the arrow and release my life.'

"Gently I pulled the arrow out. The young ascetic turned on the ground, heaved a sigh and, with his eyes fixed on me, breathed his last.

"It is this crime of mine that is now pursuing me. The agony of those blind parents who were deprived by me of their son has come now for me to endure."

CHAPTER XXIII

LAST MOMENTS

DASARATHA continued: "Listen, I shall tell you what followed.

"Having committed a sin and seeing the young ascetic die, I stood wondering what to do next. Finally I decided that it was my duty and my interest to do what he advised me. I cleaned the pitcher, and filling it with fresh water, took it and went along the foot-path he had pointed out.

"I reached his cottage and there I saw the old couple waiting for the return of their son. They sat there like two birds with broken wings shrivelled in body and unable to move. Both were blind.

"They were speaking to each other about the long delay of their son in fetching water from the stream. I was filled with terror as I slowly approached them.

"The old man, hearing my footsteps, mumbled: 'Why this long delay, my son? Quickly give me some water to drink. Your mother too is athirst. Were you making your pleasure in the stream? Was this the cause of your delay, son? Why are you silent? Even if your mother or I have offended you in any manner, you should not take it to heart. You are a perfect son and our only prop. We have lost our eye-sight and you serve as our eyes. Indeed you are more than our life to us. Why are you still silent? Are you still angry?'

"I trembled in fear when I heard the toothless old man talking thus. Gathering courage I began: 'O, holy one, I am Dasaratha by name, a kshatriya, bound to obey and serve you, though not your son.

Driven by my former karma, I have committed a terrible sin and stand in abject humility before you. I went to the river bank for sport, hoping to shoot wild beasts. I thought I heard in the darkness an elephant drinking water, and I aimed my arrow as I am a marksman that can aim by sound as well as by sight, and it was my misfortune and his fate that my arrow struck your son as he was filling his pitcher, with the gurgling I had mistaken for that of an elephant drinking. Thus, without intending it, I fatally wounded your beloved son. When I went to the spot and saw him rolling in blood with my arrow stuck in his breast, I cursed myself. I was filled with horror and stood not knowing what to do. At his request I pulled the arrow out to release him from the mortal pain. He is dead. I have told you the horrible sin I have committed. I throw myself at your mercy. I await your judgment.'

"The miserable couple were struck dumb by my dreadful tale about their son. Tears poured from their sightless eyes and the old man said: 'King, your sin is indeed great. But it was done in ignorance. And you have come yourself to tell me your crime. So you shall live. Now take us both to the spot. Let us touch our beloved son with our hands and send him into Yama's keeping.'

"I carried them to the river bank where their son lay dead. They felt his body all over, cried and blessed his soul and performed the cremation.

"Then before ascending the funeral pyre and giving themselves up to the fire, they turned to me and said: 'This great grief you have brought about for us, you too, will endure in good time. You will die of grief parted from your son.'

"Saying this, they burnt themselves and their souls joined the gods. My sin has pursued me and I am now in its grip.

"My old crime is killing me now. As food prohibited by the doctors foolishly consumed by a sick man kills him, what that old father uttered in unbearable grief has now come true. I have sent my innocent son to the forest and, unable to bear the grief, I now enter Yama's abode.

"How else could these unnatural events occur? How else could I be thus deceived and betrayed? Even if I ordered Raama to go to the forest, why should he obey my unjust command? Why should he insist on being exiled? It is the curse of that old blind couple, nothing else.

"Kausalya, I do not see you. My sight is gone. Death is fast approaching. Come nearer and let me feel you. All is over. The messengers of Yama are calling me. Will Raama come? Shall I see him before I die? Oh, I am dying. The oil is all consumed and my light is going out! Ah Kausalya! Oh Sumitra!"

His life slowly ebbed away and that night at some time unobserved by any, the King breathed his last.

As described by Vaalmeeki in the early pages of the epic, Dasaratha was one who had mastered all the *Vedas* and *Shaastras*, was a farsighted person, the hero of many battles, the performer of many sacrifices, follower of *dharma*, a far-famed king with many friends and no foes, one who had conquered his senses. His power was like Indra's. His wealth was like Kubera's. In statesmanship, he was like Manu. Fate had ordered that such a one should exile his beloved son and die of a broken heart, with none by him in his last moments but two faithful women stricken by himself with a common sorrow.

Since the King had so often fainted and recovered, his death was not immediately noticed by Kausalya or Sumitra. They were weary, too, with grief and watching, and fell into a sleep of fatigue in a corner of the apartment. At dawn, the musicians and singers, whose duty it was to rouse the King from slumber, came to his bed chamber and played on instruments and sang the usual hymns.

But they saw no sign of the King waking. The royal servants who attended to the King's morning needs waited long and wondered why he slept till so late. Then they made bold to enter the apartment and saw him lying dead.

Soon the news spread and filled the palace with grief. The widows of the great Dasaratha cried like orphaned children, embracing one another in unavailing lamentation.

CHAPTER XXIV

BHARATA ARRIVES

KAUSALYA clung to the King's body and cried: "I shall go with the King to Yama's abode. How can I live without my son and without my husband?"

The elders and officers of the palace managed to separate her from the dead King and take her away. Then they discussed about the funeral rites. They could not be performed immediately, for Raama and Lakshmana had gone to the forest and Bharata and Satrughna were far away in their uncle's place. It was decided to send for Bharata and to keep the body immersed in oil till his arrival.

The great monarch's remains were thus kept waiting for Bharata's arrival. Ayodhya, the City of Splendour, was sunk in darkness and lamentation. Crowds of women met here and there and reviled Kaikeyi. There was anxiety in men's hearts. The Crown-prince had gone to the forest. Bharata too was far away. Anarchy was feared, for no one in those days could imagine a people going on without a king.

After the long night had passed, the ministers, officers and elders assembled in the hall in the morning. Maarkandeya. Vaamadeva, Kaashyapa, Kaatyaayana, Gautama, Jaabaali and other learned men, with Sumantra and the other ministers, bowed to Vasishtha and said:

"Sir, the night we have passed was like a century. The King is no more. Raama and Lakshmana are in the forest. Bharata and Satrughna are in far-off Kekaya in their grand-

father's house. Some one must forthwith be asked to
take up the responsibility of rule. A land without a
king cannot survive. Order will disappear, son will
not obey father, nor wife her husband. The rains will
hold back. Thieves and robbers will range at will.
There will be no mutual trust among people. Neither
agriculture nor trade can flourish. Without a king,
the land must lose its prosperity. The springs of
charity will dry up. Festivals and services will cease
to be performed in temples. There will be no
expounding of *Shaastras* or epics, nor any listeners.
People will no more sleep with doors open. Culture
will decline and soon disappear. Penances, vows,
enjoyments, learning — all depend on the king's
protection. The beauty of women will vanish. The
sense of security will be lost. Men will eat one
another up as fish do. Cruelty and misery will grow
apace and lay waste the land. For good to prosper
and evil to be restrained, a king is essential."

Thus Vaalmeeki describes at length the
dangers of anarchy through the mouths of leaders in
that assembly.

"It looks as if a great darkness has enveloped
the land," they said. "*Dharma* is in danger. Let us
forthwith secure a king."

Vasishtha sent for tried messengers and said to
them: "Start at once. Go straight and swift to
Kekaya. See that you wear no sign of sorrow on your
face or show it in your behaviour. Bharata should not
know that the King is dead. Tell him simply that the
family preceptor and ministers want his presence at
once in Ayodhya and bring him along with you with
all the speed you may. Tell him nothing about
Raama and Seeta going to the forest or the King's
death on account of grief. To avoid all suspicion, take

with you the usual gifts of jewels and precious
garments for presentation to the King of Kekaya."

From this we can understand the meaning of
what the *Shaastras* and *Kural* say about Truth.
Truthfulness should be such that it needlessly hurts
no being in the world. The test for right conduct
including truthfulness is harmlessness. This does
not mean that truth is underrated.

Soon the messengers were provisioned and
equipped for the long journey and furnished with
gifts of honour. Mounted on swift and sturdy horses,
they sped past rivers and forests, up hill and down
dale, and reached Kekaya, which was somewhere to
the west of the modern Punjab, and found
themselves in Raajagriha, its capital, where the
Ikshvaaku princes were residing in the palace of
their maternal uncle. They decided to wait on the
princes the next morning.

The night the messengers arrived, Bharata had
evil dreams and woke up in the morning filled with
anxiety as to what they might portend. His face
showed the state of his mind. His companions tried
to entertain him with dance and mirth to make him
forget his cares, but did not succeed.

We still do not know all the secrets of nature
and the telepathy of affection. May be, Dasaratha's
mental anguish and death–throes reached Bharata
across space and caused him his bad dreams. He said
to himself: "It seems to me that death is approaching
my brother Raama or Lakshmana or myself. They
say that an early morning dream does not fail to be
fulfilled. And mine has been a terrible dream. I am
full of fear. I know not what to do."

Just then the messengers were announced. The
King of Kekaya and his son Yudhaajit received the
envoys with due courtesy. They paid their respects to
the King and the princes, then turned to Bharata
and said:

"The priests and ministers send you their
blessings and request you to return at once to
Ayodhya. They want us to convey to you that the
need for your presence there is most urgent. Please
touch for acceptance these garments and jewels to be
given to your uncle and to the King as gifts from the
palace of Ayodhya."

Bharata questioned the messengers after the
welfare of all at home. The manner of his enquiry
suggest that he had an uneasy premonition that his
mother's head-strong and ambitious nature might
have had something to do with this hasty summons
home. "And is my mother, the haughty and irascible
Queen Kaikeyi who believes herself all-wise and
must always have her way — is she in good health?"

The messengers must have been at their wits'
end for an answer. The best they could make was: "O
tiger among men, all are well whose welfare is dear
to you. Lakshmi, the goddess of sovereignty, whose
abode is the lotus, woos you. Get into your chariot
without loss of time." There was an enigmatic
thought in this greeting, for according to them
Bharata was to be installed on the throne.

The prince took leave of his uncle and
grandfather for returning home and preparations
were made for his departure. The old king and
Yudhaajit collected rare and valuable things of their
country to be sent as gifts to King Dasaratha and
Prince Raama of Ayodhya. Bharata and Satrughna
mounted their chariots and started with a big

retinue towards Ayodhya. They travelled fast, unmindful of fatigue, and by forced marches reached Ayodhya on the morning of the eighth day.

As he approached the city, Bharata's mind was filled with misgiving. Nothing seemed to be as it was before, and the air seemed heavy with disaster. He asked the charioteer: "Why does the city wear such a strange look? I do not see the usual crowds of people going in and coming out. In the gardens outside the city one used to see young men and women with bright, cheerful faces. But now they all seem sad."

Bharata's chariot entered the city through the Victory Gate. The streets, houses and temples were bare and unadorned. The faces of the people looked drawn and famished.

"Why are the musical instruments silent?" he asked. "Why are the citizens not decked with flowers and sandal paste? These are all bad signs. I cannot repress my anxiety."

Inauspicious omens were seen everywhere. Bharata concluded that some great misfortune had overtaken the city and that was the reason why he had been so hastily sent for. He entered Dasaratha's palace. The king was not to be seen. His anxiety increased.

He then entered Kaikeyi's palace. When she saw her son after a long absence, she jumped from her golden couch to embrace him. He bent down and touched her feet. She kissed his head and welcomed him with maternal blessings.

"Did you have a good journey?" she asked. "Are your uncle and grandfather well? Tell me all about them."

He answered: "The journey took seven days. All our people at Kekaya are happy and well. Grandfather and uncle send you their love. They have sent rich gifts for you, but these will arrive later. I have come in advance. The envoys hurried me, saying there was urgent work demanding my presence here. What is all this about? I went to the King's palace to pay him my respects. He was not to be found there and here too his couch is empty. Perhaps he is with one of my senior mothers. I must go and see him and tender my respects."

When Bharata, innocent of heart and unaware of what had happened, said this, the foolish queen intoxicated with a new sense of power answered: "My child, your father had his full share of the blessings of this life. His fame was great. He performed all the sacrifices enjoined by tradition. He was a refuge for the good. He has now entered the higher world and joined the gods."

On hearing this, Bharata fell down uttering a cry, his long arms stretched out on the ground. Rising, he looked at his father's empty bed and sobbed like a destitute orphan. The mighty hero threw his god-like frame on the earth and wept like a child in uncontrolled grief.

Looking at her son, who lay on the ground like a big tree fallen to the axe, Kaikeyi said:

"Arise, O King. Stand up. It is not right for a king thus to mourn and roll on the ground. Honour and glory are waiting for your acceptance. You are to uphold the *dharma* and perform sacrifices in the way of your royal fathers. Your intelligence shines like the noonday sun. No misfortune dare come near you. Son, strong of limb and brave-hearted, stand up."

Bharata's mind was immaculàte, spotless. He did not see all that Kaikeyi had put in this her appeal!

After lamenting long, he got up and said: "When I went to my uncle's house I had hoped that Raama's installation as *Yuvaraaja* would come off soon and that on my return I would see the great festive ceremonies. How differently have things turned out! How am I to bear this calamity? No more shall I see my father's face. What did he die of? How did he get the illness? And I was not by his side when he lay sick! It was given to Raama to tend him in his last moments. How affectionate the King was towards me! If some dust settled on my body, he would wipe it with his hand. And how soft and pleasing was his touch! And it was not given me to serve him in his need. But, mother, where is Raama? Hereafter he is both father and preceptor to me. I must see him at once and kiss his feet. He is now my sole refuge. What was my father's last message to me? I want his very words."

Kaikeyi's answer had to be consistent both with truth and her designs. She was pulled in contrary directions by her culture and her ambition. She found words which conveyed that the King did not think of Bharata in his last moments. She also wished to prepare him for the rest of the news. She said: "Your father breathed his last crying, 'Ha, Raama, Ha, Lakshmana, Ha, Jaanaki.' These were his last words. He died saying: "It is not given me to live to see Raama, Lakshmana and Seeta return. Happy they who will see their return."

Listening to this, Bharata gathered that Raama and Lakshmana too were absent from the King's side. His grief increased and he asked Kaikeyi:

"Where were they? What business took them away from our father's side during his last moments?"

Hoping to pacify him, Kaikeyi said: "My son, Raama put on the garments of an ascetic and, taking Lakshmana and Seeta with him, went to the Dandaka forest."

Bharata's amazement now knew no bounds. He asked: "I understand nothing of what you are saying. What sin did Raama commit that he should undertake such an expiation? Did he rob any Braahmana or cause bodily hurt to any innocent person or desire somebody else's wife? Why did he have to go to the forest? Who laid on him this penance?"

In those days people went of their own will or were sent to the forest as a purifying punishment for such and other heinous crimes. Now Kaikeyi shaken out of silence by this tempest of questions came out with the truth foolishly hoping for the best.

"Raama committed no crime. He neither robbed nor harmed anyone. And it was not in Raama's nature to cast eyes of desire at other people's wives. What happened was that, seeing that preparations were afoot for installing him as Crown-prince and regent, I approached the King for your sake and secured the fulfilment of two boons he had long ago granted to me. I asked that the kingdom should go to you and that Raama should be exiled to the forest. Bound by his past promise, the King agreed. Raama has therefore gone to the forest with Seeta and Lakshmana. Unable to bear this separation, your father expired of grief. Do not waste yourself in vain lamentations now. Think now what you should do. You know *dharma*. Your duty is to accept the burden of kingship. I did all this for your sake and you should accept the fruit of my action in the spirit in which I acted. The city and kingdom have come into your possession without your wanting or working for it. Following the injunctions of Vasishtha and other learned men, perform duly your father's obsequies and then prepare for the coronation. You are a kshatriya. You have inherited your father's kingdom. Attend to what has fallen to you as your duty."

CHAPTER XXV

INTRIGUE WASTED

NOW Bharata understood everything and realised the enormity of the harm wrought by his mother.

Overwhelmed by grief and anger, he could not control himself. At the thought of what she had done and the eternal infamy she had incurred, his grief grew wild and he hurled cruel words at her.

"What have you done?" he cried. "Did you ever hope to make me accept the kingdom? Deprived of such a father and such a brother, am I likely to care for power? After causing the death of the King and the banishment of Raama, you ask me to take their place and rule the land. This is like pouring oil into the fire of my grief. How unfortunate was my father to have chosen you for a wife! Kausalya and Sumitra will also die of grief. Oh, how could you bring yourself to do this to Raama who was so devoted to you? Revered mother Kausalya treated you like her own blood-sister. How could you think of plotting against her beloved son? And did you not know how much I loved Raama? Greed destroyed your understanding. How else could you so foolishly plan for my happiness? Even the great King relied on Raama and Lakshmana. How could you believe that in their absence I could rule the kingdom? And, even if I could, would I agree? Never will your wish be fulfilled through my co-operation. I can no longer regard you as my mother. I cut myself off from all relation with you and decline to regard you as my mother.

"How could you ever think of setting aside rule and custom and getting a younger son crowned? Would not the world revile us for all time? The general law of kings and the tradition of our family cannot be violated. I will not carry out your wish. I shall go to the forest and bring Raama back. I shall set the crown on his head and rejoice in being his loyal servant."

To understand Bharata's feelings, we should keep in mind his innate noble nature, his love for Raama, his grief for his father and the sense of guilt and shame that for his sake his mother had done this grievous wrong. We should not weigh his words in dry air and a chemical balance. In such contexts, poetry flashes fire. One sees it both in Vaalmeeki and Kamban.

Bharata raised his voice and spoke again: "Banish Raama indeed! It is you that ought to be banished, cruel woman, who have forsaken the path of *dharma*. So far as you are concerned you may take it that I am dead, for I would rather be dead than be son to a murderess!

"Murderess of your husband! You are not the daughter of the good king Asvapati. You are a *Raakshasi*. To what hell should you go, you, who banished the only child of mother Kausalya? What punishment would be too great for the grief you have caused her?

"Kaamadhenu, the cow-mother, had hundreds of thousands of children, yet she shed tears at the sight of the suffering of two bulls yoked to a plough and her tears scalded Indra on his throne in high Heaven. And Kausalya's only child you sent to the forest, hoping thus that you and I could be made happy!

"I shall do the obsequies and go to the forest and fall at the feet of Raama and bring him to his kingdom. And then, to cleanse myself of the sin and the shame you have brought on me, I shall lead the life of an ascetic in the Dandaka forest.

"What a flood of sorrow have you let loose on the earth? By what penitence, by what self-mortification, can you redeem yourself? I shall go myself at once to Raama and get rid of my guilt by restoring the kingdom to him."

Finding no relief for his anguish by angry words, sighing like a young elephant newly captured, hot tears falling from his eyes, he felt he could bear no longer the sight of his mother and rushed to Kausalya's apartment, there to find a better place to give vent to his sorrow.

Thus did Kaikeyi's castle in the air go up in smoke. She lay down on the floor and wept. 'The most painful of all reflexions is that of a crime perpetrated in vain.'

Among the characters in the *Raamaayana,* Bharata is the perfect embodiment of virtue. In the villages of the North, the people celebrate an annual festival for the episode of the meeting of Raama and Bharata at Chitrakoota, which they consider the most sanctifying part of the *Raamaayana* epic. There have been through the ages great and noble souls whose virtue shines eternally in the midst of the sordid self-seeking of a sinful world, as a beacon light to seekers of the right path, and as a token of the god in man.

Soon the news of Bharata's arrival spread throughout the palace. Kausalya, still labouring under her grief, heard this, and was glad and told

Sumitra, "Come, let us go and meet Bharata."
Hardly had they taken a couple of steps when they
saw Bharata himself rushing wildly towards them to
plead for mercy.

Kausalya's first thought when she heard of
Bharata's arrival was that he had hastened back to
assume the fortune which had come to him. Had not
the elders and ministers, led by Vasishtha, decided
to send for Bharata so that he might perform his
father's obsequies and be crowned king? Hence,
seeing Bharata, Kausalya, her heart desolate with
her loss of husband and son, said in a low voice:
"Bharata, the kingship is waiting secured for your
sake by Kaikeyi. You need not fear any let or
hindrance from us. Take it, and may all happiness be
yours. Only one boon I crave of you—to let me join
your father on the funeral pyre."

These words were like stinging poison in
Bharata's ears. He fell at her feet and clung to them,
unable to speak.

Kausalya said again: "Oh Bharata, at least take
me where Raama is in the forest."

Unable to bear all these piteous words of
Kausalya and unable to speak, Bharata fell into a
swoon. After a while he sat up and said: "Mother,
why do you thus torture me who am innocent? You
know I was far away and knew nothing of the wicked
things going on here. Do you not know the love I bear
for Raama? Would I ever do such a thing to him?
May all the sins of the world descend on me if I had
the least notion of the evil brewing here! I had
nothing to do with it. I have no desire to reap its
fruit."

He raised his hands and recited all the horrible sins that one could commit and invoked on himself the punishments due to them if he had any part in the plot.

In those days as now it was hard for a son to prove that he knew nothing of a scheme carried out by his mother for his benefit. Bharata could only swear his innocence again and again. He cared nothing for kingdom or wealth or power and it was a terrible torment to him that Kausalya should think him capable of greed for them at the expense of his brother. Indeed such a thought was hardly less cruel and unjust than Raama's exile! He could never accept the crown which was his beloved brother's birthright.

His passionate sincerity convinced Kausalya of the injustice of her suspicions, and her heart went out to him. Tenderly she raised him from the ground and took his head on her lap and caressed him as though he were Raama himself.

"My dear son, my grief is doubled by seeing the pain raging in your innocent heart. What shall we do, child? We are the playthings of fate. May the reward of goodness come to you in this world and the next!"

Kausalya had not believed Bharata privy to the plot, but she feared that he would condone it and yield to the temptation of its results. Now she was convinced that Bharata's heart was completely free from stain. Though her own son had gone to the forest, she was pleased that such another son had come to her in his place.

Here, Kamban beautifully sings how Kausalya shed tears of joy over Bharata and embraced him

imagining that Raama himself had returned from
the forest. Kausalya said amidst her sobs: "Many
were your ancestors who attained fame. You have
surpassed them all in glory by renouncing the
kingship that has come to you. You are indeed King
among kings."

The Kausalya and Bharata portrayed by
Kamban embody a culture. May these heroic figures
and that culture live for ever in the land of Bharata!

The obsequies of the dead king were duly
performed. Vasishtha and other learned men and
elders offered grave *shaastric* consolation to Bharata
and Satrughna. Fourteen days after the King's
demise, the ministers called the Assembly and
addressed Bharata thus:

"The King has gone to the world above. Raama
and Lakshmana are in the forest. The land is now
without a king. It is right that you should assume
the rule at our request. The preparations for the
coronation are all complete. The citizens and
ministers are awaiting your acceptance. This is your
kingdom lawfully descended from your ancestors. It
is for you to be anointed and rule righteously over
us."

Bharata went with folded hands round the
materials gathered for the coronation and said in
grave tones to the assembled elders:

"I do not consider it proper that you should ask
me thus to accept the kingdom. According to the
custom of our House, the throne belongs to the eldest
son. With all respect to you, I have decided to go to
the forest and bring Raama back to Ayodhya with
Lakshmana and see that Raama is crowned. Please
get ready the men and materials for this purpose.

Prepare the road for the journey. Let labourers be mobilised for it. It is my final and irrevocable decision not to accept the crown."

Listening to the prince's words, the whole assembly was beside itself with joy. They applauded Bharata's suggestion.

The army and a big retinue were got ready to accompany the prince to the forest. Quickly an army of workers with their tools went forward to prepare the road. Men who knew the forest, pioneers who could dig wells and canals, builders of rafts and boats, carpenters and engineers, worked enthusiastically, because they were engaged in getting beloved Raama back. Culverts were built, trees felled, a broad road for the prince and his retinue was soon laid. Ups and downs were levelled, marshes drained, resting places for the army and facilities for drinking water and all other conveniences were soon made ready.

Though thus preparations were made for Bharata's journey to the forest, Vasishtha and the other ministers formally summoned the Assembly again. They did not give up their desire to get Bharata to agree to be crowned. They sent messengers to Bharata's palace and invited him to the Hall. They approached him with music playing on many instruments. All this pained him.

He stopped the musicians and sent the messengers back and told Satrughna: "Why should they still persist in tormenting me when I have refused the kingdom? This is the result of our mother's intrigue. My father has gone to Heaven leaving me to bear all this alone. The land needs a king; without one it drifts like a rudderless and derelict ship. We must soon get Raama back."

The Assembly sat eagerly looking for the entrance of the blameless prince. He entered the Hall as the full moon rises in the sky. He bowed to the elders and sat down.

Vasishtha said: "This kingdom has been given to you by your father and your brother Raama; accept it and protect us according to ancient custom."

Bharata's heart was far away with Raama. Tears fell from his eyes. The young prince wept aloud in the midst of the royal Assembly and in a voice struggling with tears, he addressed words of respectful reproach to the preceptors:

"How can you ask one of my race and upbringing to usurp what belongs to another far nobler and more worthy than I? Can any son of Dasaratha possibly dream of such iniquity? This kingdom, and I, and all else in it belong to Raama. He is the eldest son, the noblest among us, a lover of *dharma*, an equal to Dileepa and Nahusha of old. He is the rightful king. He is fit to be sovereign of the three worlds. Standing here I pay my homage to Raama there in the forest. He is the King, not I!"

The Assembly burst into tears of joy when they heard Bharata speak thus.

And Bharata continued: "If I am unable to persuade King Raama to agree, I shall stay there performing penance. It is your duty, O Elders, to use every means to bring Raama back. I shall do all I can to make Raama come back to Ayodhya and make him King."

He then ordered Sumantra who was standing near him to hasten the preparations for going to the forest. The city rejoiced in anticipation of Raama's return, for all felt sure that nothing could resist the force of Bharata's dutiful love.

CHAPTER XXVI

BHARATA SUSPECTED

GAZING across the river Ganga, Guha, the hunter-king, noticed unusual commotion on the bank opposite. A great army had encamped there. He pointed it to his kinsmen standing by his side and said:

"Who is this and why has he come here with a large army, apparently to cross the river? The flag suggests that it is Kaikeyi's son Bharata and his army. Yes, I see the flag flying on the top of the chariot and I can recognise the tree painted on it. That is the flag of the King of Ayodhya.

"Is not Raama's enemy, Bharata, the King of Ayodhya today? Having secured the kingdom unjustly through his mother Kaikeyi, it looks as though he has pursued Raama here to slay him. Get together our warriors and kinsmen and friends. Let them stand ready on this bank. Gather all the boats and fill them with armed men ready for battle. Let us wait and see. If the newcomers are well disposed towards Raama, we shall help them to cross the river and come over to this side. But, if their intention is hostile, we shall prevent them from crossing the Ganga."

And so having made all preparations, Guha, in accordance with rules of courtesy, took some presents, got into a boat and went to meet Bharata.

On the other bank at the same time Sumantra was telling Bharata:

"Look! Guha, the hunter-king, devoted friend of Raama, has come with his people to welcome us. He is the ruler of this region. He and his kinsmen are well acquainted with every nook and corner of this forest. They could tell us where Raama is to be found and lead us safely and swiftly to the place."

Meanwhile Guha crossed the stream and, approaching Bharata, bowed and said: "Though we have been taken by surprise by your unexpected visit, still all that is mine here you may consider as your own and command me. I consider it an honour to be able to welcome and entertain you and your army."

Bharata answered: "It is very kind of you, O friend of my brother, to offer hospitality to such a large army. I wish to proceed to the hermitage of Bharadwaaja. We do not know the way, and we also need to cross this great river."

Guha bowed before him with clasped hands and said politely: "My lord, my servants and myself are ready to go with you and act as guides. But you must excuse me for expressing a doubt which occurs to me on seeing this large army you have brought. Surely you have no intentions hostile to Raama?"

Pained by these words and from a heart clear and pure as the summer sky, Bharata said: "Alas, what greater shame can come to me than this, that men who love Raama should fear and suspect me? Have no misgivings, Guha. Raama is my father now, for he has taken the place of my lost father. I have come here to beg of him to return to Ayodhya. I swear, I have no other purpose in my mind."

Guha rejoiced to see in Bharata's face his intense love for Raama and his grief at what had happened. He said: "My Lord, who in the world can equal in sacrifice? Who but you would renounce such wealth and power coming to him unsought? Your glory will shine for ever."

The hunter-king supplied Bharata's army with all it needed. The hosts and the guests retired for the night.

The meeting with Guha only increased Bharata's sorrow. Bharata was endowed with a heart of utter innocence. He sighed and said: "Alas, that it should come to this", and rolled sleepless on the ground. His whole body burned with thoughts of the infamy that had come as a cloud over him, his father's death and the parting from Raama. Guha spoke words of comfort and tried to console him. This meeting of Bharata and Guha and the way they shared their sorrow is an episode dear to the Vaishnava Aalvaars and other true Bhaktas.

Bharata questioned: "What food did Raama take when he was here? Where did he sit? Where did he sleep? What did he say? And what did he do?"

Guha answered every question lovingly and pointed the spot where Raama had slept. And when he was asked, "Where did Lakshmana sleep?" he replied: "Lakshmana said, 'When Raama and Seeta lie stretched on the bare earth, how can I sleep?' and he shed tears and, like me, stood on guard the whole night, bow in hand."

As Bharata pictured this scene, his grief became unendurable. He saw the spot where Raama and Seeta had slept that night and pointed it to the weeping queens.

Asked what Raama ate, Guha answered: "My Lord, they fasted that night, Lakshmana brought some water and Raama drank of it and handed it back to Lakshmana to drink. The food I brought was returned untasted. The following morning, they matted their locks and walked into the forest."

Bharata had found some relief from sorrow in his resolve to seek out Raama and persuade him to return, but his talk with Guha and the sights he saw brought it back in full flood.

"For my sake, Raama, you slept on the grass. I have seen the spot and still live. And they want me to wear a crown, on top of all this!" Thus he lamented inconsolably.

Then he told himself: "I shall somehow take Raama back and seat him on the throne. If he wants his vow fulfilled, I shall replace him in the forest for fourteen years. He will agree to this arrangement as it is only right and proper." Thus he calmed himself.

Early next morning, Bharata woke up Satrughna: "What? Are you still sleeping? The day has already dawned. The army has to cross the river. We should send quickly for Guha and arrange for the journey."

Satrughna answered: "I am not asleep, brother. Like you I spent the whole night thinking of Raama."

While they were speaking, Guha arrived and after courteous greetings announced that he had a fleet of many boats ready. All the baggage and the whole army were put on boats. The loaded vessels crossed the great river. The transport across raised a joyous clamour like some great festival.

The people did not see the sorrow in Bharata's heart, for they had concluded, even when Bharata set out, that Raama would surely return. They went forward rejoicing that soon Raama would be in their midst as crowned king and all their recent sorrows would pass like a bad dream.

Vaalmeeki describes the scene on the bank of the Ganga in a way that recalls to one a crowded railway station during a popular festival. When the whole army had crossed the river, Bharata followed it in a boat specially fitted up for him.

They reached the *aashrama* of Bharadwaaja.

The story of Bharata in the *Raamaayana* portraying a character of unrivalled purity and sublime selflessness is something more than an episode, and stands out by itself even in that noble epic, as holy shrines do on the banks of the Ganga. It uplifts the heart, and gives one a glimpse of the heights to which human nature can rise when cleansed by love and devotion. Whether Raama and Bharata were incarnations of the Deity or merely supreme creations of a nation's imagination this episode is among the masterpieces of the world's literature.

Jnaana and *bhakti* will automatically grow by a contemplation of the personality of Bharata. In order to recreate the scene and the person in his own mind the reader must bring into play his reverent imagination. We bring with us into this world as our inborn gift some wisdom and reverence. This gift is always in us and though sometimes obscured by prejudice or passion it keeps alive the divine in man which prevents him from reeling back into the beast.

Bharata and his retinue went on towards Bharadawaaja *aashrama*. When they reached the Prayaaga wood, they saw at a distance a beautiful grove with a cottage in its midst. Learning that this was Bharadwaaja's *aashrama*, Bharata left his retinue behind and, accompanied only by Vasishtha and a few other elders, walked towards it with due humility. Divesting himself of his silk garments and his weapons and accompanied only by the ministers he went on foot behind Vasishtha. A little further on, he left behind even the ministers, and he and Vasishtha alone went forward.

When Bharadwaaja saw Vasishtha, he rose from his seat and went to meet the illustrious visitor and bade his disciples to bring the customary water for the feet of the guests.

Bharata offered humble salutations to Bharadwaaja. Learning who he was, the *rishi* received him with the respect due to a king and made enquiries concerning his welfare. He thoughtfully refrained from making any mention of the sad fate of Dasaratha.

The narration that follows is as told in Vaalmeeki's epic. A few words by way of explanation may be useful. Bharadwaaja suspected and questioned Bharata, just as Guha had done earlier. This is, however, not so put in Tulasi *Raamaayana* which is a poem of pure 'Bhakti.' There is nothing that was not within the knowledge of *rishis*. How then could Bharadwaaja (in Tulasi *Raamaayana*) entertain any doubt about Bharata?

Kamban, the Tamil poet of *Raamaayana*, follows Vaalmeeki closely not only here but in many other places where Tulasi differs. Although Kamban carefully follows Vaalmeeki, he adds many beautiful passages out of his own imagination. With a touch here and a touch there, Kamban manages skilfully to disentangle many knots. The changes he makes are very few, while Tulasi deals freely with the story, taking such liberties as he likes with the story as a great 'bhakta' may who has made his god his own by self-forgetting surrender.

Following Vaalmeeki, Kamban reports the
conversation between Bharadwaaja and Bharata
and very beautifully expresses Bharata's indignation.

We may not, reading it all today, appreciate
Bharadwaaja's doubts about innocent Bharata. Such
suspicion was perfectly natural to Guha, but not so
in a wise *rishi*. Vaalmeeki makes the *rishi* justify
himself saying: "Don't I know you, young prince? I
put you these questions only the more clearly to
reveal your innocence."

Vaalmeeki pictures *rishis* not as omniscient
sages, but as very human wise men and seekers after
truth, liable to love and fear somewhat like the rest
of us. Just as Vaalmeeki delineates Raama as a hero
rather than as an *avataar*, so he makes Bharadwaaja doubt Bharata because of his tender affection
for Raama. Bound by his attachment to Raama, he
hurts Bharata; seeing the latter suffer, he at once
consoles him with an explanation.

All Vaalmeeki's characters are human beings
with heightened human qualities. It is only under
great stress or in exceptional circumstances that
divinity shines faintly through the human nature. In
the time of Tulasidaas, *bhakti* had reached its
noon-day height. It shone dispelling every shade.
Though *bhakti* predominates in Kamban's picture
also, he contrives to retain the humanity of
Vaalmeeki's characters and in places makes them
even more beautiful.

Bharadwaaja, after making the usual personal
enquiries, asked Bharata: "Why did you leave your
kingly duties and go over here? Should you not stay
in Ayodhya? Listening to his young wife, Dasaratha
ordered Raama to live for fourteen years in the forest

and the Prince accordingly left the city with his brother and Seeta. Do you feel that even now the way is not clear for your rule and have you come to complete what Dasaratha began and make assurance doubly sure?"

Hearing these words, Bharata wept. The tears gushed and he could hardly speak. "Death," he said, "would be better than such a life as this."

"Do you doubt me, master?" he asked. "Do not blame me for what was done by my mother in my absence without my knowledge or consent. I have come now to do my utmost and persuade Raama to go back with me to Ayodhya, and there to be crowned King. And it is my purpose to be his humble slave all my life. I have come here to ask you where Raama dwells, to go and beg of him to return home. And me, you suspect!"

Bharadwaaja said: "Bharata, I know your real nature. You are a scion of the race of Raghu. I questioned you because I wished to draw out a revelation of your affection and loyalty and thereby establish and spread your glory. Do not grieve. The Prince is dwelling on Chitrakoota hill. Stay here today. Tomorrow, you and your ministers shall go there. You will please me by accepting hospitality for a day in the *aashrama*."

Bharata said: "My Lord, your wishes and words of affection are a feast. What more is required?"

Bharadwaaja smiled because he could see that Bharata was unwilling to cast the burden of feeding an army on a poor ascetic. He said: "I am bound to entertain you in a manner worthy of your status and goodness. Why have you left behind your army and retinue?"

Bharata answered: "I followed the rule that one should not approach a *rishi's* dwelling with a retinue. There is a big crowd following me. It would be a great disturbance to you if they all come here."

The *rishi* said: "Nothing of the sort. Order them all to come up."

And so Bharata ordered.

Bharadwaaja went to the sacrificial fire and, uttering *mantras*, sipped water thrice and called on Viswakarma, Maya, Yama, Varuna, Kubera, Agni and other celestial beings and ordered them to produce a great feast for Bharata and his followers.

Then a miracle happened. The feast that was ready in Bharadwaaja's *aashrama* was like that which Vasishtha gave of old to Viswaamitra. The only difference was that here, there was no quarrel or commotion. Every one had ample accommodation. Sandal paste, flowers, food and drink, music and dance by divine performers, were all provided. Bharadwaaja's feast was more sumptuous than that given by emulous kings to one another. Dwellings, vehicles, servants rose suddenly into being. The guests forgot themselves in the feast. The soldiers in Bharata's army in the ecstasy of present enjoyment exclaimed to one another: "We shall not go to the Dandaka forest. We shall not return to Ayodhya. We shall stay here for ever."

How were they to know that the good things they enjoyed were for a day, and would disappear at dawn, like the stage and the crowd after a village play is over?

The guests ate fully and soon fell fast asleep.

The following morning Bharadwaaja said to Bharata: "At a distance of two-and-a-half *yojanas* from here runs the river Mandaakini. On its banks is an unpeopled forest with Chitrakoota hill to its south. On the slope of the hill, in a hut your brothers and Seeta are dwelling." And he explained in detail the way they should follow.

The three queens were presented to receive the sage's blessings. "This is Queen Kausalya," said Bharata, "the mother of Raama and here, to her right and supporting her, stands the mother of Lakshmana and Satrughna, sorrow-stricken and limp like a creeper stricken by summer winds." "And here is my mother, the cause of all our sorrow," said Bharata, pointing to Kaikeyi who along with the other Queens prostrated before the sage.

"Do not judge your mother harshly," said Bharadwaaja casting his gentle eyes on the sorrowing lady. "All that has happened has happened for the good of the world."

This episode of introducing the mothers is placed by Kamban in the earlier scene with Guha. Guha reverently inquires about the queens and Bharata explains. What Vaalmeeki describes as having taken place in Bharadwaaja's *aashrama* is, with more poetical effect, transferred by Kamban to its proper place.

Introducing Kausalya to Guha, Bharata says, in the *Raamaayana* of Kamban: "This is the mother of Raama. Her treasure was Raama and she lost it because of me." Of Sumitra he said: "This is the mother of Lakshmana, truer brother to Raama, who has a happiness beyond the reach of poor me." Kaikeyi in Kamban, as in Vaalmeeki, is introduced by Bharata in harsh terms.

Bharata and his great retinue took the forest path as directed by Bharadwaaja. They saw from afar the Chitrakoota hill and as they proceeded eagerly a column of smoke indicated the spot where the Prince's dwelling was and shouts of joy arose from the crowd. Leaving his following behind, Bharata went forward accompanied only by Sumantra and Vasishtha.

CHAPTER XXVII

THE BROTHERS MEET

WHILE Bharata was thus engaged in trying to undo the mischief wrought by others, in the forest hut at Chitrakoota, life went on fairly cheerfully. With Lakshmana and Seeta by his side, Raama lacked nothing. The grandeur of the mountain scenery and the forest and the sweet songs and play of the birds pleased his heart. He forgot the sorrow of his exile from kinsfolk and city.

"Look, Seeta, at those birds playing," he would say. "Look at that rock on the hill with the blue, yellow and red veins shining on it. Look at these plants and creepers with their flowers. We feared life in the forest, not knowing how pleasant it would be. I am so happy here. And I have in addition to this pleasure the feeling that I carry out my father's promise. We have the joy of duty done besides leading a happy life here. Over and above all this, I am happy that my brother Bharata is ruling the kingdom."

Thus Raama, free from sorrow himself, made Seeta happy. Descendig from the hill they would sometimes go to the river Mandaakini and spend time there. "Look at those sand hillocks," Raama would say. "Look at the swans playing among the lotuses. The stream is as lovely as yourself, beloved. The fords where animals come to drink are beautifully red with new earth. Even the river in Kubera's kingdom cannot be as beautiful as this. See the *rishis* bathing there and standing in supplication and offering hymns to the sun. Look at the flowers falling from the boughs on the water. Look at that

pearl-scattering cascade. We are indeed lucky to be
far away from the crowded city here in the forest.
There, we cannot see *rishis* and pure souls such as
we see here bathing everyday. This hill is our
Ayodhya. The birds and beasts are our subjects. The
Mandaakini is our Sarayu.

"With you and Lakshmana by me, I am so
happy and content. How pleasant it is to see the
animals drinking water in the stream without any
fear! Plunging in the water here, eating fruits and
roots, walking about in the forest and climbing the
hills, why should I think of kingdom or power?"

Thus, in the company of Seeta and Lakshmana,
Raama was spending happy days.

One day as they were sitting as usual on the
slope of the hill in utter peace, suddenly at a
distance, they saw a cloud of dust rise in the sky
which seemed moving towards them. And soon they
heard a great noise as of a big crowd. Raama saw the
forest animals stampeding hither and thither in
fear. It looked as if an army entered the forest.

"Do you hear that noise?" Raama said to
Lakshmana, "The elephants, bisons and deer are
running helter-skelter. What could it be? Could it be
some king come here hunting? Or is it that some
tiger or other fierce wild beast has come rummaging?
Just see and tell me."

Lakshmana climbed up a tall tree and looked
all around. He saw a large army approaching from
the north, a complete force of all limbs—chariots,
elephants, horses and foot-soldiers. He shouted to
Raama in warning:

"Listen, brother. A great army is approaching
with flags flying and in complete formation. Let us

be careful. Put out the fire. Take Seeta into the cave for safety. Let us don our armour and get ready for battle."

Raama said: "Do not be in such hurry. Look again at the flag on the chariot and tell me which king is leading his army here."

Lakshmana looked and was filled with anger. "O my brother, it is Bharata. Not satisfied with getting the kingdom, he is pursuing us here. I can see the tree on our flag flying in the breeze. He has come to slay us; but the son of Kaikeyi shall not escape with life from me today. What sin is there in killing this destroyer of *dharma*? The only question now is, shall we wait for them here, or shall we give them battle on the top of the hill? We will make him pay for all the harm he has done us. It is surely no sin to kill one who comes to slay us. With him will be destroyed the greed of his mother. You will soon see the forest paths running with blood. Like a tree uprooted by an elephant, Bharata will be felled to the ground by me. We shall destroy this army. We shall feed fat the beasts of prey in the forest."

Lakshmana spoke thus, beside himself with rage.

Raama proceeded to calm him. "I know you can destroy the seven worlds if you are so minded. Listen, you can easily kill Bharata and his army, but there is a thing to consider before you set to work. Disobeying and disgracing our father and killing our brother and earning infinite obloquy, what good shall we gain by battling for and winning the kingdom? What we gain by killing our kinsfolk will be like food with which is mixed poison. Why and for whom do we seek wealth and kingdom? Is it not for the sake of others, whose joy is our own?

"Who would want to acquire a kingdom by wrong means? And what joy is there in a kingdom which you cannot share with those you love? Truly I tell you, I will never look at wealth and power that you and Bharata and Satrughna cannot enjoy with me.

"I know why Bharata is coming here now and I will tell you. He knows the way of *dharma*. He is coming here to give the kingdom to me. If he had been in Ayodhya instead of in the far-away land of his uncle he would have dissuaded Kaikeyi, and saved our father from the great sorrow which has befallen him. I am certain he is coming now to take me back to the city. It is wrong of you to think ill of Bharata and speak such harsh words about him. If it is desire for the kingdom that makes you so cruel in your suspicion, tell me. I have only to tell Bharata to pass it on to you, and I make no doubt he will do it with pleasure."

Raama said this laughing, and Lakshmana shrank into himself with shame.

"Perhaps our father, the King," Lakshmana said, "is himself coming to see us."

After listening to Raama, he was convinced that his fear was improper. He wondered then why the army was marching and thought that perhaps Dasaratha was coming to visit them in the forest and a large retinue followed the King. The commentator remarks that Lakshmana, realising his folly in having spoken ill of Bharata, was trying by some explanations to cover up his shame.

Raama cheered up Lakshmana saying: "Yes, it may be as you say. Thinking that life in the forest was hard, the King might have come to take us, and

specially Seeta, back to the city. But then, we do not
see the King's great white umbrella. But whatever
be the case, you should be calm."

Lakshmana stood humbly with folded hands by
Raama.

Halting the army at some distance, Bharata
sent a few men to observe and report on the place
whence the smoke rose. They brought the news that
this was the very spot described by Bharadwaaja
and that the cottage was very probably Raama's
forest abode.

Bharata started forward with Satrughna,
Vasishtha and Sumantra. As they advanced, they
saw indications that the *aashrama* was habited.
There was a path that led to the river and the trees
were blazed on either side of it as though to make it
easy to find it in the dusk. Presently they came to a
cottage thatched with leaves, near which were
stacks of faggots and the dry dung of deer and wild
buffaloes heaped for use in winter. In the cottage, on
the walls were mighty bows and quivers full of
deadly arrows, swords which seemed to radiate
victory and other weapons all of superlative
excellence. They saw also, spread out to dry on the
branches of trees, garments of bark. Bharata beheld
all these sure signs of his brothers' residence in the
hermitage with a swelling heart. From inside came
smoke from the oblations of daily worship, and
entering, Bharata saw the altar with its blazing fire
and Raama himself seated by it with matted locks,
majestic, though in deer-skin and bark, a ruler of the
world, with his mighty arms, breadth of chest and a
countenance made to command love and obedience.
By him were Seeta and Lakshmana.

He had been thinking all the time of the infamy
that had gathered on his head, and wondering what
to say and what to do when he met Raama. But now
when he saw Raama, he forgot all this in the great
love that surged within him and submerged all other
thoughts and fears. He sprang forward to the spot
where Raama was seated. He could utter no word
beyond "Brother," and fell at his feet, and sobbed. By
this time, Sumantra and Guha joined him.

Raama saw before him lying on the ground
Bharata with hands clasped in supplication, with
matted locks and in garments of bark. With grief and
fasting, his body had grown lean and he was tanned
with fatigue and exposure. Raama embraced him,
and kissed him on the head, and said: "Brother
beloved, why did you leave our father's side and
come all this way into the forest? And why have you
grown so thin?"

Bharata was speechless. Raama put to him the
formal questions which members of the royal family
asked each other when they met after an absence.

After an interval, Bharata gathered strength
and gave answer. "Why question you me about the
kingdom, brother, as though I were its ruler? What
connection is there between the kingdom and
myself? When you are the rightful king, how could I
call myself king, or rule over the land? My duty is to
do you humble service. It has not been given to me to
do it. The eldest son should bear the burden of the
kingdom. This is the law and custom. Come with me
to Ayodhya, wear the crown and shower your grace
on our family and people. The old King's work in the
world is over and he has entered *Swarga*. When you
had left Ayodhya for the forest and before I returned
from Kekaya the King gave up his life, slain by the

grief of separation from you. Do not give way to sorrow. Perform the obsequies of our father. Thinking of you, he gave up his life. The obsequies you perform will alone satisfy his spirit." Thus Bharata steadied himself and spoke.

When Raama heard that his father was dead, he fell down like a tree felled by an axe. Bharata had no need to repeat before Raama all the apologies and explanations which he had to give to Kausalya, Guha and Bharadwaaja. Where was the need for explanations when Raama set his eyes on that grief-stricken body and that ravaged face? Bharata, whose one concern was to take Raama back to Ayodhya, spoke only of this and not at all of himself.

The princes, with Seeta and Sumantra went to the river and offered libations for the peace of the departed soul of the King. After other customary ceremonies, the princes returned to the cottage. They held each others' hands and relieved their sorrow by loud lamentation.

(In this episode, where Bharata meets Raama, we read in Vaalmeeki a long lecture on the art of government, delivered by Raama to his brother. Often in our epics, we come across such long dissertations on politics or morality. Modern fiction gives high priority to narrative vigour, dramatic suspense and surprise. In old works, in addition to plenty of these qualities, there were generous doses of didacticism. It may be added here that even old commentators noticed that the chapters of this episode have got mixed up and displaced in Vaalmeeki. Kamban has of course regularised and modernised the narrative. In Tulsidaas the meeting of Raama and Bharata is steeped in *bhakti* and there is no room for any complications.)

CHAPTER XXVIII

BHARATA BECOMES RAAMA'S DEPUTY

WHEN it was known that the four princes and the three queens were re-united and could be seen together in one place, a chorus of joy went up in the army and retinue and they came surging forward to witness that happy spectacle. They were sure now that Raama would return to Ayodhya and the people embraced one another for the very joy.

The sage Vasishtha conducted the three queens to the hut. On the way, they saw the river Mandaakini. When he showed them the spot where the princes daily took water for their use, Kausalya and Sumitra broke down and sobbed. Said Kausalya:

"From this pool in the river, Sumitra, your son takes water to the *aashrama* every day. Lakshmana is prepared to do the commonest task cheerfully for his brother. He does not mind the weight of the water pot on his princely shoulder."

They saw the spot where Raama and Lakshmana poured out libations for their father's Spirit. The *darbha* grass lay with the ends facing south, beside the oil-cake.

Kausalya clung to Sumitra and said: "O sister! This is the food that the mightiest kings have to be content with after death."

They reached the hut. There they saw the princes with faces clouded with sorrow, seated under a thatched roof. Unable to bear the sight, the royal mothers sank to the floor.

When Raama lifted Kausalya up, she stroked him with her flower-soft hands and was at once sad and happy. She embraced Seeta and said: "My child, Janaka's daughter, daughter-in-law to the King of Ayodhya, do you live in this hut in the forest? O, faded lotus-flower! O, golden image covered with dust! My heart melts at the sight of you."

Raama reverently touched the feet of Vasishtha who seemed another Brihaspati, the preceptor of the gods, come down to earth, and then sat by his mother. Bharata humbly sat apart facing Raama. The elders surrounded them, eagerly awaiting what Bharata would say and how Raama would react.

"Bharata, why have you left your kingly duties and come here in deer skin and with matted locks?" asked Raama.

Bharata attempted to speak several times, but at first could not get beyond the word 'Brother'. Then he pulled himself together with a great effort and said:

"Sending you to the forest, but unable to bear the pain, our father's soul fled to heaven. All the good my mother has got from her evil plan has been that she has become a sinner and a widow and is in deep sorrow. Despised by the world, she experiences hell on earth. Only you can save us. Undo all the evil that has been done and wipe off our tears by agreeing to be crowned. It is to implore you for this that we and the citizens and the army and the widowed queens have come and are all here waiting on your word. Grant us our prayer. This alone will put an end to our sorrow and re-establish the *dharma* of our race. Without a rightful king, the land is like a widow, desolate and helpless. You must come back and make it happy and secure. Like the full moon rising, dispel our darkness. The ministers here and I fall at your feet and beg of you. Do not refuse, O, brother!"

Saying this, the great Bharata, with tear-filled eyes, clung to the feet of Raamachandra.

Raama raised him from the ground and embracing him said:

"Child, we were born in a noble family and brought up in good ways. Neither you nor I can do anything wrong. I see no fault in you, my blameless brother! Do not feel sad and do not speak unkind words about your mother. It is not proper that we should blame her. Surely our father had the right to tell us what to do, aye, even to decree banishment, just as he had the right to order a coronation. Our duty is to honour our father and our mother. How could I disobey or question their command? Was it for me to refuse my father's command that I should go to the forest?

"He gave you kingship and he ordained for me life in the forest. He certainly had the right to settle the manner of our lives. What right have we to alter or reject his plans? Far from being wrong, it is your duty to rule the land. And I too shall do my duty and fulfil our father's last command by living fourteen years in the Dandaka forest. Failing to fulfil our father's wish, can I find contentment in the possession of the whole world?"

Bharata repeatedly besought and importuned Raama. Raama realised that Bharata grieved that it was for his sake injustice had been done and that he endeavoured to remove the blot.

"Do not blame yourself," he said. "Do not think that all these things took place for your sake. Destiny rules everything. Give up your grief. Return to Ayodhya and rule the kingdom. Let us each perform the duties assigned to us by the father we love and revere."

The people who watched the talk and saw the determination of the Prince were filled with joy and sorrow in equal measure. Bharata's affection and purity filled them with pride and joy.

Raama told Bharata his unalterable decision. "I cannot possibly disobey my father's word. You will please me by not persisting in trying to persuade me. Satrughna is there to help you in ruling as Lakshmana is here to help me in forest life. With Lakshmana by my side, I lack nothing. Let us all four, brother, do our father's will."

The learned Jaabaali, one of the priests who had accompanied Bharata, here interposed a lesson on worldly wisdom for the benefit of Raama. "You talk again and again of your father's command. Dasaratha was a physical body which has now rejoined the five elements. You talk as though there is some continuing relationship between that person who is now no more and yourself. This is sheer illusion. Why do you like the foolish prating of *dharma* and seek to give up the good fortune to which you were born? Like a woman mourning with dishevelled hair, the city of Ayodhya is plaintively longing and waiting for your return. Go back. Accept the crown. Enjoy life's pleasures. Listen to Bharata. Do not fail in your proper duties."

This lecture angered Raama. He said with much sharpness: "Sir, you seem to set little value on truth and rectitude. Your materialist talk fills me with such abhorrence that I wonder that an unbeliever like you should have been tolerated in the court."

Jaabaali hastened to explain that, far from being an infidel, he had all his life been a teacher of the *Shaastras* and that he had only spoken as he had done out of an earnest wish to persuade Raama to return. Vasishtha also intervened on his behalf and that unlucky interlude came to an end.

Vasishtha then put the case for Raama's return this way:

"On the whole, my opinion is that you should return to Ayodhya and accept the throne. Of course, your father's command also has to be considered, and reconciled to this step. You have obeyed that command at once and unhesitatingly, but now a new situation has arisen. Bharata in his helplessness, fearing infamy, has sought shelter at your feet. How can you spurn him? We all know that you love him as your life. You never refuse those who approach you for help. How then can you deny it to Bharata now? Is it not your life-principle to help those who seek refuge at your feet?"

But Raama showed no signs of relenting. Then, Bharata turned to Sumantra and said, "My brother has no pity for me. Please spread a bed of *darbha* grass here for me. I shall take the pledge of fasting unto death."

Sumantra hesitated and looked at Raama. Then Bharata himself fetched and spread the grass and sat on it.

"My child, this is not right," said Raama firmly. "Rise. Go to Ayodhya and fulfil your duties. Do not go against Kshatriya *dharma*."

Bharata got up and as a last resort appealed to the people who had accompanied him — a representative crowd of soldiers and citizens from

Ayodhya: "O, citizens of Ayodhya! Why do you stand mutely looking on? Do you not want Raama to return? Why then are you silent?"

The people answered: "Raama will not swerve from truth. He will stand firm by his father's promise. He will not return to Ayodhya. What is the use of pressing him further?"

Raama said, "Listen to them, brother. They wish well by both of us. Virtue dwells in their hearts."

Bharata said: "Here I am as guiltless as Raama and a fit substitute for him. If the King's word should be fulfilled, let me stay here in the forest in place of Raama. Let him fill my place and rule in Ayodhya."

Raama laughed and said: "This procedure of exchange cannot apply here. This is not trade or business for barter and agreement. It is true that sometimes one discharges the duties of another, when the latter is too weak and unable to do it. But how does it fit on this occasion? Can any of you say that for life in the forest I have no capacity but only Bharata has?"

Then the wise Vasishtha found a solution for the problem in which righteousness struggled with righteousness as to which should be more right. "O, Bharata, rule the kingdom under Raama's authority and as his deputy. No blame would attach to you then and the pledge would be kept."

Raama took Bharata on his lap and told him, "Brother, look on the kingdom as my gift to you. Accept it and rule it as our father wished."

A glory descended on Raama and Bharata at that moment as they shone like two suns.

Bharata said: "Brother, you are my father and my God. Your least wish is my *dharma*. Give me your sandals. That token of yours shall reign in Ayodhya till you return. And for fourteen years I shall stay outside the city and discharge the King's duties in your place, paying reverent homage to your sandals. At the end of that period, you will return and accept the kingship."

"So be it," answered Raama.

He placed his feet on the sandals and handed them to Bharata who prostrated himself on the ground and accepted them and put them on his head.

Bharata and his retinue turned back towards Ayodhya. On the way, they met the sage Bharadwaaja and reported what had happened. He blessed Bharata saying:

"Your virtue will be for ever remembered. Are you not a son of the Solar race? As water flows downwards, the virtue of your family runs its inevitable course in you. Your father Dasaratha is indeed happy. He is not dead but lives again immortally in you."

They met Guha again and crossed the Ganga and reached Ayodhya. Bharata and his followers entered Ayodhya. The city, bereft of the King and Raama, appeared desolate to Bharata. It seemed to be enveloped in the darkness of a moonless night. When he returned in haste from Kekaya, he had entered the city in fatigue and shapeless fear and suspense; but today he entered it again fully realising all the tragedy. He remembered the past and thought of the present and grieved afresh. He went to the palace and took the queens to their desolate apartments. He went to the assembly hall, and said "Great is my sorrow. But I shall bear it. I shall stay in Nandigraama and carry out my tasks as I have promised Raama. Make all arrangements for this purpose."

This was done and he solemnly announced in the assembly, "This kingdom is Raama's. For the time being, he has asked me to be in charge. In my brother's place I have installed his sandals. Deriving my authority from them I shall do my work as king."

Accordingly, Bharata stayed in Nandigraama and with the help of ministers ruled the kingdom as a religious duty until Raama should return after completing his forest life. And indeed, is it not the law laid down in Scripture that one should serve the world unselfishly and without attachment, leaving the fruit of one's work at the feet of the Lord? Raama did his penance in the forest for fourteen years and all the time Bharata too did his penance at Nandigraama near Ayodhya.

CHAPTER XXIX

VIRAADHA'S END

NOT far from Chitrakoota was an outpost of the *Raakshasas,* called Janasthaana, in charge of a famous warrior named Khara, who was a brother of Raavana, and from this station, fierce *Raakshasas* ranged the forest round, molesting the *rishis* in their isolated *aashramas.* They made life so insecure that the *rishis* abandoned their hermitages in the Chitrakoota region in spite of all that Raama could do to dissuade them.

After Bharata's departure Raama was not quite happy in Chitrakoota. The face of his beloved brother tearful with disappointment and the sad drooping form of his widowed mother were ever before his mind's eye, and now that the going away of the *rishis* had deprived him of even their companionship, the lonely hut was so full of sad memories that he made up his mind to seek some other resting place in the Dandaka forest.

So they left Chitrakoota and proceeded to the hermitage of Atri, a *rishi* who knew the country, to seek his advice as to where they might establish themselves. They were most affectionately received and Seeta won the heart of Atri's wife, the saintly Anasooya who, delighted at finding in her a perfect embodiment of wifely virtues, blessed her and presented her with beautiful garments and auspicious cosmetics that set out the charms of lovely young wives.

Anasooya was the embodiment of pure womanhood and her gifts added beauty and inner strength to Seeta. She received the gifts and said:

"My Lord the Prince loves me with the love of a mother and a father. I am indeed blessed."

Then they made enquiries concerning the way and resumed their journey.

Walking through the great Dandaka forest, Raama, Seeta and Lakshmana reached a spot where many *rishis* lived. Even as they approached the place, they saw the sacrificial materials, bark garments and deer skins spread out to dry and they knew it was a colony of holy men.

The place was beautiful to look at. Birds and animals moved about with the freedom from fear born of affectionate familiarity with their human neighbours. Ripe fruits hung from the trees. The beautiful sound of Vedic chanting was heard.

As they came near, they saw the radiant faces of the *rishis*. They welcomed Raama. "O, King! you are our protector," they said. "Whether we are in the town or in the forest, you are our king." And they gave the newcomers all they needed and a place in which to rest.

The following morning, the three took leave of the *rishis* and re-entered the forest, which was now denser than before and there were tigers and other wild animals. They proceeded slowly and cautiously.

Suddenly, a gigantic form distorted like a broken fragment of a hill rushed at them making a blood-curdling noise. It was a man-eating *raakshasa* and his roar was like thunder. He was unutterably ugly and the tiger-skin he wore was covered with blood and gobbets of flesh of the slaughtered beast were sticking to it still. The corpses of three lions and the head of an elephant recently slain were impaled

and strung in a row on the great spear which he
shook menacingly at them.

The *raakshasa* lifted his weapon, roared
horribly and, springing forward, lifted Seeta and as
he held her, shouted at the princes: "Who are you,
little fellows? How dare you enter this forest? You
look young but wear matted locks and bark
garments. You have disguised yourselves as ascetics;
yet you carry bows and arrows, and go about with
this woman by your side. Whom are you trying to
cheat? Are you not ashamed of yourselves? You are
besmirching the good name of the *rishis* by your
conduct, you hypocrites! Know that I am Viraadha
himself. The flesh of *rishis* is my daily food. I shall
have this lovely damsel for my wife, do you
understand? I shall now drink your blood, you
villains!"

Held in his grasp, Seeta trembled with fear.
Raama lost his usual self-control and said:
"Lakshmana, this is unbearable. Kaikeyi must have
known all this when she sent us to the forest!"

Raama was bewildered and did not know how to
meet the *Raakshasa*. But Lakshmana, hissing like
an angry snake, said: "Raama, you are strong like
Indra and, with me by your side, you should not talk
dejectedly. Look at what my bow and arrow can do.
The earth will presently drink this monster's blood.
My wrath which was denied outlet at Ayodhya, I
shall now direct on this monster, and shatter him as
Indra did the winged mountains of yore. I shall
attack this creature and slay him."

Viraadha roared again: "Who are you? Tell me
at once." Raama's mind now cleared. His face glowed
with courage and calmly he said: "We are princes of

the Ikshvaaku race. We have come to live in the
forest. May we know who you are?"

The *Raakshasa* answered. "And so, you are the
sons of Dasaratha, are you? My father's name is
Jaya. And I am known among *raakshasas* as
Viraadha. You puny kshatriyas carrying arms, what
can you and your ridiculous weapons do to me? I
have secured a boon from Brahma that no weapon
can hurt me. Leave this girl here and run away, if
you wish to save your lives."

Raama's eyes grew red with anger. "It is time
for you to go to Yama," he said and bent his bow and
shot a sharp arrow at the monster. It pierced his
body and emerged red with blood, glistening like fire,
and fell on the earth beyond. But the *raakshasa* was
not killed. Enraged by the pain, he placed Seeta on
the ground and, lifting his spear and opening his
mouth wide, rushed towards Raama and Lakshmana. The princes sent a shower of arrows at him. The
arrows stuck so thick on his body that he bristled all
over like a gigantic porcupine. The *raakshasa*
however laughed and shook his limbs, and down fell
all the darts. He straightened himself and lifted his
spear again. Raama and Lakshmana with two
arrows broke the spear and rushed at him sword in
hand. But he lifted them both up with his hands and
put them on his shoulders and strode off into the
forest. Seeta saw them disappear in the darkness of
the jungle and wept loud.

Raama and Lakshmana, seated one on each
shoulder, knowing that weapons could not kill him,
wrenched off his arms and threw them down. They
then attacked him with their hands and feet. Still
they could not kill him on account of Brahma's boon,
but the agony of his wounds was so great that he

howled with it. Unfortunately for him he had asked for immunity from slaughter, but not from pain.

The brothers threw down the exhausted monster and Raama planted his foot on his neck to prevent him from rising.

The touch of Raama's feet cleared the mist in which the curse incurred in a previous birth had shrouded his understanding, and in the sudden light of recollection he joined his hands and said humbly, "Your feet have touched me, Lord, and my eyes are opened. I have realised who you are. I am under a curse, but you can save me. I am not a *raakshasa* by birth, but a Gandharva.

"The boon I secured prevents my liberation. If you could somehow kill me, I shall recover my original form and go to heaven."

Accordingly Raama and Lakshmana smashed him without weapons and buried him in a pit they dug in the earth. And the *raakshasa* returned to the world of Gandharvas.

Then the Princes went back to the place where Seeta stood terrified and told her all that happened.

They proceeded to the *aashrama* of Sarabhanga. Indra was there with other gods, talking to the *rishi*. Knowing that Raama had arrived, he cut short his talk and went away. Then Raama, with his brother and wife, approached the *rishi* and humbly saluted him.

The old ascetic said: "It is for you I have been waiting. It is time for me to leave the body but my wish was to see you first. And so I have been waiting. Now my desire is fulfilled, I pass on to you all the merit of my penances."

Raama answered: "My Lord, should I not earn my own merit? How can I receive what you have earned? I have renounced everything to live in the forest. Advise me where I can best find an abode in the forest and send me forth with your blessing."

The *rishi* knew the secret of Raama's *avataar* and told him: "Learn from the sage Suteekshna where in the forest you should dwell."

Then Sarabhanga kindled a fire and entered it. The gross body perished in the flames and a youthful ethereal form rose from the pyre and floated up the heavens.

When the *rishis* of that forest heard the news of Viraadha's death they came to Raama and surrounded him. "It is our good fortune, O King," they said, "that you have come to dwell in this region. Hereafter, we shall perform our penance untroubled by *raakshasas*. Look at those bones scattered all round. They are the remains of ascetics killed and eaten by the *raakshasas*. The *rishis* on the banks of Pampa and Mandaakini live in constant fear of their lives from these man-eating monsters.

"The King's duty from which he may not fail without sin is to protect his subjects. Just as householders pay taxes, a share of the merit of our penances goes to the King's benefit. You are radiant like Indra, king of the gods. Protect us from this persecution of the *raakshasas*. You are our only refuge."

Raama answered: "I am bound, O great ones, to obey your command. I gave up kingship and came to the forest in obedience to my father's wish. If in discharging my duty as a son I can also serve you and do some good, I shall count myself twice blessed.

"I shall stay in the forest and destroy the *raakshasas* and free you from trouble. Shed your fear."

Raama's promise of help gave relief and joy to the *rishis*. Raama, Lakshmana and Seeta then proceeded towards the *aashrama* of Suteekshna. They came to a big hill surrounded by a thick forest which they entered. There they saw bark garments drying in the sun and a little later came upon the old *rishi* himself.

Saluting him, the Prince said: "My name is Raama, O holy sage. I have come to have *darshan* of you. I pray for your blessing."

The sage rose and embraced him. "Welcome, defender of *dharma*. My *aashrama* is lit up by your presence. It is now yours. When I heard you had left Ayodhya and taken up your abode at Chitrakoota, I knew you would come here, and have lived in hope of seeing you. Else I would have long ago given up this body.

"The merit I have accumulated I now pass on to you. Take it for yourself, your brother and the princess." The sage's face was bright with the light of long holy life.

It was the custom of the *rishis* thus to offer their acquired merit to those who came as their guests. From Raama's answer, we can see how such courtesies were to be received.

"O sage, I must earn merit by my own good deeds. With your blessing, I still hope to do so. I wish to dwell in the forest. The sage Sarabhanga directed me here to receive your blessing and seek your instructions as to where I could build a home for the rest of my stay in the forest."

The *rishis's* face was bright with joy and he said meaningfully: "You may live in this *aashrama*. There are many *rishis* living round about. The forest is full of fruit and roots. But evil beasts are abroad molesting the *rishis* and obstructing their penance. The sages are unable to bear this trouble. But for this, the place is good."

The Prince understood what the sage meant to convey. He bent and strung his bow and said: "Holy sage! I shall destroy these evil-doers. My bow is strong and sharp are my arrows. It is not proper that we should dwell in this *aashrama*. It may interrupt your penance. We shall find a place for ourselves in the neighbourhood. Permit us to do so."

That night they stayed in the sage's *aashrama* as his guests. The following morning, the three got up and bathed in the cool water fragrant with flowers, lit the sacrificial fire, performed their worship and touched the feet of the sage.

"By your grace, we spent a good night. We desire to see the other *rishis* in the region and receive their blessings. It is good to set out before the sun grows hot. Pray, give us leave to go."

The sage embraced the princes and blessed them, saying: "Visit the good *rishis* in the Dandaka forest. They have all gone through great austerities and obtained divine powers. The forest is indeed beautiful with deer and birds and lotus-filled tanks, and the hills with cascades and peacocks. Lakshmana, go now with your brother and with Seeta. Come to this *aashrama* whenever you feel like it."

The three walked round the sage according to custom and took leave of him. Seeta handed to them their swords, bows and quivers and the princes set out, more radiant than before because of the great sage's blessings.

CHAPTER XXX

TEN YEARS PASS

NOW begins the Aaranya Kaanda. The poet begins with an episode that prepares us for the misfortunes of Seeta. A new reponsibility has been cast on the Prince. He is to destroy *raakshasas* who molest the *rishis* in the Dandaka forest. A fear arose in Seeta's heart like a shadow cast by events to come.

"Why should you and Lakshmana who are properly to be merely ascetics in the forest," asked Seeta of her beloved husband, "take on yourselves this task of protection? You have come here to fulfil a promise of the late King. The duty of protecting the *rishis* belongs to the ruler who is actually reigning. It is not for you, engaged in penance, to protect *rishis*. To kill anyone, except in self-defence, is opposed to the vows of ascetic life. But you have rashly promised protection to the *rishis*. I wonder where this will lead us."

Thus Seeta argued in soft and affectionate words while they were going from Sage Suteekshna's *aashrama* towards some other *aashrama* in the Dandaka forest.

"Bear with me, my lord," she said, "for seeming to counsel you. I speak but as a weak woman out of my infinite love for you. You know what *dharma* is. But, men, it is said, are driven by desire into three kinds of sin: falsehood, lust and violence. Falsehood is unthinkable in one who for truth's sake has renounced a kingdom and is here in the forest. And as for lust, do I not know that you will not allow even the thought of another woman to enter your mind? But I am afraid of the third kind of sin. Should we

kill one who does not attack us? Whether it is a
raakshasa or anyone else, why should we kill anyone
who leaves us alone? You were in a hurry, I feel, to
give your word to the *rishis*. To destroy the wicked is
no doubt the duty of a kshatriya, but can that duty
still cling to you when you have renounced the
privileges that go with it, and elected the life of a
recluse in the forest?

"The duties of kingship go with actual status.
Dressed in garments of bark and with hair matted,
you are now an ascetic, pure and simple. Of course,
you know best. I am only asking you to think well
before undertaking anything."

Raama's love and admiration of Seeta rose all
the more for her misgivings. "Indeed, my love," he
said, "you speak like a true daughter of Janaka. But,
Seeta, did you not once say yourself that the
weapons borne by kshatriyas are for protecting
others? When helpless people suffer persecution,
how could a kshatriya sit still? When we came here,
the sages complained of their sufferings and
entreated our protection. They could not endure the
cruelties of the *raakshasas* who looked on them as so
much meat and made shambles of the hermitages.
Did they not show us a great heap of bones to show
what had been done? 'You are the king's son,' they
said. 'Our troubles will now end as darkness before
the rising sun. You are our only refuge.' Could we
princes hear their piteous appeal and refrain from
helping them? Every kshatriya, every one has to do
his duty, not the king alone. You are, of course,
solicitous for my safety. Even granting that what you
say is right, I have given my word and I cannot go
back. They said, 'You are our refuge,' and I have
given my word to protect them. A pledge thus given

cannot be withdrawn. What I have spoken cannot now be unsaid. You and I must tread together the path of *dharma*. How can we differ?" Talking thus, they went along the forest path.

This conversation occurs in the poem like the cloud that precedes the storm. It is the artistic creation of a changing atmosphere and not a random casting up of facile verses.

For ten years, Raama, Lakshmana and Seeta lived quietly among the *rishis*. In the great Dandaka forest, there were a number of *aashramas* where the *rishis* lived practising their austerities and living their lives of abnegation. The princes spent a month in one *aashrama,* three months in a second and perhaps a year in a third as welcome and happy visitors.

The forest was indescribably beautiful, with deer and bison, boars and elephants. The birds, the trees, the creepers, the blue waterlilies — all live again in the beauty of Vaalmeeki's poetry.

Raama was very happy these ten years, the joy of association with great and holy men being added to his joy in the quiet companionship of Lakshmana and Seeta. These ten years are disposed of in a small chapter. Time happily spent seems short and needs no length in recording.

When after ten years had thus passed, the end of their forest life was approaching, Raama wished to have *darshan* of the sage Agastya who lived in the south. The sage was, like Vishwamitra, famous 'through the three worlds'. It used to be said that if all the wisdom and spiritual merit between the Himaalayas and the Vindhyas were put on one scale and Agastya sat on the other, the southern scale would go down by his weight.

There is also the story of Agastya's service during the wedding of Siva and Paarvati. All the *rishis* had gone to Mount Kailas for the great event; Agastya alone, staying in the south, maintained the balance of the earth.

Once the Vindhya mountain steadily grew towards the heavens and threatened to obstruct the sun's passage between the northern and southern hemispheres. The gods grew frightened and approached Agastya for help. The Sage stood before the mountain which bent low in reverence before him. Then he blessed it saying: "May you ever remain thus", and so the mountain stretches low and long even now. So goes the story.

Two *raakshasas,* Vaataapi and Ilvala, gave much trouble to the *rishis.* The former had obtained a boon that no matter into how many pieces his body was cut up, they would all reunite and his body would be whole and strong as before. Ilvala, disguised as a braahmana, would go to the *aashrama* of one *rishi* after another and say, "O Learned One! Go over to my humble home and oblige me by accepting the consecrated food prepared for my manes."

On no account, according to ancient rule, could one refuse such an invitation. The *rishis* therefore had to accept the invitation. To them Ilvala served as food his brother Vaataapi cut up and cooked lusciously and after the unsuspecting guests had eaten the meat, the host would, according to custom, ask the guests, "Are you satisfied?" The answer would be "Yes. We are content." Then, Ilvala would shout, "Vaataapi! Come out!" And at the call of

Ilvala, Vaataapi reunited into life would come out tearing the bowels of the guests. Many *rishis* had to die in this way.

One day, Ilvala tried to play this trick on Agastya. As usual, Vaataapi entered Agastya's entrails as meat. Agastya of course knew this, but he was a devotee of Ganapati and had obtained the power to digest the *raakshasa.*

"Are you satisfied?" asked Ilvala.

"Yes, I am satisfied," answered Agastya.

Ilvala shouted, "Vaataapi, come out."

Agastya, laughing, said, "Vaataapi has been digested, my host!"

"What?" cried Ilvala. "Have you killed my brother?" And he rushed against Agastya.

The Sage opened his eyes in indignation and the *raakshasa* was reduced to ashes. No *raakshasas* would thereafter come near Agastya and he protected the other sages also.

Raama first went to the *aashrama* of Agastya's younger brother and obtained his blessings before visiting Agastya himself. Proceeding south and approaching Agastya's place, Raama noticed the brightness of the whole region, the birds and animals playing about without fear and braahmanas gathering flowers for worship.

He told Lakshmana to go in advance and announce him to the sage. Lakshmana met one of the disciples of the sage and sent word through him: "Raamachandra, son of Dasaratha, has come with his brother and wife to seek the great sage's blessings."

Agastya warmly welcomed the princes. He said: "I heard of your having come to dwell in Chitrakoota and I was looking forward to your visit. The end of your exile is approaching. Stay here during what remains of it in peace. This place is free from the fear of *raakshasas.*"

Raama answered: "I am happy to receive your blessing and I thank you for your gracious welcome. But I have promised protection to the *rishis* in Dandaka and now that I have received your blessings, I must return to that forest."

And Agastya answered: "What you say is right." Then the Sage gave to Raama the bow made by Viswakarma for Vishnu and an inexhaustible quiver, as well as a sword. He blessed him saying, "Raama, destroy the *raakshasas* with these weapons which of yore Vishnu gave me."

Agastya advised the prince to spend the rest of his exile at Panchavati.

"May God bless you, O, Prince," said Agastya, "take good care of Seeta who for love of you cheerfully submits to hardships to which she was not born or accustomed. Women are by nature fond of comfort and averse to hardship but no such weakness is found in Seeta. She is like Arundhati. Wherever you are, Raamachandra, with Lakshmana and Seeta by your side, the place will be filled with beauty. But Panchavati is itself a beautiful spot and Seeta will love to live there, secure in the protection of you both. Fruit and roots are there in abundance. Stay there on the bank of the Godaavari. The period of your exile is coming to an end. You will soon fulfil your father's plighted word. Like Yayaati, Dasaratha is served by his eldest son."

CHAPTER XXXI

THE SOORPANAKHA EPISODE

THE Princes and Seeta, following Agastya's instruction, took the way to Panchavati.

On the way they met a huge figure perched on a big tree. They took it to be a *Raakshasa*.

"Who are you?" asked Raama in an angry tone. The vulture however answered in a voice full of mildness and affection: "My child, I am your father's aged friend." Then he proceeded to tell his story.

Jataayu was the brother of Sampaati, the son of Aruna the dawn-god, who was brother to Garuda the great Eagle-vehicle of Vishnu.

He said: "When you leave Seeta alone and go hunting in the forest, I shall be looking after her safety."

The prince was pleased and accepted the offer of the bird with gratitude. They then proceeded on their journey.

Raama was thrilled by the beauty of Panchavati and gratefully offered praise in his thoughts to Agastya for recommending the spot to them. He told Lakshmana: "We can build our *aashrama* and enjoy our stay here for any length of time. Those hills are near and yet not too near. Look at those herds of deer. The trees with their flowers and the sweetly singing birds, the river, the clean sand—everything is beautiful. Choose for us a good site and build a cottage."

Lakshmana did as he was told. He constructed an *aashrama*.

Vaalmeeki pauses here to explain the skill and swiftness of Lakshmana's workmanship. He describes in detail how the mud walls were raised and the thatched roof was made. Raama admires Lakshmana enthusiastically.

"You are more than a father to me," said the Prince shedding tears of love and joy.

We, too, may pause to think how the noble prince Lakshmana acquired this skill. We may infer that in those days education even of princes included a knowledge of the realities of life and development of manual skill such as could enable one to collect materials in a forest and put a neat cottage for oneself.

In the *aashrama* at Panchavati, Raama and Seeta lived happily, lovingly served by Lakshmana.

One morning in early winter the three went as usual to the Godaavari for their bath and to offer their morning prayers and fetch water for the day's needs. They walked conversing about the beauty of the season. Lakshmana thought of Bharata and how he would then be busy performing the ceremonies appropriate to the month.

He said: "Bharata is entitled to live in ease but he has taken on himself a life of hardship because we live a life of hardship in the forest. My heart is full of sorrow for him. Even in this cold weather poor Bharata no doubt eats sparingly and sleeps on the bare floor. This cold morning he too is probably walking towards the Sarayu. How fortunate we are to have such a noble brother! Pure in mind and speech and conduct, renouncing all pleasures, he lives a life of austerity for our sake. He is exactly like our dear father and quite the opposite of his mother.

How could so cruel a woman as Kaikeyi bear so good a son?"

Raama stopped him, saying, "Talk as much as you like of Bharata and our father, but stop condemning Kaikeyi. All that you say of Bharata is true and my thoughts too to-day go to him in love. How long yet to see him again? When shall we have that pleasure, Lakshmana? When shall we four brothers live together again? Bharata's loving words are still sweetly ringing in my ears."

Thus thinking longingly of home and Bharata they bathed in the Godaavari on that early winter morning.

After offering oblations to their ancestors and prayers to the sun, Raama rose transfigured like the Lord Siva and returned to the *aashrama* with Seeta and Lakshmana.

Their morning duties over, they sat whiling the hours with wistful talk of old days and tales of long ago.

While they were thus recapturing the past in sweet companionship suddenly there came a *Raakshasa* woman and saw them. She was Soorpanakha, Raavana's sister who was roaming the forest full of the idle thoughts of well-fed ill-taught youth. She was horribly ugly, but had the magic power to assume any lovely form at will. When she saw the god-like beauty of Raama, she was filled with uncontrollable desire for him and accosted him.

"Who are you, dressed like an ascetic but accompanied by a woman and carrying warlike weapons and arrows? Why are you here in the forest that belongs to the *Raakshasas*? Speak the truth."

On such occasions it was the courtesy of those
days for the person accosted to announce himself and
recite his name, city and history and enquire of the
newcomer concerning his or her family and the
purpose of the visit.

Raama began, "I am the eldest son of the great
King Dasaratha. My name is Raama. This is my
brother Lakshmana. And this, my wife Seeta.
Obeying the behests of my father and mother and in
fulfilment of *dharma*, I am now in the forest. And
now please announce who you are. What is your
family? You look like a woman of the *Raakshasa*
race. What is your purpose in coming here?"

She answered, "Have you heard of Raavana, the
heroic son of Visravas and the king of the
Raakshasas? I am his sister. My name is
Soorpanakha. My brothers Kumbhakarna and
Vibheeshana are also renowned warriors. The lords
of this region, Khara and Dooshana, are also my
brothers. They too are mighty men-at-arms and
wield great authority in these regions. But I am not
subject to their control, but am a free person—free to
do what I like and please myself. Everybody in this
forest is, as a matter of fact, afraid of me." She said
this to strengthen her wooing position.

"The moment I set eyes on you", she continued,
"I fell in love with you. You are now my husband.
Why do you wander around with this midget of a
woman? I am the mate worthy of you. Come with me.
Let us wander at will through the forest. I can take
what shape I please. Do not mind this girl of yours. I
shall eat her up in a trice and dispose of her. Do not
hesitate."

Under the influence of lust, she thought in the
manner of her race and prated thus.

All this amazed and amused Raama. He smiled and said: "Oh beautiful one! Your desire for me will end in trouble for you. My wife is here with me. I do not care to live the life of a man with two wives. But my hefty brother here is untrammelled with a wife, and is as good-looking as myself. He is the proper husband for you. Offer your hand to him and leave me alone."

Raama said this, being confident that Lakshmana would deal with Soorpanakha suitably.

The *Raakshasi* took Raama's advice seriously and approached Lakshmana saying, "Oh, my hero, come with me. Let us together wander at will in joy through this Dandaka forest."

Lakshmana entered into the humour of the situation and said, "Do not be foolish. He is trying to cheat you. What is your status and what is mine? I am here a slave to my brother, while you are a princess. How could you become my wife and accept the position of a slave's slave? Insist on Raama's taking you as his second wife. Do not mind Seeta. Soon Raama will prefer you to her and you will be happy with him."

Some critic might ask whether it was proper thus to torment a woman, especially a woman in love. But if we exercise our imagination and have before us a monster of ugliness we can understand the situation. It is true that she could assume a charming form she chose, but in the intoxication of lust, she seems to have omitted even this allurement.

"This ugly, corpulent and paunchy *Raakshasi*, with leering eyes blood-shot with lust, her red hair all dishevelled and her voice hoarse with passion, accosted the handsome, beautifully built and smiling Raama," says Vaalmeeki. The Tamil poet Kamban varies the situation by making Soorpanakha assume a lovely shape from the outset.

Impelled by brute passion, the *Raakshasi* did as she was told by Lakshmana and went again to Raama. She thought and acted like a *Raakshasi* for she knew no other way of life.

The sight of Seeta enraged her. "It is this wretched little insect that stands between you and me. How could you love this girl without a waist? Look. I shall finish her off this instant. I cannot live without you. Once I have put her out of the way, you and I shall live together happily." Saying this, she sprang on Seeta.

Raama intervened just in time to save Seeta. The farce had gone too far and threatened to become a tragedy. Raama shouted to Lakshmana, "Look, I have just been able to save Seeta. Attend to this monster and teach her a lesson."

Lakshmana at once took up his sword and maimed Soorpanakha and drove her out. Disgraced and mutilated, Soorpanakha uttered a loud wail and disappeared into the forest.

Bleeding and mad with pain and rage, she flung herself on the ground before Khara, as he sat in state with his colleagues. Yelling with anguish, she related the story of her wrongs. The scorn and mutilation she had suffered was an insult to the *Raakhshasa* race which only blood could efface.

She said: "Look at me. Raama and Lakshmana have done this and they are still alive and roaming in your domain. And you sit here doing nothing."

Khara stood up and said: "My dear sister, what is all this? I understand nothing. Calm yourself and tell me what has happened. Who dared to do this thing to you and is he in this forest? Who is he that wants to become food for crows and vultures? Who has stirred up the black cobra? Who is that fool? Where is he? Tell me, and he shall die at once. The earth is thirsty for his blood. Stand up and tell me everything as it happened."

"Two handsome young men," said Soorpanakha, "have come into the forest, dressed like ascetics and accompanied by a girl. They say they are the sons of Dasaratha. These two together, making an excuse of the girl, attacked me and have hurt me thus shamefully. I am thirsting for the blood of these villains. Slay them first. Everything else can wait."

Khara ordered his generals: "Go at once, slay these men and bring their lifeless bodies. Drag hither the woman also. Delay not."

Fourteen generals set out to do his bidding.*

---

*   There are some people who pose as critics of our holy books and traditions saying, "This hero killed a woman. He insulted and injured a woman who offered him her love. He killed Vaali from behind, rather than face him and accept honourable defeat. He unjustly banished Seeta to the forest at the end of all the adventures. If the banishment of Seeta was not unjust and if he rightly suspected Seeta's fidelity, why then, we too, must suspect her fidelity."
All such criticism is based on a mentality of hatred. We have unfortunately plenty of barren, heartless cleverness, devoid of true Understanding. Let those who find faults in Raama see faults, and if these critics faultlessly pursue *dharma* and avoid in their own lives the flaws they discover in Raama, the *bhaktas* of Sri Raama will indeed welcome it with joy. If they exhibit the virtues of Raama and add to these more virtues and greater flawlessness, who can complain?

In Kamban's *Raamaayana*, Soorpanakha is
delineated as having come in the shape of a beautiful
young woman, entirely human, who tried to tempt
Raama. Kamban departs widely from Vaalmeeki in
this episode and he makes a beautiful episode of it as
will be seen in the next chapter.

CHAPTER XXXII

KAMBAN'S SOORPANAKHA

RAAMA and Lakshmana drove out Soorpanakha, as one takes a stick and drives out a donkey straying into a garden. Such is the brief and simple treatment of this incident by Vaalmeeki.

Kamban, the Tamil poet, however, deals with it more elaborately and has made a number of changes in the story.

Sitting on the river bank, Raama watched a swan walking and then looked at Seeta, also walking. Noting the similarity in the gait, Raama was pleased and smiled. Seeta, for her part, observed an elephant returning from the river and, reminded of Raama's gait, smiled.

Thus in Panchavati, beside the river Godaavari, love flowed smoothly between the banks of *dharma*. Just then Fate conspired with Lust to drag Soorpanakha to the presence of Raama.

The Lord Vishnu had left the Ocean of Milk and taken birth as Dasaratha's son, to rid the earth of the enemies of the gods. But how was Soorpanakha to know this?

Beholding the beauty of his person, she wondered: "Is this Manmatha or Indra or Siva or Vishnu? But Manmatha has no body. Indra has a thousand eyes and Siva has third eye in the forehead, and Vishnu has four arms; so he cannot be Indra, Siva or Vishnu.

"Perhaps, after all, this is Manmatha who has recovered his body through penance, after it had been reduced to ashes by Siva's wrath.

"If it be Manmatha, why should this handsome hero still perform penance? Why should this lotus-eyed youth waste his time in *tapas*?"

So she stood there wondering, watching, unable to turn her eyes away. She thought, "My own form would fill him with disgust. I shall change my appearance and then approach him."

She transformed herself into a beautiful young woman and appeared before him like the full moon. Her slender frame was like a golden creeper climbing up the *Kalpaka* tree in Heaven. Her lovely lips and teeth were matched by her fawn-like eyes.

Her gait was that of a peacock. Her anklets made music as she came near. Raama looked up and his eyes beheld this creature of ravishing beauty. She bowed low and touched his feet. Then she withdrew a little with modesty shading her eyes.

Raama welcomed her, imagining that she was a visitor from some distant place and enquired: "Which is your place? What is your name? Who are your kinsfolk?"

She answered: "I am the daughter of the grandson of Brahma. Kubera is a brother of mine. Another is Raavana, conqueror of Kailaasa. I am a maiden and my name is Kaamavalli."

"And what is your purpose in coming here?"

"It is not proper for a woman to speak out trouble in her mind. And yet I suppose I must speak it out. The God of Love has invaded my heart. You can and should save me."

She paused. Raama remained silent. And she went on.

"You may wed me with Gandharva rites. You know it is permitted for lovers to come together in this manner. Once we are joined in this way, not only will happiness be ours, but friendship between you and my brother, the great Raavana, will follow. You are alone in this forest and the *Raakshasas* will molest you. Even if you do not provoke them, they will give you trouble because you are dressed as an ascetic. If you marry me, you will be free from all this danger. Not only that, my powerful people will be ready to serve you in all ways. Consider this well."

Thus she pleaded for the fulfilment of her desire, citing authority and appealing to Raama's self-interest also.

Raama laughed revealing his beautiful pearly teeth. Just then, Seeta was coming towards them through the plants and creepers, herself looking like another creeper. Soorpanakha saw and marvelled at her loveliness.

Not knowing who she was, Soorpanakha, angered by lust, told Raama: "This girl is a *Raakshasi* in human form. She has come to deceive you. Beware of her. This is not her real form. She is a *Raakshasi* that eats raw meat. Throw her out. Have nothing to do with her."

Raama laughed again. "You are indeed wise," said he. "You have found out the truth about her."

Meanwhile, Seeta had come and stood by Raama. Soorpanakha could not understand what Raama was laughing for. In her lust, she had quite lost her wits. She hissed at Seeta: "Why do you approach this hero of mine, oh *Raakshasi*? Go away from here."

Seeta, bewildered and afraid, hung on the prince's shoulder, and she then seemed like a lightning flash hugging a rain-bearing cloud.

Raama now saw that the joke had gone too far and said: "Dear lady, please stop, lest my brother should hear you. He is quick-tempered and terrible when angry. I advise you to go back quickly the way you came." Saying this, Raama took Seeta with him and went into the hermitage.

The fire of her desire unquenched, the *Raakshasi* spent the night somewhere, somehow. In the morning, she thought: "I shall die if I do not get this man. So long as this girl is with him, he will never come near me. I must contrive to carry her off and put her away somewhere and then I may secure his love." Thus resolved, she came again to the *aashrama*.

Raama had gone to the river for his morning ablutions and prayer and Seeta was alone in the *aashrama*. Soorpanakha reckoned this was her chance to carry her off. She did not notice that Lakshmana was in the wood nearby. She rushed towards Seeta. Lakshmana shouted and sprang on the *Raakshasi*. Catching hold of her hair, he kicked her and drew his sword.

Soorpanakha when attacked resumed her own shape and attacked Lakshmana. Lakshmana easily caught hold of her and multilated her and drove her off.

Soorpanakha ran into the forest, bleeding and loudly appealing to her kinsfolk: "Oh, brother Khara! Oh, brother Raavana! Oh, Indrajit! Oh, kings of the *Raakshasa* race! Are you all asleep? A mere man has insulted me and cut off my nose. Do you not hear my lamentations?"

This is Kamban's version of the episode. Soorpanakha approaches and tries to attract Raama, hiding her true form and appearing like a beautiful human girl. This variation is supported in a way by Vaalmeeki's description of Soorpanakha as 'Kaama-roopini,' that is, one able to assume what form she liked.

The Tamil poet appears to have felt something wrong or wanting in Vaalmeeki's story and has woven an episode showing how bestial passion works.

CHAPTER XXXIII

KHARA AND HIS ARMY LIQUIDATED

ACCOMPANIED by the fourteen generals of Khara, Soorpanakha came back to Raama's *aashrama*, determined to avenge herself and drink the blood of the princes. Pointing to the two young men, she told her escort, "Look, there stand the men who insulted and mutilated me. Slay them immediately."

Raama understood the situation at once and told Lakshmana: "Take care of Seeta for a while, while I deal with those fellows." Saying this, he took up his bow.

Following the prevailing rules of war, Raama announced himself to Khara's generals and said, "Tell us the reason that you come here. Know that we are here in the forest at the bidding of the *rishis* for the purpose of destroying their enemies. If you wish to escape with life, leave us alone."

But the *Raakshasas* wanted not peace, but war. And the battle began. It did not take long for Raama's arrows to annihilate the *Raakshasa* generals.

Once again, lamenting loudly, Soorpanakha went to Khara. The destruction of the powerful detachment he had sent was inconceivable — he could not believe it. He sought to soothe his disturbed sister with soft words.

"I have sent warriors unconquerable, each one like Yama. They must have by now fulfilled their mission. Why do you weep? Why need you bewail while I am here?"

Soorpanakha rose, and wiping the tears from her eyes, said: "True, you sent your fourteen warriors with me. But the fourteen now lie stiff and cold in death, slain by Raama, whose skill with weapons baffles description. If you have a spark of pride in you, start at once, fight with Raama and save the *Raakshasa* race. If you do not, the destruction of our people is certain. But if you are afraid, tell me so and I shall understand. These young men who have entered your satrapy are determined to destroy your race, unless you first meet and destroy them."

These words, spoken by his sister in a loud voice before all his courtiers, pierced Khara's heart.

"Why do you speak thus terrified by a puny human being? Hold yourself in patience for a moment and you will have his blood to drink." So saying, Khara rose.

"Do not go alone!" she said, "Take your army with you."

Khara gave orders accordingly. A great army, fully armed, went in advance under the leadership of Dooshana. Behind the army Khara proceeded majestically in a chariot. On the way he met with many bad omens which affected the sprits of his host. He laughed and reassured his army, saying:

"Never have I been so far defeated in battle. Do not mind these portents. We shall soon crush these two little men and return in triumph."

The army took heart at these bold words of their leader.

Hearing the tumultuous noise of the approaching army, Raama and Lakshmana prepared for battle. Raama told Lakshmana: "Do you see the signs? It is certain that the *Raakshasas* of Janasthaana are coming here to their death! I see in your face the glory of the victory that awaits us. Arm yourself and take Seeta with you to a cave in the hill and look after her. I shall encounter the *Raakshasa* hordes and destroy them. Go at once. I do not require any help." Saying this, Raama put on his armour and strung his bow.

Lakshmana did as Raama bade and took Seeta to a mountain cave.

A great battle was to follow. So the Devas and Gandharvas hovered in the heavens to watch the fight. They uttered benedictions and prayed for Raama's victory. The *rishis* had misgivings. How was Raama, standing single, to meet and quell this huge army? As Raama stood there, bow in hand, the radiance of his face was like that of Rudra himself when he bent *Pinaaka* his great bow.

The *Raakshasa* force advanced in proud array, with drums and trumpets and the clanking pageantry of war filling the quarters with clamour and causing the denizens of the forest to stampede in all directions. Raama stood holding his bow with his hand on the string. Like great black clouds disturbing the sun the *Raakshasa* hordes surrounded him.

The battle began; but while even the Devas wondered how he could withstand the yelling masses which rushed on him, a constant stream of deadly arrows sped from his bow before which *Raakshasa* ranks withered and fell like moths before a blazing fire.

Dooshana himself now stood in front of Raama. Raama bent his bow and sent his shafts in all directions in an unceasing stream. Like rays from the sun, and with speed of light, arrows shot out from the spot where Raama stood, spread out in all directions and brought down warriors, chariots, elephants and horses.

The shafts pierced the bodies of the *Raakshasas* and came out, covered with their blood shining like fire. The army was utterly destroyed and Raama stood still, like Siva at the end of Time.

Dooshana came again with another great army. For a while he seemed indomitable. But soon Raama's arrows laid low his chariot, drivers and horses. He jumped down and sprang towards Raama. Raama's arrows, however, severed his arms from his trunk. And the monster fell dead on the ground like a huge elephant. Other *Raakshasas*, who saw Dooshana falling, rushed against Raama and were also slain by the arrows that sped from his *Kodanda*.

In this way, the whole army of Khara was destroyed. It had come roaring like an ocean and now it lay still, a mass of corpses and severed limbs and derelict weapons and broken chariots.

Only Khara and Trisiras remained. As Khara rushed forward to meet Raama, Trisiras stopped him saying: "I shall go first and kill Raama. Or else, I shall be killed. After I am dead, you may meet him."

The three-headed *Raakshasa* mounted on his chariot attacked Raama with his arrows. Raama met them with arrows that hissed like deadly serpents. At last Trisiras collapsed and fell spitting blood. His followers fled like deer.

Khara, seeing this, cried "Hold" to the fugitives and directed his chariot against Raama. His

confident pride was gone but he fought manfully.
The shafts sent by the two warriors covered the sky.
Khara stood like Yama in his chariot, sending his
stream of arrows. For an instant, Raama leaned on
bow. In that interval Raama's armour was pierced by
Khara's arrows and showed the Prince's body
shining like the sun.

Raama now took up the bow of Vishnu and laid
low Khara's chariot and cut his bow in twain. Khara
then took his mace and approached Raama. The
Devas and *rishis* watching the battle became
anxious and renewed their benedictions.

"You have been a terror and a plague to
mankind!" exclaimed Raama. "Strength of body is no
protection to an evil-doer. You have persecuted and
killed *rishis* engaged in penance in the forest. You
will now receive the punishment due for these sins of
yours. The spirits of the *rishis* whose flesh you fed on
are now witnessing your punishment from their
aerial chariots. I have come to the Dandaka forest to
destroy wicked *raakshasas*. My arrows will pierce
the bodies of all your kinsfolk. Your head will soon
roll on the ground like a ripe fruit."

"Human worm!" exclaimed Khara. "Son of
Dasaratha! Have done with boasting! You are proud
because you have killed a few common *Raakshasas*.
A hero boasts not as you do. Only a Kshatriya
banished by his people can talk boasting like this.
You have shown you can brag. Let us see now if you
can fight! Your words have blazed up like burning
straw with little heat or life. Here I stand, mace in
hand, like Yama to take your life. Evening
approaches. Be prepared to lose your life. I am here
to avenge the death of these my followers whom you
have killed."

So saying, he whirled his mace, and hurled it at Raama. The mace was split by Raama's arrows into splinters which fell harmless on the ground.

"Have you finished speaking, *Raakshasa?* Now you shall die. This forest will be safe hereafter and the *rishis* will live in peace," said Raama.

Even while Raama was speaking, Khara pulled out by its roots a huge tree, and gnashing his teeth, threw it at Raama, but this too Raama split by his arrows. And, fearing further delay, he aimed deadly darts at Khara. The wounded *Raakshasa* sprang on Raama intending to close with him; but the latter avoided contact by stepping back, and laid him dead with a shaft which clove his breast.

The Devas showered flowers from on high and cried in joy: "Raama has killed the sinful *Raakshasa.* Men can live in peace in the Dandaka forest hereafter. Within an hour Raama has destroyed Khara, Dooshana, Trisiras and their whole army. Indeed he is a hero."

Seeta and Lakshmana returned from the cave. Lakshmana embraced Raama and rejoiced that single-handed he had fulfilled the promise of safety he had given to the *rishis*.

How did Raama all alone perform these feats? If one observes a cow guarding her calf and scattering a whole crowd of men, one can realise the power of love. Love is a supreme quality which according to occasion manifests itself in diverse heroic forms — such as valour and self-sacrifice, just like gold which can be changed for silver or goods or other things of value. When God assumes human form and is engaged in fulfilling His promise to save the helpless, His limitless power comes into play.

CHAPTER XXXIV

THE PATH OF RUIN

AKAMPANA, one of the few *Raakshasas* who survived the great slaughter at Panchavati, fled to Lanka and seeking audience of Raavana, said: "Almost all our people who occupied Janasthaana are dead and Janasthaana is now an empty ruin. I alone have managed to escape with life."

Raavana was furious with anger. He stared and violently shouted, "who destroyed my lovely Janasthaana? Was it Yama or Agni or Vishnu? I shall deal death to the god of Death. I shall burn up both the god of fire and the sun. I shall strangle and suffocate the god of wind. Tell me, who was it that destroyed Janasthaana and killed my men heedless that I am here to avenge? Speak out at once."

It was ever dangerous to carry unpleasant news to tyrants. Akampana was frightened by the king's rage and said, "I shall speak, if you give me protection." He then told his tale: "Raama, son of Dasaratha, a young warrior, lion-like in fierce valour, a hero who has already acquired fame among men, fought with Khara and Dooshana at Panchavati and destroyed them."

The *Raakshasa* king hissed like a cobra and said, "What are you talking? How did this happen? Did Indra and the divine hosts come down to earth and fight on Raama's side?"

Akampana answered: "No such thing happened, great king. Alone did Raama stand against our whole army and its commanders and destroyed them all, and Khara and Dooshana too were slain. The deadly arrows issuing from Raama's bow like five-headed serpents pursued the *Raakshasas* wherever they went and destroyed them." And he went on to describe at length Raama's skill and speed in the use of his weapons.

And so Raavana learnt that Dasaratha's son, Raama, with his younger brother Lakshmana was at Panchavati and that he, alone without even his brother's aid, had done it all and that no gods had come to their aid.

"Well," said Raavana, "I do not understand this but I shall start at once. I shall destroy these little worms of men and return." And he rose.

"Hear me, great king, before you go," said Akampana, and explained once again Raama's strength and courage.

"Listen to me. 'No one can fight with Raama and conquer him. When I say 'No one,' I mean 'No one.' Not even you can do it. Because you have promised me protection, I dare thus to tell you the plain truth. There is only one way of killing him. His wife is with him. The whole earth holds not her equal in beauty. If you contrive to carry her off, separation from her will kill Raama; so great is his love for her. Consider how you can do this. Do not think of battle with him."

When he heard of Seeta's beauty, the *Raakshasa's* desire was kindled. He began to think that the defeat of Khara and his hosts was indeed a fortunate event that brought him an opportunity for gaining one more beautiful queen and wife. He welcomed Akampana's advice and said, "Tomorrow morning I shall go. I think your plan is good."

Accordingly Raavana set out in his mule-yoked flying chariot which gleamed like the moon among the clouds as it sped fast in the air. He went straight to Maareecha's dwelling.

Maareecha duly welcomed his king and enquired what urgent necessity brought him there. Raavana answered, "Hear me, Maareecha. You and you alone can help me. Janasthaana has been destroyed and so too the whole army I had stationed there. All this is the work of Raama, son of Dasaratha. Isn't it amazing? To avenge myself, I am resolved to carry off his wife. In this I need your advice and help."

Maareecha whose experience of Raama's prowess had seared into his soul was horrified, and tried to dissuade Raavana from his mad enterprise.

"What plan is this? Some enemy determined to destroy you, but pretending to be your friend, has given you this plan of carrying off Seeta. Whoever gave you this advice wishes the end of the *Raakshasa* race. It is like advising you to put your hand into the mouth of a sleeping cobra and pull out its fang. Haven't you a happy home and devoted wives? Return to them, and enjoy your life and prosperity. To hanker after Raama's wife is the highway to disgrace and destruction and the annihilation of the *Raakshasa* race."

Ten-headed Raavana went back to Lanka, for Maareecha's counsel appeared right to him. Raavana must have then remembered the omission in the series of boons he had secured. He had obtained immunity from the attacks of all beings except men. Raama's shafts had conquered and killed the whole army with Khara, Trisiras, Dooshana and other mighty warriors. Thinking of all this, Raavana accepted Maareecha's advice.

But Fate would not let him be. Raavana was seated on his throne with his counsellors around him. Majesty shone on his face like a sacrificial flame fed with ghee and his mighty body showed the scars of many wounds received in victorious battle against gods, *asuras* and others. His strength and courage were limitless, — so was his *adharma*. He had no equal in persecuting Devas, spoiling sacrifices and carrying away women. The hosts of Devas and *asuras* were mortally afraid of him. He was a terror to all creatures. Enjoying wealth and varied pleasures, freed from the fear of death, the ruler of Lanka knew no master or rival and feared neither God nor sin.

With his ten heads, large eyes and huge limbs, his figure was terrible, but it also possessed the marks of royalty. Gorgeously dressed and bejewelled as he sat on his throne, surrounded by his ministers in the midst of the splendour of the despoiled world, there suddenly appeared before him like the vision of the doom to be, his sister Soorpanakha, bleeding and mutilated, a shape of pain and sorrow and shame. While all looked at her with horror-struck eyes in stunned silence, her anguish broke out in burning words.

"What a fool are you that, sunk in sensual pleasures and arrogantly secure of sovereignty, you are not awake to the deadly danger that threatens your existence at your very doors! Surely that king who is drunk with self-importance and dead to all portents that threaten his state is doomed to shame and destruction! No object is of less account or more contemptible than a ruler who falls through his own remissness. Know you not that your brothers, Khara, Dooshana and Trisiras and your gallant army of fourteen thousand fierce *Raakshasas* have been exterminated by Raama, a mere man, and that your outpost at Janasthaana has been destroyed? One moment I saw a single warrior stand proud in the glittering pageantry of war and the next, they lay dead slain by that man's arrows, strewing the ground like ripe crops devastated by a terrible hail-storm; and you see me, your own sister, disgraced, mutilated and heart-broken! Have you no thoughts of vengeance — you, a hero, a brother, king?"

Stung by her contempt and heart-struck by her suffering and sorrow, Raavana said: "Be sure you shall have vengeance. But this Raama, who is he? What sort of man is he? What are his weapons? How does he fight? What seeks he in Dandaka forest? And how happened it that you were so cruelly mutilated?"

She gave a description of the brothers and Seeta, dwelling on the virile beauty and powers of the brothers — probably with a view to provoke the envious jealousy of the *Raakshasa* — and growing enthusiastically eloquent about the superlative loveliness of Seeta.

"I have no words to describe her perfections. I have never seen such sublime beauty in any created thing — be it Gandharva or *kinnara* or a daughter of man. And now, I will tell you why this ghastly outrage was perpetrated on me. On seeing this Seeta, I felt that none but you deserved her and that she was fully worthy to share your bed and out of my love for you I tried to carry her off for you. Lakshmana, who was standing by, prevented it and, springing on me, disfigured and disgraced me thus. For your sake, all this I have suffered. If you wish to avenge this insult and protect the honour of the race, rise and go at once.

"Apart from revenge for the insult I have suffered, secure for yourself a wife worthy of you. If you capture her and disgrace Raama, the spirits of the warriors who were slain in Dandaka would be satisfied. I too shall feel that some amends have been made for the dishonour done to me.

"You do not know your own strength. You can easily secure Seeta, and make her your own. And can you remain indifferent to the insult to your race? Khara and Dooshana lie dead in Janasthaana because they dared oppose Raama. Think of all this and do what is right. Save, oh, save, the honour of our race."

Listening to these words of his sister and her praise of Seeta's beauty, Raavana dissolved the council and retired to muse alone. He had to think and think again, because he remembered what Maareecha had told him. He turned in his mind the pros and cons and finally coming to a decision ordered a chariot to be kept ready in secrecy.

It was ready, his golden chariot, drawn by mules bearing demon faces. Mounting it, he passed over sea and land and cities. As he looked from his magic chariot at the sights of the summer season down below, his passion grew stronger.

He reached Maareecha's *aashrama* and met Maareecha who, with matted hair and bark garments, lived the life of an ascetic. Seeing his king and kinsman, Maareecha welcomed Raavana duly and said: "Why have you come all this way a second time and unannounced?"

Raavana, skilful in speech began: "I am in great trouble from which only you can save me. I beg you for help. Do you know how my brothers, under my orders, ruled Janasthaana and how they and their warriors knew no opposition all these years? But now this man Raama has killed them and their whole army. Without a chariot, and standing on the ground, his arrows have pierced to death all our kinsmen. Today, in the Dandaka forest, rid of *Raakshasas,* the *rishis* live fearless lives. This Raama is a worthless prince banished by his father, no doubt for some crime. He has been wandering in the forest alone with his wife, Seeta. This fellow, dressed like an ascetic but enjoying sense-pleasures, this renegade from *dharma,* proud of his strength and for no other reason, has mutilated the face of my sister and insulted our race. My sister who has suffered this pain and shame had come and complained to me. If, with all this, I sit still and do nothing, would I still be a king?

"To avenge myself I have decided to carry off Raama's wife from the Dandaka forest. To disgrace and punish this Raama is a duty I owe to my race. And for this I need your help. With you to help me, I have no fear. In courage, strength, skill and magic powers, none on earth can equal you. That is why I have come to you. You cannot refuse me. I will tell you how you can help me.

"You should turn yourself into a golden deer — a golden deer with silver spots, casting a spell on all eyes. In that shape romp in front of Seeta near Raama's *aashrama.* True to the character of women, she will insist on Raama and Lakshmana pursuing and capturing you for her. When they are thus engaged and she is left alone, I shall easily carry her off.

"Seeta is a most beautiful woman. Raama losing such a wife is sure to languish in sorrow and lose his manly spirit. It will then be easy to kill him and avenge ourselves."

Maareecha stared at Raavana. His face became pale and his mouth grew parched. He was frightened by Raavana's plan. With his experience of Raama's prowess and his own wisdom born of penance, Maareecha saw what was going to happen.

He knew that Raavana's sinful purpose had not the ghost of a chance of success. It was clear to him that the noose of fate was round Raavana's neck dragging him to inevitable ruin. He had spoken no doubt of the honour of the *Raakshasas,* of the duties of kingship and of the insult to Soorpanakha; but he was really impelled by a lustful desire to possess Seeta. All this Maareecha saw.

We should analyse Soorpanakha's motives too. She had suffered because of her own uncontrollable carnal desire. Though it was Lakshmana who mutilated her she was not so angry with him as with Seeta who stood between her and her desire and whose beauty and virtue she hated as darkness hates light.

The one desire that now burned in her heart was to avenge herself by bringing disgrace on Seeta. In order to use Raavana for this purpose, she described Seeta in such glowing terms to him and kindled his lawless passion. The rest of her talk was ancillary to her main purpose. Reference to the honour of the race, the security of his empire, the slaying of his kinsmen and so on was only to serve her main purpose which was to rouse Raavana's lust and make him desire Seeta. And he was caught in the snare.

CHAPTER XXXV

THE GOLDEN STAG

MAAREECHA told Raavana, "I have listened, my king, to all that you have said and I am filled with boundless sorrow. It is easy to flatter. Flattery is ever pleasant to the ears. Those who utter good though unpalatable advice are few; and fewer still are those who welcome it when given; yet it is my duty to speak to you the harsh truth. Sweet words might please you now, but will surely lead you to danger and ruin.

"Your informants have not told you the truth about Raama. Do not be deceived by what you have heard from others about this Raama. He is neither a renegade nor a criminal, but a dutiful son who is in the forest to honour his father's word. Far from being a weakling or coward, he is a mighty warrior, whose equal in arms does not exist.

"Do not make him your implacable enemy and bring ruin on your people and your kingdom. From what you are bent upon, it looks as though Seeta was born only to compass your ruin. The race of *Raakshasas* and Lanka itself will soon be destroyed on your account.

"Who is the enemy that has put this disastrous thought into your head? Who has given you this bad advice to take you, your kingdom and your race to danger and destruction?

"Who told you that he was a lover of pleasure and falsehood? Raama is the embodiment of *dharma*. He employs his strength and courage in the service of *dharma*. As Indra is surely the first among the gods, Raama is first among mortal men.

"How dare you, how could you, cast longing eyes on Seeta? Will Seeta ever yield to you? Take her from Raama indeed! Can one deceive the sun and steal from him his light? You will be reduced to ashes if you approach the blazing fire of Janaka's daughter. Do not fall a prey to Raama's shafts. Do not seek your own death. Do not approach the fire guarded by Raama.

"One should not launch on a course of action without full thought. You can never vanquish Raama in battle. O, ruler of the *Raakshasas*, do not turn a deaf ear to my words. Do you remember how, in olden days, proud of my strength, I disturbed the rites and sacrifice of the sage Viswaamitra. In those days Raama was but a boy; yet Viswaamitra had, with Dasaratha's permission, taken young Raama to protect his sacrifice. That sage knew Raama's prowess. I approached the place to put out the sacrificial fire with contaminating blood and flesh and then I came up against the boy Raama. What do you think happened? He let loose an arrow which killed Subaahu on the spot and with another he swept me off my feet and hurled me into the sea. Raama the boy is now a man, immeasurably stronger and more skilful in arms!

"Do not incur his wrath. Do not bring ruin on your people who are now enjoying wealth and pleasure. Do not harbour thoughts about Seeta and bring down destruction on your rich and beautiful city and certain death on yourself. If you persist in your foolish project, O Raavana, I see before my eyes the ruin that awaits you. I see Lanka in flames and her streets littered with death, and her widows and orphans loud in lamentation. Avoid this great sin. If you are angry with Raama fight him face to face and meet your death like a hero. Do not follow a fraudulent path and drag me into it. Go back and be happy with your numerous wives. Do not invite Yama to your land and race!"

Thus Maareecha earnestly pleaded for the good of Raavana who, however, was far from pleased or convinced. How could good advice prevail on a victim of lust? Like a sick man rejecting medicine, Raavana refused to listen to Maareecha's counsel.

"If a king," said Raavana, "wants to know whether a thing should or should not be done, it is open to his adviser to examine its advantages and disadvantages. But I have not come to you for such advice. I am king and I have come to tell you that I have decided to do this. I expect and want your help to carry it out. You forget the loyalty due from you and dare tell me that what I contemplate is wrong. On this matter, I have considered everything and reached a decision. This insignificant creature whom you extol is unworthy of the honour of a formal challenge to battle from me. What more is he than a man driven out of his own country, a fool who has allowed himself to be cheated by a woman and has been deprived of his rights? The proper treatment for such a fellow is to disgrace him by carrying off his wife. This is a matter determined and concluded. Your remarks are therefore irrelevant. You should do what I want you to do and that is not much. Transform yourself into a strange and beautiful stag and appear before Seeta and attract her attention. Seeta will send Raama to pursue and capture you. You should draw Raama away to a distance and simulate Raama's voice and cry 'Ah, Seeta, Ah, Lakshmana!' Hearing this Seeta will conclude that Raama is in danger and she will force Lakshmana to go to his help. When thus she is alone, I shall carry her off to Lanka. Once you have rendered me this help, you will be at liberty to do what you like. But if you will not help me now, understand, your life shall be forfeit."

Maareecha thought within himself. "The frenzied Raavana who is already under the shadow of doom will not listen to advice. Sinful desire is driving him to Yama. It is better for me to be killed by Raama than by Raavana. At least then I would yield my life to a foe."

And so he agreed to the proposal.

He said: "I have given you good advice, but you will not listen. If I carry out your wishes, I am sure to die, but not more sure than that you will also perish, not long after with all that is yours. So will our race. Some enemy of ours wishing our destruction has set you on this course, someone who envies you. I would rather be killed by a foe whom I respect than by you. Come, let us go to Dandaka."

Raavana was overjoyed and embraced Maareecha saying, "Now you are again my dear old Maareecha."

The two ascended the chariot and proceeded towards the Dandaka forest. They flew over cities, mountains, rivers and kingdoms. Reaching Dandaka, they espied Raama's *aashrama* in a banana garden.

They alighted at a distance and Raavana took Maareecha by the hand and, pointing to the *aashrama*, told him to do his part according to their plan.

At once Maareecha transformed himself into a wonderful deer. Every part of the animal had its own different hue and exquisite beauty. Like a rainbow in the sky, it charmed the eye of the beholder. Gold, silver, diamonds, gems and flowers seemed to appear in succession on its beautiful skin. It was like a living stream of jewels flowing on a beautiful golden body.

With such surpassing beauty the magic deer wandered here and there, now resting for a while and now pursuing its graceful gambols. It would sometimes bend and nibble the grass on the ground, again lift its head up to eat the tender leaves of plants; sometimes walk slowly near the *aashrama* and again jump away and disappear and re-appear at a distance. Sometimes it would join a herd of deer; then it would part from it and walk alone. The other deer would smell him and move away in sudden terror.

Seeta, who was then gathering flowers in the forest, looked at the stag and stared spell-bound at its wondrous beauty. The deer, too, stared back at her and ran here and there in front of her, shedding a new beauty on the landscape.

"Do come and look! Do come and look!" cried Seeta, eager that Raama and Lakshmana too should see that wonderful stag.

"Come quickly, quickly!" she cried. Raama and Lakshmana came out of the cottage and saw the exquisite creature and marvelled at its beauty.

Lakshmana grew suspicious. It seemed to him it was no ordinary deer, but a *Raakshasa* in disguise. Both Raama and Lakshmana had heard about Maareecha and had been told how, assuming the form of a deer, he would often beguile and destroy those who came for hunting deer in the forest.

Lakshmana said, "This is no ordinary animal. This is a trick of the *Raakshasas*."

But Seeta said: "Do catch this deer for me. We shall bring it up as a pet in the *aashrama*. This is the most beautiful creature I have so far seen in this forest. Look! Do look at it: What colour! What playfulness!"

And so she went on, talking of the deer and desiring to possess it. And she pleaded, "Do somehow catch it for me."

She begged Raama, "Soon we shall have to return to the city. Should we not take some rare thing from the forest to Ayodhya? How beautiful it will be, this exquisite creature moving in the inner apartments of our palace? Bharata would be so pleased. I should love to give it to him. Do, my beloved, catch it for me. Somehow catch it for me."

Seeta saw that Lakshmana did not seem to like her importunity. This only made her more determined to persuade Raama to get it for her. If a strong desire creeps into our heart and some one stands in the way of it, we are angry with him no matter how dear he may be to us.

This unfortunate truth about the way that desire works in the human mind is explained clearly by the Lord in the *Gita*. It was demonstrated by what happened in Seeta's heart now.

"Look!" she exclaimed, "it is all gold! Look now! It is all silver! If you cannot capture the creature alive, at least bring it down with an arrow and let us take the skin home. We shall never again see such a beautiful skin. It would be a lovely thing to sit on. Look. It is going away. Do go and catch it alive. Or else, let me have at least the skin."

Again she said, "Look, look again. All these long years, I never saw such a beautiful thing in these forests. It is like a cluster of shining stars!"

Raama could no longer resist her entreaties.

He said to himself: "Even if Lakshmana be right and the creature is a *Raakshasa* so much the better reason for killing it. What is there to be afraid of? If I cannot catch it alive, I can bring it down with an arrow and give the skin to Seeta. When she is so keen on having it, is it not my duty to get it for her?"

And he told Lakshmana to bring him his bow and arrows. Lakshmana's heart was not in it, but he obeyed.

And Raama set out saying, "Mind, Lakshmana, remain by Seeta's side and guard her vigilantly. I shall come back soon with this stag alive or killed. Do not be anxious. Even if this is a *Raakshasa*, what does it matter? It will share the fate of Vaataapi. If this has come here to cheat me, as Vaataapi tried to cheat Agastya, why then, it will be the victim of its own deceit. What can this animal do to me? Stag or *Raakshasa*, it is all the same."

Again he said, "Be careful. Mind Seeta. Anything might happen at any time. Be vigilant."

Destiny had set the stage for misfortune. Strangely enough Lakshmana, who was by nature hasty and quick to act, was suspicious on this occasion and Raama, who was usually circumspect now yielded to Seeta's foolish wish and, disregarding Lakshmana's warning, went in pursuit of the Maareecha-stag.

In order to give Raavana plenty of time and opportunity, Maareecha kept within sight of Raama, but beyond his reach, and drew him on and on like

Fate. The deer would take a few steps, then stop and turn and stare at the pursuer. Then suddenly it would start as if in fear. Pricking its ears, it would spring drawing up its hooves to its breast. It would disappear for a while among the trees. Emerging soon on some tall mound, it would display its lovely outline framed against a passing cloud. Sometimes it allowed near approach as though tired and so easy of capture but presently it would spring up and bound far away.

This went on until Maareecha took Raama far out. Then the *Raakshasa* realised this game would not go on for ever and that his end was near. Raama, tired of the pursuit, bent his bow and sent forth an arrow. It pierced the stag. Maareecha resumed his natural form and simulating Raama's voice called out, "Ah Seeta, Ah Lakshmana!" and fell dead.

"Lakshmana was right," said Raama to himself. "This deer was indeed a *Raakshasa*."

He thought further, "Hearing his last cry, may be, Seeta will be deceived. She is likely to be overwhelmed by fear."

He then said to himself again, "What if Seeta entertains false fears? Lakshmana is there by her side."

His heart then swelled with pride and joy, that he had a brother like Lakshmana, so loving and so steadfast. How could Raama guess what was happening at that very instant in the *aashrama*, and what painful words Lakshmana had to hear from Seeta? Truly, the way of Destiny is cruel.

CHAPTER XXXVI

THE GOOD BIRD JATAAYU

"ALAS, alas! Ah Seeta! Ah Lakshmana!" So cried Maareecha simulating Raama's voice. And Seeta was deceived. Trembling like a plantain tree in a storm, she cried, "There, Lakshmana, do you not hear your brother's voice? Run, run at once to his help!"

Overwhelmed by fear and seeing Lakshmana unwilling to move, she appealed to Lakshmana again and again in an agony of anxiety, "I hear my Lord's voice in distress. Go, go at once! Do not delay!" she cried. "He is in some great danger. Did you not hear his cry for help? Why do you still stand here? Your brother is no doubt surrounded by *Raakshasas* and cries for help. Instead of rushing to his rescue, you stand still here!"

Lakshmana knew the wiles of the *Raakshasas* and remembered his brother's command. He would not move.

Seeta grew furious in her agony of fear and doubt. She beat her breast with both hands and shouted in uncontrollable fury: "Son of Sumitra! Have you too turned foe? Have you been an imposter all these years? Have you been with us waiting only for Raama to die? Pretending to be his friend, were you hoping all the time for his death to secure me thereafter? Why else do you stand here, wicked wretch, and refuse to go to his rescue when he cries for help? Traitor! Imposter!"

These cruel words pierced Lakshmana's heart like poisoned arrows. He closed his ears with his hands. He spoke gently to Seeta, who was in tears of wrath: "Vaidehi, Raama can encounter and vanquish

any foe in the world. There is no need to fear, O more
than mother! Calm yourself. None in the universe is
strong enough to touch our Raama or do him harm.
What you have uttered is unworthy of you, my
mother. Do not fear or grieve. You will surely see
Raama return with the body of the stag you wanted.

"The voice we heard was not his. It is a
Raakshasa's trick. Do not be deceived and grieve for
nothing. My brother has posted me here to watch
over you. Do not ask me to leave you alone and go. I
cannot disobey my brother. Since we slew the
Raakshasas of Janasthaana, their people are trying
to avenge themselves in various ways. We should not
be misled by their false forms and voices. It was not
Raama's cry for help. You need not be afraid in the
least."

But Seeta's fear grew to a frenzy and with eyes
red with anger she uttered terrible words: "Taking
advantage of what you call your brother's command,
you stand unmoved by his cry of anguish and are
prepared to let him perish! Oh, how completely have
you been deceiving us, Raama and me, all these
years! Base, wicked, selfish wretch calling yourself
brother! O, you false friend, do you rejoice that
Raama is in dire peril? I now see why you followed us
into the forest. Have you been set on by Bharata?
Have you all become my lord's enemies? Have you all
joined together in a wicked conspiracy? I, who have
lived with Raama, shall I ever look at you or
another? When Raama dies, I die with him. Know
this for certain."

Seeta burst into a rage which completely
overwhelmed Lakshmana. Her cruel words pierced
and burnt into him like poisoned arrows. His hairs
stood on end. He clasped his hands in worship and

said: "O Mother! O Goddess! How can such words issue from your mouth? Like red-hot iron they burn my ears. Cruel and unjust are these thoughts of yours. With all the gods for witness, I swear, your suspicion is wrong. I see now that after all you are a woman like other women quick to think evil of others. I fear a great tragedy is about to befall you. Otherwise you could not have thought and spoken evil of me."

And innocent Lakshmana trembled in fear of some dire calamity that was to come over them.

But Seeta said: "Look here, here is plenty of dry fuel. I shall light a fire and fall into it. Or I shall drown myself in the Godaavari. Or I shall hang myself dead — unless you run immediately to the help of Raama. Now, once again, I ask, will you not go? Or shall I perish?"

She beat her breast and cried. Lakshmana could bear this no longer. He raised his hands in solemn worship and said:

"Very well, sister. I shall obey you and disobey my brother. I shall leave you alone. May you be safe and well! May the gods of the forest protect you! I shall do your bidding. I see bad omens. I fear greatly. I wonder if I shall ever see you with Raama again. Yet I shall go!"

And he went, unwillingly and looking back every now and then.

Lakshmana walked, his heart troubled and heavy with anger and sorrow. How could he bear to hear the cruel words of Seeta? How could he forget them? Sorely wounded was the heart of the prince who had renounced everything to be with his brother.

Lakshmana went in the direction that Raama had taken. Raavana, who had been waiting for this, now approached Raama's *aashrama*. He transformed himself into a mendicant ascetic, clad in clean saffron clothes and his lips uttered beautiful *vedic* hymns while in his heart was ugliest evil.

Seeta was standing at the entrance of the cottage, her eyes fixed on the forest, eagerly looking for Raama. Raavana beheld Seeta.

At sight of her, the desire planted in his heart by Soorpanakha took good root and grew rapidly irresistible. He was more determined than ever to possess Seeta.

Seeing this wandering ascetic, clad in saffron clothes, carrying his water-pot and staff, Seeta greeted him respectfully, according to the courtesy due to holy men. He desired hospitality. As in duty bound, she offered him a seat and placed before him some fruits and roots as was the custom.

The ascetic sat and looked again at Seeta. His desire grew stronger. Sinner and *Raakshasa* though he was, he had an instinct that made him wish to win her heart; he wished not to ravish but to secure Seeta's willing consent and make her his wife.

The King of Lanka wanted and hoped to persuade Seeta. He thought she would yield to him for his wealth and power, turning her back on poverty-stricken Raama. He thought also that this would be the best way of disgracing and punishing Raama. He expected Seeta to behave like other women he had known.

Seated in front of the fruits and roots offered by Seeta, the ascetic began to praise Seeta's beauty in terms too warm for a genuine ascetic. He dwelt on the charms of her person and asked: "Who are you? Why are you here alone in the forest haunted by *Raakshasas* and wild beasts?"

She was astonished but answered his questions. She hoped the prince would return at once and kept her eyes fixed on the door-way.

Little by little the visitor revealed who he was and described the greatness of his origin and family, his power and wealth. After exalting himself, he proceeded to run down Raama and concluded:

"Be my wife and live a glorious life with me in Lanka. Come, let us go!"

In this unexpected situation, Seeta's purity gave her courage to defy the powerful monster whom she now knew for what he was.

"Base and wicked fellow! Your destruction is near. Leave this *aashrama* if you would escape with life!" she said, hissing like an angry cobra.

The *Raakshasa* was furious. He completely threw off all pretence of disguise and gentleness and assumed his real imperious wickedness. With one hand he caught hold of her hair and with the other lifted her up and carried her to the chariot which waited for him behind the trees, and forcing her into it, rose with her into the air.

Seeta cried aloud: "O my lord! Where are you, my Raama? Oh Lakshmana, most faithful of friends, why did I, with obstinate folly, drive you away?"

The *Raakshasa* held her firmly down and drove on in the aerial car. Seeta addressed the trees and plants down below and begged them to tell Raama of her fate.

It happened that old Jataayu, half-asleep upon a tree, saw the chariot flying past. Startled by a woman's cry of distress he was wide awake in a moment and recognised Seeta by her voice. She also saw him and appealed to him for rescue.

Jataayu's blood was fired by the sight of her piteous plight and he threw himself in the way of the aerial car crying: "Hold, hold! What is all this?"

"The King of Lanka is carrying me away by force," wailed Seeta, "but what can you do to prevent it, my poor old friend? O, fly to Raama and Lakshmana and tell them my helpless plight!"

But Jataayu's fighting blood, the blood of generations of lordly ancestors who ruled the air and knew not fear, was on fire; he cared not for Raavana and his might; he only saw a princess in distress; he thought of his friend Dasaratha and his promise to Raama and he was resolved that this outrage should not occur while he lived to prevent it.

Jataayu now addressed Raavana directly, "Oh king, I am Jataayu, king of the eagles, a king like you. Listen to me, brother king! Forbear from this wicked act. How can you call yourself a king and do this shameful wrong? Is it not the rule of kings to protect the honour of women? And Seeta is a princess. I warn you, you shall surely perish unless you leave her and go. Her very look will reduce you to ashes. You are carrying a venomous cobra in your bosom. The noose of Yama is round your neck and dragging you to perdition.

"I am old and unarmed and you are young, fully armed and seated in a chariot. Yet I cannot look on, while you carry off Seeta. Why do you do this cowardly act behind Raama's back? If you have any grievance against him, meet him face to face. O, you would fly away from me, would you? You shall not escape while I am alive! I care not for your chariot or your ten heads, or your glittering arms! Your heads shall roll on the ground that you have polluted with your presence. Get down from your car, and fight if you are not a coward as well as a thief!"

Raavana flared up in a rage. He attacked Jataayu. It was like a clash between a mighty wind and a massive rain-cloud. The battle raged in the sky above the forest. Jataayu fought like a winged mountain.

Raavana aimed deadly darts at him. But the eagle intercepted them all and with his talons tore Raavana's flesh. The enraged *Raakshasa* despatched sharp, serpent-like missiles against the bird.

The bird-hero was desperately wounded, but fought on undauntedly while Seeta watched the unequal combat with beating heart and tearful eyes. The sight of her made Jataayu all the fiercer in his attacks on Raavana. But his years were telling on him and he felt he must gather all his strength for a supreme attempt to conquer. Regardless of the wounds, he attacked Raavana fiercely and with his wings broke off and threw down his jewelled crown and deprived him of his bow. He attacked the chariot and killed the demon-faced mules and the charioteer and smashed the vehicle into a thousand pieces. Raavana fell on the ground, still clutching Seeta. The elements rejoiced to see Ravana fall.

The gallant old bird swooped down on Raavana's back and tore great chunks of flesh off it, and tried to wrench off the arms which held Seeta. But Raavana had twenty arms, and no sooner was one pulled off than another took its place and Seeta was held in writhing helplessness.

At last Raavana let go Seeta and unsheathing his sword cut off the bird's wings and talons. The old bird was now helpless and fell on the ground unable to move.

Jaanaki ran and embraced Jataayu and cried: "O my father! You have given away your life for my sake. You are a second father to my Lord! And now you are no more. O our devoted brave friend!"

Then Raavana turned towards her to take her up again. Helplessly she ran hither and thither, crying. She clung to the trees and cried. 'O my Raama, where are you? O Lakshmana, where are you? Won't you come to my rescue?" The *Raakshasa* at last caught her and rose in the air.

As the dark and massive Raavana flew in the sky with her, Seeta struggling in his grasp looked like a flash of lightning across a great black cloud. The *Raakshasa* carrying her appeared like a mountain covered by a forest-fire. The body of Raavana, lit up by Seeta, coursed through the sky like a calamitous comet.

Thus was Seeta carried away by the *Raaksha-sa*. The sun grew dim and untimely darkness descended on the earth.

All beings lamented: "*Dharma* is destroyed. Righteousness has disappeared. Virtue and pity are no more."

The dumb creatures of the earth, looking upwards, shed tears.

Raavana, cruelly clutching the princess, flew — as towards his ruin. As she was carried away, the petals fell down from the flowers she was wearing at that time and as they were strewn along the path

below, they seemed to announce the scattering of
Raavana's fortune and affluence.

CHAPTER XXXVII

CLOSELY GUARDED

SEETA opened her eyes red with anger and grief, and facing Raavana cried: "Base fellow! You boasted of your fame and your great origin and your warlike qualities, but have you behaved like a brave warrior? Are you not ashamed of yourself? What sort of warrior is he who waits for the husband's absence to steal his wife and carries off a lonely helpless woman when no one is nearer to prevent it?

"What heroic deed to kill the old bird that tried to save me! How brave was your talk in the *aashrama*! The world will no doubt remember and praise this great hero who dares not fight but is prepared to steal! If indeed you come of a noble family, what a shame you have brought upon it!

"And what do you hope by thus carrying me off? How long do you hope to live? Very soon Raama's arrows will seek you out and end your life. Know that the moment Raama sets eyes on you, you are dead. Do not hope to escape. Your death is certain at his hands. What then do you gain by this cheating? I will never be yours. I shall die before I yield to you and you cannot escape my lord, having incurred his wrath. Very soon you will see the river Vaitarani in hell. The red-hot image is awaiting you there for your embrace. So is the tree with iron spikes. Raama within an hour slew your army of myriad *Raakshasas* in Janasthaana. Will he let you escape? Soon will he send you to Yama."

While Seeta was speaking words of contempt and warning, Raavana, chariotless, sped like an arrow across the sky towards Lanka. They went over many mountains and rivers and Seeta saw some people below standing on a hill-top. She took off her sash and tying up her jewels in it threw the bundle down.

She did this hoping that the ornaments thus dropped may be seen by Raama and give him a clue of the direction in which she was carried away.

Crossing the Pampa and then the sea, Raavana entered the city of Lanka. He went to his apartments with the grief-stricken Seeta. The fool thought that he had secured the prize, but he was taking home his own death in a woman's form. Then, summoning some demon-like *Raakshasis*, he ordered them to keep watch over Seeta, specially commanding them to let none approach her without his permission.

"Give her whatever she wants, clothes or gold or jewels. Serve her and do her honour as you would serve and honour me," he enjoined them.

And he added the warning: "Anyone who utters a word which might offend her will be punished with death. No one, knowingly or unknowingly, should cause her anger or grief."

Having thus installed Seeta in the inner apartment, he considered what should be done next. He sent for some clever spies and gave them this mandate:

"Go at once to Janasthaana where Khara lived. Watch carefully and bring me word what Raama is doing. So long as that Raama is alive I cannot sleep. He is my greatest foe. Somehow, he should be killed. Go boldly now and do your job and return."

Imprisoned within a fortress in a sea-girt island, Seeta did not know where she was or how far from Raama. She expected that her lord would somehow arrive, kill Raavana and redeem her.

Though full of grief, thinking of the strength and powess of her lord she was bold and steady in mind. It was also some consolation that the *Raakshasa* king did not behave like a beast with her.

Having despatched his men to Janasthaana, Raavana returned to Seeta's presence. He saw her overwhelmed by grief and shedding tears. The *Raakshasis* were watching her with care.

He thought that if she saw his wealth and power she would yield to him. She was therefore taken round in the great palace and shown the wealth and grandeur there displayed. No king on earth had ever possessed such wealth and means of enjoyment.

Seeta was shown gold and jewels and silks in plenty; curiously — wrought platforms, vehicles and towers; thousands of maidservants and every symbol of wealth and royal power. But her thoughts were elsewhere.

Raavana tried to convince her also of the vastness of his army. But then she had already formed her opinion of his prowess and had described it to him in scathing terms.

Yet, Raavana argued: "All this you can count and enjoy as your own. You shall be my queen, dearer to me than life itself. I have many wives but you shall be mistress of them all. Hereafter my love shall be for you and you alone. Listen to me. Do my desire. For hundreds of miles the sea surrounds this island which is guarded by thousands of mighty soldiers. No one can enter this city. No one among the gods or *asuras* can match me in might; and they know it. What pleasure or honour is it for you to stick to a poor human creature banished from his kingdom, a destitute wandering in the forest? To match your beauty, you need my wealth. Do not waste the years of your youth. You are never again going to set eyes on Raama; be certain of that. Raama cannot approach this city. Treat this whole kingdom as yours. Treat me and all the obedient gods as your slaves. Till now, because of your sins in some previous birth, you have suffered hardship. Hereafter you will enjoy with me the fruits of your former merits. You will be the queen of Lanka and the wife of the Lord of Lanka, the conqueror of Kubera. Let us take our pleasure floating about the world in the Pushpaka *Vimaana*. Let the cloud of sorrow disappear from your face and let the moon of joy appear."

As Raavana went on speaking thus, tears flowed from Seeta's eyes. She covered her face with the end of her sari as she did not want her enemies to think that she was afraid.

Raavana begged and importuned her: "Do not be shy. There is nothing wrong in accepting me, nothing to be ashamed of. It is laid down that one should accept the gifts of God. O beautiful one! I bow my head at your feet and beg you for your grace. I am your slave. Forgetting my greatness and power, I thus beg for your favour. Never in my life have I bowed in this way before anyone."

He really thought he could persuade her and gain her affection.

If one's mind is clear, one can courageously face any situation. In spite of her grief, therefore, Seeta spoke boldly to the *Raakshasa*. She placed a little bit

of grass between Raavana and herself before
answering him.

Boastful words were uttered by Raavana in
sanyasi garb, sitting in front of the fruit served by
her in Panchavati. Imprisoned Seeta now spoke as if
in echo of those words.

"Know who I am. Dasaratha was famed in all
the three worlds and reigned long years and stood as
a bulwark of *dharma* and defender of truth. His son
Raama, of god-like presence and lion-like valour, is
my husband. He and his brother Lakshmana will
surely take your life. You know how Khara and his
army were destroyed in Janasthaana by my lord. As
easily as an eagle carries a venomous serpent, he
destroyed your huge army in Janasthaana. Because
you have secured a boon that no god or *Asura* can kill
you, you have dared to make Raama your enemy.
You think your boon will save you. But I tell you, you
cannot escape. You will surely meet your death at
his hands. You are, like the goat tied to the
altar-post for sacrifice, doomed to death. The
moment Raama sets his angry eyes on you, you will
meet your fate. My lord will dry up the sea or bring
down the moon, if necessary, to kill you and redeem
me. It is certain. Your evil deed will bring
destruction on yourself and your kingdom. My noble
lord lived unafraid in the midst of the *Raakshasas* in
the forest. Like a hero, he fought and killed the
Raakshasas who encountered him. Like a thief, you
stole me in his absence. But you cannot escape. Your
fate impelled you to this sin because the hour of your
ruin and the destruction of your race are near.

"You ask me to accept you. How foolish! Can the
crow approach the swan? Can a heinous sinner be
allowed near the sacrificial fire? I do not value life or

body. Do you imagine I would wish to live despised by the world? Do not dream that out of fear or for saving my life I shall yield to you."

Having spoken those words, she was silent.

"Is that so?" said Raavana. "Very well then, I shall give you twelve months' time. If you agree to accept me, well and good. If, at the end of that period, you refuse, my cooks will make meat of your body for my breakfast."

After warning Seeta thus, he gave orders to the attendant *Raakshasis:* "You should break her pride and ostinacy by some means or other. Put her alone in the Asoka garden and skilfully use fear and temptation to bring her to her senses. As we tame a wild she-elephant, you should train her to submission." And angrily he went to his palace.

The *Raakshasis* took Seeta to the Asoka garden. It was a beautiful park attached to the women's apartments. The trees were full of flowers and fruits, and beautiful birds played among them. Here, surrounded and guarded by terribly ugly *Raakshasis,* Seeta was kept prisoner.

Though overwhelmed by grief, she had the faith that Raama and Lakshmana would somehow discover where she was and rescue her, that her lord would destroy Raavana and take her back to a happy life with him.

Sustained by this faith, she was neither frightened by threats nor deceived by temptations. Not for one day, or two, but for months, Seeta suffered thus a close prisoner in the Asoka garden.

The day was yet far off when the mighty Hanumaan, crossing the sea, would visit Seeta in her sorrow and bring her the message of hope and love and the assurance of relief: "Raama loves you infinitely: he will be here soon. Be not afraid."

All the women in our land who suffer sorrow in any way are so many replicas of Seeta. May all the men be, like Hanumaan, pure and heroic helpers of such suffering women!

We shall now go to Raama and Lakshmana.

CHAPTER XXXVIII

RAAMA DISCONSOLATE

WHEN Maareecha was struck by Raama's arrow and was about to die, he resumed his own *Raakshasa* shape and cried aloud in a voice which was an exact imitation of Raama's, "Ah Lakshmana, Ah Seeta!"

Raama now realised how the *Raakshasa* had beguiled them and how he had been drawn away a long distance by the crafty Maareecha, and he was full of anxiety as to what it all could mean.

"Alas, we have been badly deceived. It would be terrible if Lakshmana is also deceived by this cry and leaves Seeta alone to come to my succour. It looks as though the *Raakshasas* have planned this ruse to carry off Seeta and eat her. When Seeta hears what she will take as my cry of distress she is sure to insist on Lakshmana leaving her and rushing to my help. The howling of jackals and the behaviour of birds do portend disaster. There is trepidation in my heart and it is a portent in itself of some danger close at hand."

Saying thus to himself, Raama hurried back to the *aashrama*. On the way he saw Lakshmana running towards him. "Alas, the worst I fear has happened," exclaimed Raama.

He held Lakshmana's hands and cried in sorrow. "Why did you leave Seeta alone in the forest, Lakshmana? You may be sure the *Raakshasas* have killed and eaten her. It was not right for you to leave her and come away. It is now all over with Seeta!"

Fatigued and thirsty with the futile chase, and now overwhelmed with anger and unbearable anxiety, Raama cried again: "If I do not see Seeta in the *aashrama* when we return, I shall surely die, Lakshmana. You will return to Ayodhya, the survivor of us three, and tell them what has happened. O, how will Kausalya bear her grief? Lakshmana, you have more than fulfilled Kaikeyi's wishes. The *Raakshasas* will by now have visited on Seeta, poor unprotected Seeta, all their pent-up hatred against us. They must have killed and eaten her up by now. How could you leave her alone and come away? How could you be deceived by Maareecha's false cry? What shall I do now? I shall see Seeta no more. The *Raakshasas*' plan has succeeded. My trust in you was misplaced and I shall never see Seeta. How could you leave her and come away, how could you, Lakshmana?"

Lakshmana answered with tears in his eyes: "What else, brother, could I do? When Seeta heard the cry, 'Alas Seeta! Alas Lakshmana!' she was frightened. Quivering with fear she urged me to go to you at once and would tolerate no delay. She persisted, whatever I said to the contrary. I told her again and again not to be afraid and assured her that no foe was strong enough to do you harm, and that the cry of distress was not yours, but she would not listen. She charged me with having turned traitor to you and with having come to the forest with treasonable intentions, and, O brother, she found it possible in her anguish to say I would be glad of your death out of sinful intentions towards herself! I was half dead with horror on hearing those words of hers and then she announced that she would kill herself if I did not go on the instant. Mad herself, she maddened me with her words of reproach and I ran towards you not knowing what else to do."

But Raama was not satisfied. "Whatever a foolish woman might have said in her fright, you should have stayed and not left her unprotected. How could you do such a foolish thing? You have bought calamity on me. I shall never see Seeta again!"

The two hurried to the *aashrama*. Many bad omens appeared on their way. And Raama repeated, as he saw them one by one: "I fear, I fear we shall never see Seeta again!"

Reaching the *aashrama*, they found it, as they had feared, empty. Seeta was not there. The deer skin, the *kusa* grass, the mat spread as a seat, all lay scattered on the ground.

Raama wept and ran hither and thither in the grove round the cottage. The leaves and flowers on the trees had faded. Seeta was nowhere to be seen.

He wandered about like one mad. His eyes were bloodshot. He cried, "Alas, have they eaten her up? Have they carried her away? O, how she must have trembled in terror! I cannot bear the thought of it. Could it be that she has gone to the river to fetch water? Could it be that she has gone out to cull flowers? Let us see."

And he went searching among the trees, hoping that perhaps she was hiding and playing a practical joke on him.

His sorrow swelled like the sea and seemed to have drowned his reason. He called the trees one by one by their names and beseeched them for help.

"Oh, Asoka tree! Be true to your name, remove my sorrow. You must know the truth. Tell me where

Seeta is now. Oh tall palm tree! You must be able to see where Seeta is. Tell me where she is."

He talked to the animals too. "Oh tiger!" he said, "the elephant and the deer are afraid to tell me the truth. But you know no fear. You can tell me what has happened. You know everything. Tell me then the truth."

He cried: "Oh Seeta, you are hiding somewhere. There! There! I see you there! Stop this fooling. I can stand it no longer."

After wandering and weeping in vain for a long time he fell on the ground, moaning, "Ha Lakshmana! Ha Seeta!" He cried like an elephant trapped in a pit.

"Lakshmana, Seeta is nowhere. The *Raaksha-sas* have captured her and torn her to pieces and eaten her up. How can I live any more? My end is near. But when my father sees me in the other world, he will say, 'Why have you come here, my son, before fulfilling my command?' I have failed. In everything, I have failed."

Lakshmana could bear this sight no longer. "Brother, it is not right that you should cry like this," he said. "Let us search through the forest. You know how fond Seeta is of entering caves and thickets. She may be bathing in the river or playing somewhere or culling flowers. Let us search again. She is only testing us. Come, let us search again. Do not cry."

The two searched again all over the place on hills, by pools and on the river bank. But they did not find her.

"Seeta is not to be seen, Lakshmana," said Raama. "What shall I do now?"

Lakshmana tried to encourage him with words of hope, but Raama was inconsolable. "No, no, my brother. There is no hope," he said, "Seeta is nowhere. I have lost her for ever. I shall live no more."

He lay unconscious for a time. Then he came to himself and lifted his voice and wept. Nothing that Lakshmana said could comfort him.

"Lakshmana, how can I go back to Ayodhya?" he cried. "Won't they laugh at me for returning alone after allowing Seeta to be killed and eaten by *Raakshasas*? Having brought her to the forest and having failed to protect her, what shall I tell Janaka?

"No, you should go alone to Ayodhya. Go and look after our mothers. Greet Bharata from me and tell him it was my dying wish that he should continue to rule as king."

All Lakshmana's efforts to console him were in vain. He was convinced that the *Raakshasas* had carried away Seeta and torn her to pieces and eaten her up. He pictured to himself in detail the horror of her suffering and cried in his grief: "I must have committed terrible sins. How else could such suffering come to me?

"Seeta who accompanied me, thinking I could protect her, has been eaten by the *Raakshasas* and I can do nothing about it. Is there another sinner like me in the world?"

Lakshmana said: "Do not lose heart. You must be bold and energetic. A resolute mind can conquer fate. But you must first conquer your weakness. Let us make a more thorough search of the forest. Instead of yielding to unavailing sorrow, let us be manly and active." But Raama would not listen.

Raama behaved as a human being, not an *avataar* of Vishnu. Though elsewhere his words and actions give room for a different view, here Vaalmeeki describes Raama as a mere man enveloped in the gloom of a supreme misfortune.

His feeling and behaviour are exactly those of any noble and virtuous man who has lost his beloved wife, dearer to him than life itself, and that in a forest infested with *Raakshasas*. We see that all the efforts of Lakshmana to console him had no effect.

Our common human *dharma* is illustrated by the sorrow of Raama. We see here the picture of true and equal love between a virtuous man and woman and the anguish of loss.

The episode may also be interpreted allegorically. Raama's sense of privation, when he misses Seeta, is a measure and image of the mind of God when a single human soul is lost through sin.

One may ask whether God can lose, or can suffer pain of mind. If one realises that all life is divine *leela*—the play of God—no further exegesis is needed. Sin, merit, devotion—all are aspects of that sport.

Each one of us is beloved of the Lord. If for any reason we are swept away from the right path, He suffers like a lover who has lost his love. And His sorrow too is a part of His great play.

CHAPTER XXXIX

A SECOND FATHER DIES

THE two brothers searched every mountain, forest and river-bank calling Seeta's name aloud. But all in vain, and they did not so much as find a clue anywhere. Baffled and grief-stricken, Raama cried out against the river Godaavari, against the gods and against the five elements.

The Poet-Sage ascribes the silence of the rivers and the gods and elements to their fear of the powerful *Raakshasa* king. A herd of deer, however, moving southwards seemed to indicate to Raama and Lakshmana that they too should travel in the same direction. They did so and, after a time, found some flowers scattered on the way.

Raama at once recognised the flowers and cried excitedly: "These are the very flowers I gave her. They must have fallen from her hair."

His grief and anxiety grew greater and he sobbed aloud fearing the worst for Seeta.

They searched the forest all around the spot where they found the flowers. They noticed the marks of a *Raakshasa's* big feet and little foot-prints which they knew were Seeta's.

They found some gold beads spilt from Seeta's jewels. Raama cried again: "Look! The *Raakshasa* has been chasing her like a beast of prey to tear her tender flesh!"

Then they saw several fragments of a chariot and great clots of blood, as also royal headgear and jewels scattered on the ground. They wondered what these things could mean.

Soon they came upon a large bow broken, flag torn and armour crushed. A little later they saw the dead bodies of a charioteer and of mules. It was clear that a vehement battle had been fought on that spot.

"Two powerful *Raakshasas* must have struggled here," groaned Raama, "each claiming the sole right to eat Seeta."

Conjecturing and lamenting in this way, Raama went on: "*Dharma* could not save Seeta! No god came to her rescue! It will be right to destroy this wicked world." Raama was beside himself and talked wildly.

Lakshmana did his best to calm the distracted Raama. "Great sorrow unbalances all minds, even the strongest," he said. "Else why should you thus lose self-control? Why should you hate and curse the whole world for the evil deed of one person? How often have you, my brother, calmed my anger and led me on the right path! But now a great grief has upset your mind and it is the turn of the younger brother to give courage and counsel patience to the elder and restore him to his natural heroism. Let us find out who our enemy is and deal with him."

With such loving words Lakshmana sought to give courage and consolation and both walked on. They had not proceeded far when they came on Jataayu, bloody and mutilated, unrecognisable, lying on the ground.

At first Raama thought it was some *Raakshasa* disguising himself to deceive them and, wild with anger, cried: "Look! There is a *Raakshasa* who has eaten Seeta!" and rushed towards him, bow in hand.

Then raising his ruffled and gory head with great pain, Jataayu spoke in a feeble voice that seemed struggling with death. "Do not kill me, dear Raama, who has but a few moments more to live! The dear princess you are searching for has been carried off by Raavana and he could do so only by first robbing me of my life!

"Seeing Seeta in his flying chariot in the air, I intercepted it and gave him battle. I struck down his bow and smashed his chariot. His charioteer I slew. The marks of my last great fight you can see all round this place. I did my best — how I wish it were better for your sake! At last as, weary with toil, I was still waging a hopeless combat — age against youth, beak and talons against keen weapons and panoply of steel, he cut off my wings 'and legs and as I fell wounded to death, he lifted Seeta and flew with her into the sky in a southern direction. Though racked with the pangs of death, I have clung to life for love of you to tell you what I know. Now that I have done this, bless me and let me die."

Tears flowed from Raama's eyes as he listened to Jataayu's tale. He flung aside his bow and embraced the bird. The princes' sorrow knew no bounds. They lamented loudly, rolling on the ground.

"I am the most unhappy man alive, Lakshmana," said Raama. "Giving up the kingdom, I came to the forest, and here I have lost my Seeta. This Jataayu, who was a second father to us, has laid down his life for my sake.

"Why, if I fell into the fire, I fear my bad luck will put even the fire out. If I fell into the sea, I fear it would dry up. What a terrible sinner I am, Lakshmana! Who knows, one day I might lose you too, Lakshmana."

Embracing Jataayu, he said: "O, my father! Really, did you see Seeta?" But Jataayu lay speechless on the ground.

After a few moments Jataayu spoke again in a low voice: "Be not afraid, Raama. You will surely find Seeta. No harm will come to her. Regaining the treasure you have lost, you will greatly rejoice." With these words, he spat out blood and gave up life.

They were foolish and committed errors of omission and commission and lost Seeta. Trying to save Seeta from the calamity that their carelessness had brought upon her, Jataayu, old, unarmed, had fought with wing and beak and talon and given up his life. When their father died in Ayodhya, his obsequies were performed by Bharata and Satrughna. Raama and Lakshmana were denied this privilege because they were away in the forest. They regarded Jataayu as their own father and in performing his obsequies derived some consolation for not being by Dasaratha's side and performing the last offices to him. What other help or honour could they accord to heroic Jataayu?

The *bhaktas* worship Jataayu as the best of *bhaktas*. Exercising our imagination, we should behold with Seeta's eyes the poor old bird's hard struggle against the *Raakshasa* king. Then we would realise the love and gratitude and sorrow that must have surged in her heart as she watched his sufferings. Thus we shall be purified by the grace of the Mother. What wonder is there in the rank assigned to Jataayu among the *bhaktas?*

Later, when Raama fights and is victorious in Lanka, Seeta does not see it; she is a prisoner in the Asoka forest. She has to be content with listening to reports of the battle and of the prowess of her lord.

But Jataayu's devotion and heroism Seeta saw with her own eyes in the Dandaka forest. Unarmed, he opposed the *Raakshasa* who had all his weapons and armour, and humbled his pride at the cost of his own life.

Jataayu's battle with Raavana is more important than the battles in Lanka. Hence the pious revere Jataayu along with Bharata and look upon him as an *Aalvaar,* a guide in the holy path.

"Lakshmana," said Raama, "gather dry faggots. I shall churn the fire. We failed to perform our father's obsequies—let us do it for the eagle-father who gave up his life for us."

The princes chanted holy invocations as they poured libations to the departed spirit: "O king of birds, may you enjoy all the bliss of the virtuous who perform great sacrifices! May you enjoy the bliss of Vaanaprasthas who have performed great penance! May you enjoy the bliss of those who have made great gifts of land! May you enjoy the bliss of those who fight heroically in the field of battle! May the bliss of all good people be yours!" After the ceremony Raama became steadier and stronger in mind.

To millions of men, women and children in India, the *Raamaayana* is not a mere tale. It has more truth and meaning than the events is one's own life. Just as plants grow under the influence of sun-light, the people of India grow in mental strength and culture by absorbing the glowing inspiration of the *Raamaayana.*

When we see any helpless person in danger or difficulty, let us think of Jataayu and with firm mind try to help regardless of circumstance.

Raama's losing health and lamenting in sorrow may be compared to the behaviour of another incarnation honoured by another faith. It is said in the Bible that Jesus, nailed to the cross and about to give up his ghost, cried with a loud voice, *"Eloi! Eloi! lama sabachthaani!"* which is Hebrew for "My God, my God, why have you forsaken me?"

The mystery of incarnations is ever the same. They are weighed with the dust and tears of the body they have taken and suffer and grieve like mortals.

CHAPTER XL

LEFT EYELIDS THROB

IN face of the unexpected difficulties that overtook them one after another, Raama and Lakshmana often lost heart. Their fortitude yielded place sometimes to great despair. But they managed to encourage each other and proceeded on their way.

Passing through the forest, the two princes were suddenly caught by a tremendously big *Raakshasa* of ugly form without head or feet. His mouth was in his great belly and he had two enormous arms which, without moving from his place, he would stretch out and clutch tiger, bear or any other living thing within reach, and swallow them.

He had only one eye which was placed in his chest but which was terrible to behold.

Caught by this monster, the princes were, for a while, bewildered and did not know what to do.

Then Raama told Lakshmana: "Let us not be confused. You will cut off one arm, I shall cut off the other."

And so they did. The name of the monster was Kabandha, which means the barrel-shaped one. Once his arms were severed, he was helpless and began to explain:

"On account of my evil deeds I was cursed by Indra to bear this form and this name. I believe you are Raama and Lakshmana. Indra promised me freedom from the curse when you two should come and cut off my arms and commit this body of mine to the flames."

The princes set fire to his body as desired by the
unfortunate monster and there arose from the
flames a lovely being which entered a heavenly
chariot and ascended to the celestial world.

Before going, he said to Raama: "You will
assuredly regain Seeta. Go to the beautiful banks of
the Pampa and seek the help of Sugreeva living
there on the Rishyamooka hill. Driven out of the
kingdom by his brother Vaali, he lives in constant
fear and danger. Gain his friendship, and you will
succeed in your attempt." Saying this Kabandha
disappeared.

Raama and Lakshmana now set forward in the
direction of the Pampa. In that lovely region they
visited the *aashrama* of the aged *sanyaasini,* Sabari,
the disciple of Rishi Matanga, and accepted her
hospitality.

Sabari was a woman of a forest tribe and a
faithful serving sister in the *aashrama* of the old
saint Matanga. When he departed this life, she
wanted to die too; but he said the time was not yet
and she should await the arrival of Raama, an
incarnation of Vishnu, for the bliss of his *darshan*
was in store for her. So the old and wrinkled woman
lived her saintly life, looking faithfully after the
aashrama as of old and keeping it sweet to receive
the promised guest.

When the princes came, she produced the fruits
she had gathered and kept for them, and described
and showed to them the wonders of the Matanga
aashrama. Then with their leave, she kindled a fire
and entering it ascended to heaven.

The meeting with this saintly woman and the
waters of the river Pampa gave strength of mind to

the princes. They thought over what should be done next.

Said Raama: "Lakshmana, I am beginning to think that we shall succeed. Let us search the forest for Sugreeva whose help we should obtain."

They went all over the Pampa area. The place was lovely, but the loveliness of the spot and the animals, birds, trees and creepers only increased Raama's grief.

Every beautiful object wrung his heart and made him think, "How much would Seeta have enjoyed this?" Try as he might, he could not control the human sorrow which by his incarnation he had undertaken to endure.

Lakshmana tried to revive his spirit. He said. "Even if Seeta is kept hidden in the womb of Aditi, the mother of the gods, we will discover her. Raavana cannot escape. It is certain we shall kill him and redeem Seeta. It is not proper that you should thus despair. How can you let anxiety or weakness come over you? If we lose a precious thing, we should work for its recovery with perseverance. Sometimes our very affection becomes our enemy. Too much love brings on grief and grief weakens effort. What need is there for me to tell you all this? You know it all. Let us not lose hope; let us forget the grief brought on by love and bend our mind and body to exertion. Be brave. Be hopeful. We shall succeed. Get rid of your sorrow, brother!"

The younger brother thus advised Raama. Commentators look upon Lakshmana as Aadisesha. Aadisesha, the serpent, is said to be ever the protecting spirit of Vishnu. So Lakshmana ever tried to give Raama fresh energy and enthusiasm.

The fugitive *Vaanara* prince Sugreeva and his faithful adherents with the watchful vigilance of fear saw Raama and Lakshmana roving in the forests and were troubled with doubts. Having been ejected from his kingdom by Vaali, Sugreeva chose this mountainous spot because he believed that it was made by the curse of a rishi inaccessible to Vaali. And now he feared that here, too, Vaali in disguise was following him in order to kill him.

Or else, he feared, some *Kshatriya* warriors taking the side of Vaali were there to kill him. The other *Vaanaras* ran hither and thither in panic.

Hanumaan was Sugreeva's chief minister. He reassured Sugreeva, saying: "This is not Vaali, nor are they friends of Vaali, it seems to me. There is no ground for fear. I shall go and talk to them and find out the truth."

Sugreeva was pleased and said: "Do it, but be careful. Go, find out the truth and come back. Use all your skill. I am full of suspicion. They behave as if they are searching for some one. Could it not be that it is me they seek?"

Taking the form of a *braahmana*, Hanumaan approached Raama and Lakshmana. As he went and stood in front of them, a confident feeling possessed his heart. Straight he started speaking out frankly.

Hamumaan went forward to learn the truth without discovering himself. But as he went on speaking, he threw all caution away and told in detail all about himself and the *Vaanara* King.

Looking on Raama and Lakshmana, he was besides himself, as a devotee in the presence of the Lord, and praised them. He said that he was a

Vaanara and had come there in disguise as desired by his King.

"Royal saints," he said, "your presence here fills my heart with joy. There is an aura round you as if you were gods. I take it, you are here in the forest for doing *tapas*. But why have you come to this inaccessible spot? Please tell me who you are. This river and this forest are made lovelier by your presence. Your faces and forms are radiantly beautiful. The creatures in the forest look on you with reverence and awe. Your strength and courage are manifest. Who are you? From which country do you come? It is clear you are entitled by birth to rule some mighty kingdom and yet you are dressed like ascetics. With matted hair and bark garments you carry also bows and arrows.

"Why are you silent? Here Sugreeva, the *Vaanara* King, driven out of his kingdom by his brother Vaali, is in hiding. He is full of grief. I am his minister. My name is Hanumaan. I am the son of Vaayu. As ordered by my king, I put on the appearance of a *brahmachaari* and am now here before you."

Listening to these courteous words of Hanumaan, Raama said to Lakshmana: "Brother, this speech of Hanumaan has inspired me with confidence. I trust him absolutely. Did you notice the beauty of his language and how correct and rhythmic his enunciation is? He speaks like one who has mastered the Vedas and the science of grammar. An ideal messenger he is. Fortunate is the king who has such a messenger. He whom we are searching for is himself in search of us. We came here to see Sugreeva and he has sent this messenger to us. Let us welcome him."

Then they began to talk freely to one another. Raama and Lakshmana on the one hand and Hanumaan on the other related their history, their joys and sorrows, hopes and fears.

As a result of this talk, Lakshmana conceived a great affection for Hanumaan.

He said to Hanumaan: "My brother, born to great wealth, the eldest son of an emperor, has left his kingdom and come to the forest. Here his wife, dearer to him than life itself, was abducted by Raavana, who had by a fraudulent trick inveigled us far away from the hermitage where she was. We seek Sugreeva's help to rescue her and recover her, for a *daitya*, who under a curse took on the form of a *raakshasa*, told us, 'If you secure the help of Sugreeva, the *Vaanara* King, you will regain the princess stolen by the *Raakshasa*.' And so we are here. We seek the friendship of your king."

Hanumaan answered: "Sugreeva too has been persecuted by Vaali and deprived of his kingdom and his wife. It is now certain that he will regain both. My king will gain much by your friendship and with his help you will also succeed in your efforts."

Then the three went to Sugreeva. The way was such that only *Vaanara* could traverse it. Hanumaan resumed his natural shape and carried both the princes on his back.

The hearts of good men meet and instantly come together. As the *Kural* says, the spontaneous mutual attraction of two hearts and not long acquaintance creates friendship and this friendship was part of the divine dispensation. It was pre-destined that Hanumaan's sublime devotion should be at Raama's service for the fulfilment of the purpose of the incarnation—and so there was acceptance at first sight.

His carrying the two princes on his shoulder was an outward symbol of inward union. As friends and lovers embrace each other, Hanumaan, the loving servant, rejoiced in carrying his Lord on his shoulders.

Ascending the Malaya hill, Hanumaan went in advance to Sugreeva and, announcing the visit of Raama and Lakshmana, said:

"Raama is a prince full of wisdom and virtue. He is the eldest son of the famous Emperor Dasaratha. To fulfil his father's promise, he left Ayodhya with his brother and wife and came to the forest. King Dasaratha was compelled by his younger wife, in fulfilment of an undefined promise given long ago, to banish Raama. In the forest, taking advantage of the princes' absence, Raavana carried away the wife of Raama. Raama has come here, seeking your help in finding her. The princes are worthy of your friendship. You too will gain greatly from friendship with such heroes."

Sugreeva assumed the form of a handsome man and had a long heart-to-heart talk with the princes. Stretching forth his hand to Raama, he said:

"Princes, if you care for the friendship of a *Vaanara*, here is my hand, accept it. Hanumaan has told me all about your virtue and greatness."

Raama clasped his hand and embraced him.

Soon Hanumaan got together some faggots and kindled a fire. Circumambulating the flames Raama and Sugreeva swore mutual friendship: "Let us share our joys and sorrows." They vowed: "Let our friendship be eternal."

They cut down the branch of a tree and sitting on it, Raama and Sugreeva were engaged in cheerful talk and so, too, were Hanumaan and Lakshmana seated on another.

Sugreeva narrated the story of his life—how greatly he and his elder brother, the mighty Vaali, were once devoted to one another, and how malignant fate had through no fault of Sugreeva's made deadly enemies of them. It had come about this way. Once a *Raakshasa* named Maayaavi came at midnight to the gate of Kishkindha, their capital, and vauntingly challenged Vaali to instant combat in pursuance of an ancient feud. Vaali, who never refused a fight, rushed forth impetuously, followed by Sugreeva; and seeing them, the *Raakshasa* fled. Pursuing him they saw him disappear into a great cave the mouth of which was overgrown with brushwood. Vaali bade Sugreeva—exacting an oath from him — to wait at the entrance for him and plunged into the darkness of the cave after the foe. Sugreeva waited long, but no Vaali came and as he stood racked with doubt, indistinct shouts and groans, which seemed to his horror-struck ears his brother's, issued from the cave and presently there gushed out of it foaming blood which made him sure that Vaali had perished in the struggle. To make sure that the victorious *Raakshasa* would not rush out in the elation of triumph and destroy Kishkindha, Sugreeva blocked the entrance of the cave with a huge rock and retuned to Kishkindha with his tale of Vaali's death. As a rulerless state invites disaster, he was persuaded by the ministers and elders to occupy the vacant throne. While he was enjoying the sweets of power, like a bolt from the blue, Vaali burst on them, haggard with wrath and wounds, and accusing him of treason and unnatural conduct towards one who was at once his brother and his king, drove him out with scorn and contumely as a wretch too vile to live, but whom he forebore to slay only because he was unfortunately also his brother. So by a cruel fate he had been deprived of his home, throne, and all, including even his wife, and had to seek asylum in the forest with a few faithful friends. Here at least he was safe, for Vaali had been forbidden by a *rishi* from entering the precincts on pain of instant death.

This incident between Vaali and Sugreeva is a good example of the moral teaching conveyed in the *Puraanas*. There was nothing terribly wrong in the conduct either of Vaali or of Sugreeva. Anger confuses the mind. One who yields to anger loses the capacity to see the truth. That way lies destruction. Vaali's anger led to his end. Sugreeva humbly confessed the truth, but Vaali would not listen. He was beside himself with rage. Sugreeva, too was guilty of imprudent haste. He concluded too quickly that his brother had died. He was afraid that the *Asura* who was victorious would come out and kill him also; so he closed the entrance of the cave and returned home. At first he was not keen on becoming king and yet he allowed himself to be persuaded by the people. He yielded to a sub-conscious desire without sufficient thought. So difficulties came upon him. Thoughtless action leads to unhappiness. This is what we learn from the story of Sugreeva.

One should not desire what belongs to another. One has to exercise great care, and control one's desires. In contrast to Sugreeva, when the ministers and subjects in Ayodhya pressed Bharata to accept the crown, he was firm in his refusal. Bharata's strength of character was great. But Sugreeva was different. He was weak, and suffered in consequence. Bharata had the courage to refuse and his name lives for ever.

In every episode of the *Raamaayana* some lesson which we should learn for our daily life is taught. The meaning is in some places plain; in others it may lie hidden. If we read with reverence and think deeply, we can always see the moral.

Sugreeva concluded his story with a piteous appeal to Raama. "For fear of Vaali I am a wanderer in the forest. I live concealing myself here. Could you, will you, kill Vaali and restore to me my kingdom and my wife?"

Raama answered: "Certainly I will. Vaali cannot escape this bow. Be assured."

As Sugreeva and Raama were talking thus, in the Asoka grove far away, the left eyelids of Seeta throbbed, which is a good omen for women. At the same time, the left eyelids of the *Raakshasa* king also throbbed as an evil sign.

CHAPTER XLI

HE SEES HER JEWELS

THEN Sugreeva heard the story of the calamity that had befallen the Raghu princes at Panchavati and how Raama's heart was breaking with the ache of separation from Seeta and anxiety as to her fate. Deeply touched, Sugreeva tried to console Raama. "I have heard everything from Lakshmana," he said. "Lay aside all doubts and fears. We shall surely discover Seeta, wherever she may be concealed, and that, soon.

"My companions and myself noticed a *Raakshasa* carrying a weeping lady and speeding fast across the sky. She was crying 'O Raama! O Lakshmana!'

"She too noticed us and, removing her sash, tied up in it her jewels and threw down the little bundle. We picked up and have kept it. See if the jewels are Seeta's."

On hearing this Raama excitedly shouted, "Fetch the bundle, fetch it."

They brought it from the cave and when Raama saw the sash he was beside himself with grief. The little bundle brought before his eyes the suffering of Seeta at the hands of the *Raakshasa*.

He closed his eyes and told Lakshamana to untie the bundle and examine the jewels since he himself could not bear to look at them.

Lakshmana did so. "Indeed these are Seeta's anklets," Lakshmana said. "There is no doubt they are hers. These I know, for often have I seen them while laying my head on her feet in worship. The others I am not familiar with, never having presumed to look closely at them."

How full of loving reverence is this speech which Vaalmeeki puts in the mouth of Lakshmana and how cruelly must Seeta's unjust words have pierced his heart on the fateful day when she drove him from her!

Raama took all the jewels in his hands and pressed them one by one to his eyes. He said: "They must have fallen on the soft grass and so they are intact."

Then, grief giving place to rage, he said: "Yama's gates are wide open to receive the *Raakshasa.* Soon will he be destroyed with all his people."

Seeing Raama's grief and wrath, Sugreeva became somewhat anxious. Though their mutual friendship and help had been pledged in the presence of the sacred fire, Sugreeva was concerned over the question of priorities.

Sugreeva's heart went to Raama in his suffering — indeed, he himself knew what it was to lose kingdom and wife — but then, first thing must come first. He must approach the subject guardedly and not seem to place his own affairs before Raama's. That might jeopardise their new-born friendship. But it was not purely selfish to say that he, as King of Kishkindha and lord of his tribe, would be a far more serviceable ally than he could be as a fugitive pretender. Besides, if he launched on the enterprise of reclaiming Seeta when Vaali was still king of the *Vaanaras,* one could not guess what Vaali's course may be. Oh no! There could be no doubt that the first move in the enterprise must be to secure the resources of the *Vaanara* kingdom by killing Vaali and placing himself on the throne.

This alone would bring success to Raama as well as himself. But realising Raama's state of mind, he resolved to act with circumspection.

He said: "I do not know the strength or the dwelling place of this wicked *Raakshasa*. We do not know where he has taken Seeta and where he keeps her hidden. Still, I promise you solemnly, wherever Seeta may be, I shall find her and her captor and find ways of destroying him and recovering her. You will kill the wicked *Raakshasa* and win glory. Do not despair or yield to grief that weakens the spirit. Look at me. Like you, I have lost my wife; I have been turned out of my kingdom and disgraced. And yet I control my sorrow and keep my courage up. If I, a *Vaanara*, can do this, it should be for easier for you. If sorrow overwhelms, one becomes helpless and can do nothing. Therefore, friend, I beg of you to control your grief."

These words of Sugreeva made an impression on Raama's heart. He wiped the tears off his eyes and embraced Sugreeva. He got over the weakness that possessed him at the sight of Seeta's jewels and recovered his fortitude and self-control.

"Sugreeva, your friendship is dear to me," he said. "I shall follow your advice. Think out when and how we should begin the search for Seeta. I shall make your cause mine, and place you on the throne of Kishkindha and I, who say this, have never uttered a vain or false word in my life and never will. Tell me frankly how I can bring you relief. I shall do it."

Sugreeva and his ministers were overjoyed to hear Raama's words. They were convinced that soon their troubles would end and Sugreeva would once again become king of the *Vaanaras*.

CHAPTER XLII

SUGREEVA'S DOUBTS CLEARED

SUGREEVA was keen on regaining his kingdom and family, but he could not see how this was to be. Vaali's strength stood as an impossible barrier between him and the fulfilment of his desire.

Hanumaan, his minister, tried to convince him that he would succeed with Raama's help, but Sugreeva's doubts persisted. Could Raama's strength overcome Vaali's? It all looked hopelessly impossible. Vaali's body was like steel. How was Raama going to kill him?

Sugreeva had these doubts about Raama. But he had none else to help him. And he was not prepared to give up his desire. He decided to test Raama's strength.

But how is one to subject a friend to a test without discourteously betraying one's suspicion? Raama had promised to get the thing done. How was an occasion to be created to measure his ability? Sugreeva thought long and formed a plan.

He told Raama softly: "My Lord Raama! Your words have banished sorrow from my heart. I know your valour. An arrow from your bow can destroy the three worlds. How can Vaali's frame stand against it? Still it is my duty to tell you all about Vaali's strength. He can go round to the four oceans to take up in his palm and sip the water with the morning prayers. He can toss and play with a heavy rock as if it were a ball. He can pull out mighty forest trees as if they were blades of grass. Once Dundubhi, an *Asura* in buffalo form possessing the strength of a thousand elephants, challenged Ocean to a fight.

Ocean evaded saying: 'You should fight with an equal. There in the north stands Himavaan. Go and challenge him. Leave poor me alone.' Dundubhi agreed and, speeding northwards, met and challenged Himavaan, going his rocky side with his horns. Himavaan controlled his temper and said: 'Why do you assault me? I am not a fighter. I spend my life in the company of sages who love to stay with me.' Dundubhi answered: 'Very well, then. But tell me of some one I can fight with. I want a worthy foeman today.'

"Himavaan said: 'There is one in the south who is a foe worthy of you. He is Vaali, the *Vaanara* king. His strength is like his father Indra's. If you care, you may go to him and challenge him to fight.'

"Dundubhi went straight to Vaali's place and raised a loud uproar at the entrance of Kishkindha. He tore up trees and pulled down the gate and roared, 'Come out and prove your strength in a fight with me.'

"Vaali was then resting with his queen. On hearing the challenge he came out accompanied by the women of his palace. 'Why O Dundubhi, do you raise this clamour at my city gate?' he asked. 'Are you tired of life?'

'Vaali's scornful address enraged the *Asura* who said: 'Don't boast of your strength in the presence of your admiring women. I have come here for a fight with you. If you have any manliness in you, come out and show it. You will say you are too drunk now to fight; but I am willing to wait till you become sober. If you like you may spend the night in your pleasures and bid a tearful leave of all your dear ones and come to me in the morning to be slain by me.'

"Vaali laughed at Dundubhi's words and said: 'My dear women, go inside. O *Asura*, I am not the worse for drink and if you want a fight, there is no time like the present. Have at you!' So saying and with a laugh he took hold of the *Asura* by his tail and whirled him round and flung him. Dundubhi spat blood and fell on the ground.

"After a while the *Asura* rose again and a great battle followed. Vaali, son of Indra, pounded the *Asura* to death. And he flung the dead buffalo so that it fell on the ground at the distance of a *yojana*.

"Drops of blood from the *Asura's* body were carried by the wind and fell on the *aashrama* of Matanga. The sage was wroth and soon found out who was responsible for this contamination. He saw at once that Vaali in his pride had flung a bleeding carcass and desecrated the holy spot. The sage pronounced a curse, 'If this Vaali enters the precincts of this *aashrama,* he will lose his life.' That is why, O Raama, with my friends I am living here in safety. Vaali dare not approach this place for fear of the curse. Look at these *sal* trees. He can pluck one of them and just shake all the leaves off as one dusts a jacket. Such is his strength. How could I, having incurred this terrible brother's enmity, feel secure?"

Lakshmana understood that Sugreeva needed a demonstration of Raama's prowess to give him confidence and he said: "How would you like Raama to show you his confidence to conquer Vaali?"

Sugreeva answered: "Indeed, I have no doubts. I know Raama's prowess though now it is hidden as embers in ashes. I have sought refuge under him. And yet, when I recall Vaali's mighty deeds, I tremble. That is all."

Seeing Sugreeva's faith in him and his great
fear of Vaali, Raama resolved to put an end to his
doubts. By a playful flip of his toe he sent the
enormous skeleton of Dundubhi which was lying
there, flying in the air to a distance of ten *yojanas*.
But Sugreeva though impressed was not convinced.
"When my brother sent Dundubhi's carcass hurling
in the sky, it was full of flesh and blood and far
heavier than this weather-beaten skeleton," he said.

Then Raama bent his bow and, pulling the
string to his ear, sent forth an arrow. It pierced the
sal tree pointed out by Sugreeva and six other trees
standing behind it. Piercing the seven trees the
beautiful arrow touched the earth and returned to
Raama's quiver.

Sugreeva, seeing this, was beside himself with
joy. He was now certain that Raama's arrow could
pierce the adamant frame of Vaali. He fell prostrate
before Raama and said: "With my own eyes I have
now seen your prowess. Even if all the gods with
Indra at their head should come and oppose you,
your victory is certain. Why then talk of Vaali? I
have gained your friendship and I have no more use
for fear or grief. Slay Vaali and save me. Let us go to
Kishkindha today."

Both Raama and Lakshmana agreed. They
talked how to set about and it was finally agreed that
Sugreeva should appear in Kishkindha and
challenge Vaali to single combat. Vaali was sure to
come out, and as the brothers were fighting, Raama
would kill Vaali with an arrow. They proceeded to
Kishkindha. Sugreeva went ahead. Raama followed
him and stood away behind a tree in the dense forest.

Sugreeva shouted. Vaali heard the shout and in great rage emerged from the fortress, radiant like the morning sun.

The two brothers fought each other fiercely.

But Raama, who was standing bow in hand behind a tree was bewildered. As they wrestled together the brothers were so similar in form and feature, in equipment and method of fighting, that Raama could not distinguish Vaali from Sugreeva and was afraid to shoot lest he kill the wrong combatant.

Meantime Sugreeva, having the worst of the fight, broke from his brother's grip with a desperate effort and, wounded and weary, disappointed and despondent, fled for life and reached Rishyamooka forest.

Even this he was able to do because Vaali did not wish to slay him and was not unwilling to give his brother another lease of life.

Raama and Lakshmana rejoined the woebegone Sugreeva. He looked down at the ground without lifting his eyes. He was angry that Raama had broken his word and failed to help him.

"If you did not like to kill Vaali,"said Sugreeva, "you could have told me so earlier. In that case, I, who know Vaali's might, would never have challenged him to fight. On the contrary, you made me believe you, and I have had such a drubbing that it is a wonder I am alive."

"Do not be angry, Sugreeva, but listen," said Raama. "There was a good reason why I could not send forth my deadly arrow. You and Vaali were alike in height and girth, in gait and shouts, in dress and ornaments. Once the fight began, I could not distinguish you from Vaali. And I stood bewildered and helpless. It would have been terrible if I kill you instead of Vaali. Do not be angry. Challenge Vaali once again. This time I shall surely slay him. Here, Lakshmana, fetch that flowering creeper. Tie it round Sugreeva's neck as a garland. I shall then know who is our friend and who is Vaali as they fight. Now, Sugreeva, you shall see Vaali rolling on the ground.

Sugreeva was satisfied. His spirits recovered. Lakshmana tied the creeper round his neck. Once again, and handsomer than ever, Sugreeva proceeded to Kishkindha. And Raama and Lakshmana followed him as before.

CHAPTER XLIII

THE SLAYING OF VAALI

EVENING was approaching. Once more Sugreeva roared at the gate of Kishkindha and challenged Vaali to fight.

Vaali who was then resting happily was startled and for a moment paled with puzzled concern, but was presently overwhelmed with rage and sprung stamping the earth as though he would split it.

Taara, his queen, her heart full of loving fear, held him in arms in a close embrace and tried to restrain his impetuosity with affectionate counsel. "Put away this wrath, my dear lord, as one puts away a used garland, for you have had enough fighting today. Tomorrow would do as well for another battle, for you lack neither enemies nor valour. I pray you not to rush out on the instant. It seems to me you should think calmly before going out now to meet your brother. I am afraid there is a deep game. Your brother was defeated and disgraced and ran for dear life and concealed himself for safety. Now he has returned and raises this noise. Your brother is not such a fool as to challenge you again so soon after the punishment you inflicted on him unless he was assured of help and protection from an invincible ally of tried prowess. Did you not observe that his very roar of challenge had a new note of confidence in it? I shall tell you what I heard from Angada who had it from our scouts who range the forests. Two princes of unrivalled valour, Raama and Lakshmana, have come from Ayodhya and Sugreeva has secured the promise of their assistance. After all,

my lord, your brother is virtuous and brave. Why
should you hate him? Who in the world is closer to us
than he? He will be your devoted servant and strong
ally. It is best to forget the past and make it up with
Sugreeva. My dear Lord, listen to my words!"

Vaali disliked this advice. Anger clouded his
intellect. Caught and dragged by the noose of death,
he could not see reason and only became more fixed
in his resolve.

Taara, bright and beautiful as became her
name *taara* meaning star, spoke in vain.

"What are you saying?" he said. "Am I to hear in
silence the ringing challenge of this enemy-brother?
When a foe calls to battle is a warrior to hang back?
Death would be better than such cowardice. Don't
you worry about Raama. He knows *dharma*; he is
one brought up in the fear of sin. Oh, let me alone,
will you? I may tell you I shall not kill Sugreeva —
only I will teach the presumptuous fellow a lesson he
won't forget and let him go. Let me go, I tell you. You
have spoken out of the fullness of your love for me. I
shall humble Sugreeva and send him back and
return soon with victory. Have no fear for me."

Thus Vaalmeeki pictures Vaali—his chivalry,
his dauntless and impatient valour, his tenderness.
It is true Vaalmeeki's hero has to kill the *Vaanara*
king — the epic requires it — but the slain warrior
was a noble knight, worthy of the reader's
admiration and tears.

Taara, with tears in her eyes, circumambulated
him and praying for his success, returned to her
apartment full of grave apprehension. Leaving
Taara and her companions behind, Vaali issued from

the fort hissing like an angry cobra and went to meet
Sugreeva.

As he saw him standing there, radiant and
courageous, he girt his loins and sprang on him. And
Sugreeva too ran forward to meet Vaali.

"If you love your life," warned Vaali, "run away.
Do not fall a victim to this fist of mine!"

Sugreeva retorted angrily and the battle began.
Fierce with remembered wrongs and keyed up above
himself by the certainty of Raama's help, Sugreeva
maintained for long an equal combat, but presently
Vaali's greater might began to prevail and Sugreeva
was in such obvious distress that Raama who was
watching with ready bow knew he could not hold out
much longer. It was now or never and placing a
deadly arrow on the string and pulling it to his ear,
Raama sped it at Vaali's mighty chest. Pierced by
that irresistible shaft Vaali crashed down as falls a
great forest tree cut asunder by the woodman's axe
and lay stretched on the ground empurpled with
blood as lies the festival flag-staff pulled down when
the festival is ended.

Even so, he was radiantly handsome, his noble
figure shining like a cloud lit up by the setting sun.
The divine necklace given to him by Indra shone on
his breast, which guarded his life and fortune. This,
jewel, Raama's dart, the bleeding wound, all added
lustre to his mighty body.

Vaalmeeki describes beautifully the majestic
appearance of the fallen hero. A true warrior is never
so beautiful as when he lies dying on the field of
battle.

Astounded at being hit and laid low, when he
least expected it from an unknown quarter, Vaali

looked round in perplexed surprise, and saw Raama and Lakshmana approaching him bow in hand. With tears of indignant wrath, and in a voice faint with approaching dissolution, he accused them of ignoble perfidy in dealing causeless death to a person engaged in combat with another.

"Raama," he said, "you are the son of Emperor Dasaratha. Born of noble race and famous by your own exploits, how did you bring yourself to do this deed? The world is full of praises for your valour and virtue. And yet, while I was absorbed in a battle with another, you came unseen and, from behind, shot a fatal arrow at me. How false and undeserved is your reputation for manly virtue, for truth and forbearance! What will the world think of you now? What harm have I ever done to you? Did I come out to fight with you? You have killed me like an assassin concealing yourself behind the trees. For a royal prince to kill an innocent person in this way is grievous sin. You are unworthy for kingship. The goddess Earth will never consent to take you for a bridegroom. My greatest sorrow is that I am killed by a base and sinful wretch. If it was battle with me you wanted, I would have given it to you, and slain by me in fair combat you might have been lying in the dust as I do now.

"Or if it was help to recover your Seeta I would have won her back for you in a day. I would have killed Raavana and dragged his body with a rope round the neck and placed it at your feet. No matter where he has hidden Seeta, I would have discovered her and restored her to you.

"All who are born must die. This is the law. I do not therefore grieve for my death. Still, your sin is great in killing me in this treacherous way."

Thus Vaali, son of Indra, reproached Raama with his dying breath. And all this is fully set out by Vaalmeeki, the divine poet, as well as by Kamban. Against this accusation what defence could Raama offer? Vaalmeeki has it that Raama gave some explanation with which Vaali was satisfied. But I am omitting all this as pointless and pray that the learned may forgive me. What I think is that an *avataar* is an *avataar* and that among the sorrows that the Lord and His consort had to endure in their earthly incarnation, this liability to have their actions weighed on the earthly scales is a part.

Vaali, bruised and bleeding from the many wounds of his fight with Sugreeva, lay in the throes of death. He lived just long enough to see his queen and his beloved son Angada — poor bewildered lad who at his mother's bidding 'to fall at the feet of his father who was going on a long long journey' prostrated himself in silence, too stunned to realise the extent of his loss. This will be narrated later. Vaali's words were addressed to Raama.

"All is over, I shall blame you no more. My dear, dear son Angada is orphaned. You and Sugreeva should look after him. I entrust him to you. Look after him. It is your duty to see that he does not pine away like a withering lotus-plant in a dried-up tank. Tell Sugreeva that he should not imagine that it was Taara who set me up against him. Ask him to treat Angada as he should treat a prince, with honour and affection. Do this for me. I want no more. The warrior's Heaven is calling me!"

So ended Vaali's life.

Owing to the protective virtue of Indra's necklace, Raama could not have met Vaali face to face and vanquished him, just as Raavana could not be conquered by the gods. Raama could kill Vaali only when himself unseen. And still the question stands, why should Vaali have been killed at all?

Perhaps the answer is to be found in what Kabandha said to Raama in gratitude for being released from his curse. 'Through Sugreeva's friendship you will recover Seeta" — Sugreeva's help, not Vaali's. And so Raama went in search of Sugreeva, found him and pledged his friendship and consecrated it by fire. Sugreeva had committed no unforgivable offence against Vaali; yet Vaali, with his supernatural strength, persecuted his brother. Hearing the latter's complaint, Raama had pledged his word to kill Vaali and restore to Sugreeva his wife and make him king as his part of the contract of alliance. Thereafter, Raama had no alternative. To kill Vaali from cover became an inevitable necessity.

Raama erred in running after the magic deer to please his wife. Consequent on this, difficulties and sorrows and conflicts of duty pursued him. If we keep in mind that when God takes a lower and limited form by His own ordinance, limitations follow and we should not be confused thereby. This is my humble view as against other explanations propounded by the pious.

CHAPTER XLIV

TAARA'S GRIEF

THERE was panic in Kishkindha when the news came that Vaali had been slain by an archer, and the *Vaanaras* fled hither and thither in hopeless confusion. Taara, seeing this, laid aside her own grief and like a queen put courage in her husband's subjects saying: "Till this day you walked before the King to battle! Why then do you flee in fear now? There is no danger for you. Raama killed Vaali only to make Sugreeva king. Your lives are in no danger; you will only have a different ruler; that is all. You need not fly or fear."

When she tried to go to the spot where her husband lay dead, the *Vaanaras* stopped her saying: "We shall crown Angada king and we shall make safe the fortress. We shall defend the town against Sugreeva and his allies."

But she said: "Now my noble lord is dead, nothing matters." And boldly she went straight to where Raama and Lakshmana were standing.

When she saw her husband lying wounded to death she could not control her sorrow; she sobbed and cried.

"Ah my hero!" she wept embracing the wounded Vaali. "How many heroes have you laid low and now you lie low yourself! And you have left me here!"

Soon Vaali's son Angada reached the spot. And Sugreeva, witnessing this scene, was filled with remorse at the thought that it was all for him that this calamity had happened. The remorse was no doubt genuine, for invariably revenge — especially revenge wreaked on those who have been friends in other days — brings nothing but bitterness and grief, and the momentary feeling of triumph is all ashes to the taste. How few of us realise this in the confusion created by desires and anger!

Taara rolled on the ground and lamented: "Leaving dear Angada an orphan and myself a helpless destitute you have gone on the journey from which there is no return. My lord! My hero!"

Hanumaan tried to console her: "The dead reach their places in heaven. Why lament for Vaali? Angada will be crowned in due course and we shall then rejoice. It is our duty to look after Angada. Let us now think of performing Vaali's obsequies."

"I care for nothing," answered Taara. "It is for Sugreeva to perform the obsequies and to look after Angada. What is there for me to do? Can a thousand Angadas equal in my eyes my husband? With him I shall enter the house of Yama. That alone will please me."

Vaali, unconscious till now, opened his eyes for the last time and addressing Sugreeva said: "Brother, we two could have been friends and reigned happily over the kingdom; but it was not given to us to be so wise and happy. I am more to blame than you, but why talk about that now? Hereafter you shall rule the kingdom. I have entrusted to you Angada, my son, dearer than life itself to Taara and me. He is a warrior equal to you in prowess. Be a father to him and look after him with kindness. This is my only request to you. And be kind to Taara who was not only a blameless and affectionate wife, but also a very wise and far-sighted counsellor. Whatever she foretells is bound to happen. Do not disregard her advice on any matter. Here, take the necklace that Indra gave me and take with it its secret power. My life is over and so is my resentment. May you be happy!" Thus the generous Vaali blessed his brother Sugreeva.

He gave good advice to Angada: "Sugreeva is now your king. Be loyal to him and give him patient, affectionate service."

Like a flowering creeper embracing a forest tree felled down by an axe, Taara lay on the ground clinging to Vaali.

Neela, as gently as he could, drew out the dart from Vaali's chest.

Blood gushed out of the wound and spread into a pool. Vaali's life left his body. Taara lamented loudly. "For the last time salute your father," she bade Angada in heart-broken accents. "O my husband! your dear son is bowing before you. Will you not say a word to him? Alas! I am a widow and he is an orphan."

The sight of all this struck Sugreeva to the heart. He said to himself: "Moved by desire I closed the entrance of the cave and leaving Vaali there, I seized and enjoyed his wealth. What a sinner have I been!"

It may be that in his penitent mood Sugreeva accused himself wrongly, but it is also true that, without our knowledge, desire corrupts our mind and leads us to wrong actions and entangles us in sin. Sugreeva felt that desire had unknowingly blinded and betrayed him.

Kaama in Sanskrit stands for lust and greed and every kind of desire. *Kaama* is man's internal foe which he has to vanquish. This is the lesson taught in the last seven *slokas* of third chapter of the *Gita*. Sri Krishna concludes his exhortation with these words: *Jahi Satrum Kaamaroopam Duraasa-dam.*

If desire corrupted Sugreeva's mind, anger corrupted Vaali's. When Vaali saw that Sugreeva had barred the entrance and left him shut up in the cave he felt convinced that Sugreeva had accompanied him in his pursuit of the *Raakshasa* not as a brother but with a treacherous motive. He concluded that Sugreeva had planned to sacrifice him to the *Asura* and usurp his place.

He became a prey to his own fury. He disgraced and drove out his blood-brother and nursed his anger. Anger (*krodha,* as it is called in Sanskrit) betrayed Vaali into sin.

Indeed *kaama* and *krodha* are the ultimate causes of all sin. Unless we defend our heart against these foes and keep them out, we cannot escape sin.

Sugreeva lamented: "Though my sin was great, he would not kill me. He drove me out and allowed me to escape with life. That was all. But I conspired to slay him and succeeded. There is no sinner like me in the world and yet with his last breath he gave me the kingdom to rule and gave, too, the gift of Indra, the necklace of power. Indeed he was noble. Why should I still cling to this base life, I, who brought about the death of my heroic brother?"

At least once a year, men that follow ancient custom utter the prayer *Kaamokaarsheet manyura-kaarsheet.* That is, "Desire lured me into sin, anger lured me into sin.' So saying many times with humble penitence, they seek to cleanse their hearts. This is a practice that all should follow, to repent and purify the heart and surrender it to the Lord,

Kaamokaarsheet   manyurakaarsheet,
Naaraayanaaya namah.

With fear and hesitation, Raama gently
approached the weeping Taara. But there was no
sign of anger on her face. The words she addressed to
the slayer of her husband were worthy of a hero's
queen. "With the weapon with which, O Warrior, you
killed my husband, kill me too and enable me to join
him. Even in heaven, he will not be happy without
me. Do not fear it would be a sin. It will be a
meritorious act to unite husband and wife. This will
cleanse your sin, your treacherous slaying of my
husband."

Vaalmeeki says at this stage that Taara knew
the truth of Raama's incarnation and saw Vishnu in
him. The traditional belief is that, like Sumitra, the
mother of Lakshmana, Taara, the wife of Vaali, was
a *jnaani*, a knower of Reality. Though at first she
hated Raama for his treachery, yet when she saw
him face to face she saw his divinity, so it is said.

Those who read the *Raamaayana* as a mere tale
would find all this pointless. But to the followers of
bhakti maarga, this will not sound improbable.
Tulasidaas sings at this point that Siva explains to
Paarvati: "Look, Uma, how Raama — the Supreme
Being — moves all creatures like puppets tied to
strings!" *Bhakti* is needed to realise the full meaning
of ancient mythology.

Even on a rational basis, Taara comes out as a
diplomat, an expert in statesmanship. She had the
intelligence to anticipate coming events. What had
happened had happened. By his address and good
fortune, Sugreeva had secured the alliance of
Raama; Vaali was no more; Angada's welfare was all
that she should care for hereafter. Could Angada

afford to antagonise Sugreeva with Raama and
Lakshmana ready to support him bow in hand?
Peace, not war, was indicated.

Hence, when she concealed her anger from
Raama and put on an appearance of patient
submission to events, she was really securing the
best interests of Angada and winning for him the
compassion and sympathy of all.

Vaali's obsequies were performed with due form
and ceremony. After the auspicious bath, Sugreeva
was crowned king and Angada was made *Yuvaraaja*.

CHAPTER XLV

ANGER AND RECONCILIATION

THE rainy season began. Sugreeva and his companions spent the time in Kishkindha in enjoyment but Raama and Lakshmana spent the weary days waiting in a cave nearby. The forest paths were flooded and became rushing torrents, impossible to traverse. The search for Seeta, therefore, had to be suspended. Raama brooded over Seeta's predicament and was plunged in sorrow. Lakshmana counselled him to bear with the delay till the rainy season ended. And Raama held his soul in patience.

The edge of the keenest sorrow wears with time and perhaps Heaven's kindest gifts to men are sleep for the fleeting cares of the day and forgetfulness for the deep-seated injuries of the heart. Kishkindha mourned her Vaali for a time, and then rejoiced in Sugreeva and the survivors; Sugreeva forgot the privations of his exile and the remorse for his brother's death, and enjoyed to the full of his present prosperity and even Taara reconciled and adapted herself to altered circumstances in the interests of her son. The royal palace of Kishkindha was full of joy and wassail, and the gloomy months of rain, which the Raghu brothers spent in leaden-footed repining, sped with golden-winged enjoyment for Sugreeva and his household. Only Hanumaan felt anxious. He could not forget Raama's business. He was looking out for an opportunity to remind the king of his pledge to Raama.

At last, the rains ceased and the sky was cleared of cloud and lightning. The air was sweet with the perfumes of flowers and the songs of birds and joy came to life in the forest again. The intelligent and highly virtuous Hanumaan now approached his king. Sugreeva had entrusted all official duties to the ministers and was absorbed in pleasure. Hanumaan knew that the wisest and best of men neglect their promises in such circumstances and addressed the king with great politeness:

"You have regained the kingdom of your ancestors and are in secure possession and enjoyment of it. But something yet remains to be done. You must fulfil your promise to your allies and so increase your fame and strengthen your power. Even at the sacrifice of one's own interests and pleasure, one should carry out the business of one's friends according to one's promise. Only so can a king's authority and reputation grow.

"It will be best to fulfil one's promise before the due date; in any case delay should be avoided. Fulfilment after the promised date is worse than useless. One should not wait to be reminded by one's friends of what had been promised to them. All this you know without my telling you. Remembering what Raama had done for us, we must take steps to fulfil our promise without waiting to be reminded by him. The rainy season is over. There is no ground for further delay. We can no longer postpone the task of searching for Seeta. Raama may be very patient, but that does not justify any further delay on our part. Did not Raama kill your foe promptly, not minding the danger or the blame involved? We should fulfil our promise with equal promptness."

Thus politely did Maaruti convey his advice to Sugreeva. The latter accepted it and, thanking Hanumaan, ordered Neela to mobilise the *Vaanara* army. "All the world must be searched and Seeta found," he said. "Order therefore the most powerful *Vaanaras* to come and join up at once. Those who fail will be summarily punished." Having said this, Sugreeva went back into private apartments.

Raama and Lakshmana spent the time in their cave waiting for the end of the rainy season and the fulfilment by Sugreeva of his promise. But when the rains were over and the forest and its creatures shone with renewed beauty, Raama grieved intensely at the thought of Seeta suffering at the hands of the *Raakshasas*.

"The world is full of life and joy," said Raama. "But Seeta is in agony somewhere. And I sit still here, awaiting the favour of this ungrateful *Vaanara* king. Alas, she walked cheerfully through the Dandaka forest, as if it were a palace-park; she did not mind the stony ground and the thorns in the path. What must be her suffering now? But this king, drowned in his cups and revelling in the company of his women, has forgotten his promise to me.

"Lakshmana! Go at once to Kishkindha and tell this base king: 'Remember! Know that the path still yawns open whereby the slaughtered Vaali went to his doom. Do not follow him, but fulfil your promise to me. Ruin awaits him who forgets kindness and neglects friends. Beware of Raama's arrows. The four months of the rainy season are over. These four months were like four ages to Raama, but to you, steeped in pleasures, they have perhaps sped like minutes! By delay you incur Raama's wrath and seek your destruction.' Go, Lakshmana, and tell him this."

ANGER AND RECONCILIATION 291

This was the angry and impatient message Raama wanted Lakshmana to take to Sugreeva.

Carrying this freight of his brother's grief and anger, Lakshmana was about to leave. Then Raama thought again. He knew Lakshmana's nature and feared danger from his rashness. So he called him back and said to him: "In conveying my complaint to Sugreeva, do not be harsh. Whatever his faults, he is our friend. Point out his faults to him, but say nothing harsh."

Lakshmana agreed, but he found it hard to control his own anger as he approached the gates of Kishkindha.

Noting the severe face of Lakshmana who was fully armed, the *Vaanara* sentry became alert and made ready to guard the fortress. This enraged Lakshmana still further.

Some *Vaanaras* ran to the inner apartments and reported to Sugreeva: "Lakshmana, furious with anger, is coming here bow in hand. We could not stop him.

But the *Vaanara* king was tipsy and surrounded by women and he took no notice. The king's servants ordered the sentry at the gates to stand firm and prevent the entry of any one. Lakshmana's anger became quite uncontrollable. Lakshmana forced his way in. There he met young Angada, the thought of whose youth and misfortunes took away something of the edge of his wrath. "My child, go and tell the *Vaanara* king," he said, "that Lakshmana is waiting at the palace gate to have audience of him on behalf of his grief-stricken brother."

Angada went accordingly to the king's apartment and informed him of Lakshmana's visit. But

Sugreeva was in no condition to understand. Angada saw this and took counsel with the ministers as to what should be done. Hanumaan and some of the fellow ministers gently explained what was happening and Sugreeva was at last roused from his tipsy condition.

Sugreeva said: "I am not at fault, am I? Why should my friends Raama and Lakshmana be angry with me? Some enemy must have carried tales and set them up against me."

Hanumaan answered: "It is my duty, O king, to say these things and I say them. Do not be angry with me. We have delayed in carrying out our promise to Raama. We have forgotten Raama's grief. It is late, but not too late. Hence let us do quickly what we should. Let us seek forgiveness from Lakshmana. Let us, without further delay, take steps to fulfil our promise to Raama."

Then Sugreeva agreed to receive Lakshmana.

As Lakshmana went into the *Vaanara* town, he marvelled at its beauty and the culture of Kishkindha. Passing through beautiful streets, he stood outside the king's palace. Hearing the sounds of revelry, of dance and song, proceeding from within, he saw that the *Vaanaras* had forgotten their promise and were lost in enjoyment. He could hardly control his anger. Still he held back from entering the women's chamber and, standing in a corner, outside, he twanged his bow-string. The sound filled all Kishkindha with fear and trembling. Sugreeva, hearing it, realised that the prince was, indeed, angry. He saw the danger and asked Taara to go and pacify the prince. "A chivalrous man like Lakshmana will find his anger slip from him when he speaks to a lady and it will be impossible for him to continue wrathful," said the king, shrewd even in his tipsy condition.

Taara advanced towards Lakshmana. In looks, in knowledge of the world and skill in speech, Taara was unrivalled. She said to Lakshmana: "After enduring for a long time poverty and persecution, Sugreeva is enjoying the pleasures and the prosperity you have secured for him. This enjoyment has gone to his head and he has lost his senses. I know his fault, but you should forgive him. The highsouled who know the foibles and imperfections of our common nature should temper their censure with compassion. So be not too harsh in judging of King Sugreeva's surrender to temptations of the flesh—especially after his long trials and privations. But I can assure you, he has never lost sight of his debt or his duty to you. He has already issued orders for mobilising the *Vaanara* warriors from all quarters. Today or tomorrow they will all be here. Then the search for Seeta and the war against Raavana will begin. Have no doubts. And now, pray come in and see the King."

Lakshmana, now no longer angry, entered the apartment. Sugreeva, descending from his seat, welcomed Lakshmana.

"Forgive my faults," he said. "With Raama's friendship and help I am King today. How can I ever forget what I owe to the valorous and good Raama? He can destroy his foes without any help from me. I, with my armies, can only follow him; that is all. Surely Raavana will perish. The search for Seeta will soon begin. Do forgive the delay of which I am guilty."

Lakshmana was pleased. "Raama is your equal in honour and prowess, none else," he said. "Come with me to Rishyamooka and give him words of comfort in his grief."

Sugreeva and Lakshmana went in a litter to Raama and, explaining the arrangements already made, satisfied him.

Raama was pleased. He said: "You indeed are a real friend. Like the clouds yielding rain, the sun destroying darkness and the moon pleasing human hearts, a good friend comes to one's help spontaneously. I am happy in your friendship. Now the end of Raavana and his race is certain."

Even as Raama was expressing his gratitude and joy, great multitudes of *Vaanaras* under their respective leaders arrived and assembled. They came from distant forests, mountains and coasts. The dust they raised darkened the sky. Millions of monkeys and bears in a variety of shapes and colours were there.

Sugreeva addressed this enormous army and showed them their appointed camping places. Later, he divided the host into eight divisions and sent each under its commander, thoroughly to search in the eight directions for Seeta.

One point is worth noting here. The Tamil poet Kamban describes Taara as a chaste widow living a life of discipline and privations. It is different in Vaalmeeki, who includes Taara and the other women as part of the inheritance Sugreeva won from Vaali—in fact, as an appurtenance of the throne. When Sugreeva lost himself in bodily pleasures and forgot his duty to Raama, Taara shared his revels and is described as being flushed and unsteady with wine when she went out at her lord's command to allay Lakshmana's resentment.

In ancient times, when as elder brother died leaving a wife, there was a custom in royal and other noble families for the younger brother to take the widow as wife and protect her. It is difficult for people of one age to judge the customs of another age. Imagination and great flexibility of mind are needed to assess the merits and defects of usages with which we are not familiar.

CHAPTER XLVI

THE SEARCH BEGINS

"LOOK, Raama, at this *Vaanara* army," said Sugreeva. "All these myriads, of wondrous strength, are yours to command. They are willing and able to do you all the service you demand. Consider this huge army as your own and bid them to do whatever you wish."

Raama, beside himself with joy, embraced Sugreeva. He said: "First we should find out whether Seeta is alive, and if so where she is. Next we should know Raavana's whereabouts. Then we shall do what needs to be done. But it is for you, not for me or Lakshmana, to command this army. You are their King. Besides, you know best what needs to be done and how to do it. Blessed am I to have a friend like you and a brother like Lakshmana!"

Then Sugreeva issued stringent orders to his commanders at once to send divisions of the army to the four quarters of the earth to make a thorough search for Seeta.

After sending away the other leaders, Sugreeva took Hanumaan aside and told him: "Son of *Vaayu*, possessing the strength and splendour of your father, you alone can succeed in this task. You have strength, courage and intelligence and on you I rely to take up and discharge this responsibility of discovering Seeta."

Raama too felt that Hanumaan's efforts would be crowned with success. Whatever obstacles turned up, he felt that Hanumaan would find a way of overcoming them. He gave his signet-ring to Hanumaan and said: "Take this ring. I am full of hope that you will dicover Seeta. This ring will tell her that you are my messenger. Dear Hanumaan, may you bring Seeta and me together again!"

Readers should realise the solemnity and pathos of the scene, Raama full of abiding trust in the devoted loyalty and valour of Hanumaan placing the ring as though it was his own hungry heart in his servant's hand and the ideal servant accepting the sacred trust with a deep reverence and an unshakable resolve never to fail his master.

Sugreeva gave orders to his army. "Seeta must anyhow bĕ dicovered. No matter where she is hidden, you can and must find her. Within a month you must return with news of her." And the army swarmed out like ants from an ant-hill and spread in the four directions.

Satabali and his army proceeded northwards. Vinata went east, Sushena westwards, Hanumaan, Angada and General Taara travelled southwards.

All were equally enthusiastic and equally eager to catch and kill Raavana and redeem Seeta. Each group was anxious to be first to return with success. There was tumultuous rivalry.

Raama enquired of Sugreeva: "You describe every quarter and region of the earth like one who has seen the whole world with his own eyes. How and when did you see it all?"

"You will remember, my Lord," said Sugreeva, "how Vaali pursued me in all directions. Wherever I went, he still pursued me. And so I had to wander over the face of the whole world. I thus had occasion to see every part of this planet. Later, I learnt about the spot where *Rishi* Matanga had built his *aashrama*. If Vaali entered that region, his head

would go to shivers by the sage's curse. I knew that
he would not come to that place and could not harm
me even if he came. So there I lay protected."

The hordes that went north, east and west
returned in a month and reported that Seeta was not
to be found anywhere. "Carefully we searched
forests, mountains, rivers and cities, but nowhere
could we find her. Hanumaan, who had gone
southwards, is the lucky one. Did not the *Raakshasa*
carrying Seeta also travel southwards? And
Hanumaan has not yet returned."

Raama, hearing this, was satisfied that the
Vaanaras had done their best.

Hanumaan and Angada entered and searched
the caves and forests of the Vindhyas. Then they
came upon a desert, where a *rishi* was performing
tapas. By his curse it was devoid of trees and plants,
of birds and beasts. Travelling further south, they
saw a big *Asura*. The cruel one, regarding the
Vaanara crowd as a good meal, sprang up to catch
them. They thought at first that this was no other
than Raavana.

Angada rushed towards him and gave him a
mighty blow. Unable to stand it, the *Asura* spat
blood and fell on the earth and lay dead like a great
hill. Rejoicing in the thought that Raavana was
dead, the *Vaanaras* searched the forest for Seeta.
But, there was no sign of her. And so they carried the
search elsewhere.

Often they would weary of their fruitless search
and sit down in blank despair. At such times,
Angada, Gandhamaadana or some other leader
would encourage them and make them resume the
search. Many days were spent in this way. Yet Seeta

was not to be seen and they dreaded Sugreeva's displeasure.

Very far they travelled southwards in their search.

Passing through a desert, fainting with hunger and thirst, they saw a cave from which issued a variety of birds full of the joy of life. The gentle breeze which came out of it covered them with the pollen of lotus flowers and filled them with fragrance. The *Vaanaras* concluded, "undoubtedly there was water where the birds and perfume came from." And the *Vaanaras* forming a chain with linked hands plunged cautiously into the dense darkness of the cave with hearts full of hope, though too parched with thirst even to shout. At long last, all of a sudden, light appeared and they saw a lovely grove with streams of pellucid water and trees bowing under their wealth of fruit. Then they came to a city, with streets paved with jewels set in gold, and great palaces beautiful as a dream. They went along and then they saw an aged *tapasvini* clad in the garments of a recluse and seated on a dark skin. The *Vaanaras* trembled before the divine splendour of her face.

Hanumaan took courage to approach her. Bowing low before her, he said: "Salutations to you, Mother. May we know who you are? Thirsty and tired, we entered the dark cave hoping for some water. And now that we see this unpeopled golden city with trees and tanks, we are afraid, lest this be a vain vision arising from the madness of too great sufferings. Explain all this to us and remove our fears."

She answered: "How did you find your way into this cave? You will have plenty of fruits and drink here. This palace was built by Maya, the architect of the *Daanavas*. He learnt the art from Sukraachaarya.

"Long and happily did Maya live here, till he incurred the enmity of Indra, who slew him. Later Indra gave this golden palace to Hema, my friend. These buildings and parks are hers. At present she has gone to the abode of the gods. But what is your purpose in coming here? Why did you weary yourselves wandering in the forests? First eat, drink and refresh yourselves and then tell me all about yourselves."

They ate and drank and refreshed themselves and were happy. Then Hanumaan explained to the ascetic the purpose of their wandering.

"Raama, son of Emperor Dasaratha, for some reason, left his kingdom and lived in the forest with his brother and wife. Then a *Raakshasa* carried off Seeta, the wife of Raama. The two went out searching for her. They made the acquaintance of Sugreeva, the *Vaanara* King, and became friends with him. He has sent us on this mission to search for Seeta and find her for Raama. Our King fixed a time-limit for us to return with a clue. We lost our way in the darkness of this cave and the period is now over. Now we do not know what to do. Sugreeva is a strict master. For failure to do his bidding within the time set, he is sure to visit us with the penalty of death."

Swayamprabha, that was the name of the ascetic woman, said: "Alas! You cannot by yourselves go out of this cave. No stranger who enters it can go out of it with life. But yours is a great mission and I must, by my *tapasya*, transport you out. Now shut your eyes."

Accordingly they shut their eyes. All at once they found themselves on the sea-shore.

Reaching the sea-shore, they looked round and they were startled to discover that it was the beginning of spring. Angada lamented: "Alas! The time set has been transgressed. If we return to Kishkindha without any clue about Seeta, the King will surely punish us with death. He hates me. It was under pressure from Raama that he agreed to make me *Yuvaraaja*, not because of love for me. Instead of going there and losing our lives, let us fast and seek death here and now." Many of his companions agreed with Angada.

The *Vaanara* General Taara said: "I do not agree. Why should we end our lives? Let us return to the cave of the *tapasvini* Swayamprabha and live there happily. There is everything in plenty there. Neither Sugreeva nor any one else can reach this spot. We shall spend the rest of our lives, free from care."

But Hanumaan said: "What unworthy talk is this! What pleasure is there in eating, drinking and sleeping in the cave, leaving our families in faraway Kishkindha? Sugreeva is a good king, whom we need not fear. And if indeed Sugreeva is angry with us and determined to punish us, how can this cave give us sefety? Can it stand against Lakshmana's rage? Will he not smash it to pieces and kill us? I see no benefit in Taara's counsel. Let us return and tell Sugreeva the whole truth and beg for his forgiveness. This is the only way to safety."

"I do not agree with Hanumaan," said Angada. "Sugreeva has no love or pity for me. He is sure to kill me. He is of a cruel nature. Remember how he killed my father. He does not want me to live. He will find some excuse or other for killing me. He regards me as an obstacle in his way and that of his progeny, who but for me would inherit Kishkindha. To break a promise is nothing to him. Did he not forget his solemn pledge to Raama that he would search for and recover Seeta? Was it not only for fear of Lakshmana and his bow that he sent us on this search? My poor bereaved mother has succumbed to fear and accepted Sugreeva's protection. She clings to life for my sake. Hearing that I am dead, she will end her life. Alas! I am miserable and know not what to do."

"My death is certain", he said again, "if I return to Kishkindha. It is far better to fast to death here."

He spread on the ground the *kusa* grass in the manner prescribed for the vow of death, bowed to the gods and the dead and sat facing east, determined to die.

When Angada the *Yuvaraaja* took this vow and sat in the posture of a fast unto death, the other *Vaanaras* cried in grief and, resolving also to fast with him and die, sat facing east.

From a neighbouring hill, Sampaati, the vulture King, saw this crowd of *Vaanaras*, resigning themselves to fate. Having lost his wings and being unable to move, Sampaati had been famishing for a long time. He now rejoiced, saying to himself, "So many monkeys are going to die here together. I shall have enough food for a long while without effort."

Meanwhile, the *Vaanaras*, expecting death, were recalling the past and talking to one another and loudly lamenting over all that had happened. "Because of Kaikeyi, Dasaratha died," they said: "Because of Dasaratha, Raama had to dwell in the forest. Raavana carried off Seeta. The heroic Jataayu lost his life in the attempt to save Seeta. If the heroic bird had strength enough to continue the struggle a little longer, Raama and Lakshmana would have arrived on the spot and recovered Seeta. By fate did all these things happen and the end of the tale is that we are dying here. In what curious ways does fate work!"

Listening to these lamentations, Sampaati stared at the mention of Jataayu who was his brother. Hearing him spoken of as dead, he naturally wished to hear the whole story.

Sampaati was very old. He and Jataayu were the children of Aruna, the god of Dawn and brother of Garuda, Hari's vehicle. Jataayu and Sampaati in their youth competed with each other as to who could fly higher and rose in the sky. As they approached the sun the heat became intolerable and Jataayu was about to be burnt up. But Sampaati spread his wings and protected his brother from the fury of the sun. Jataayu was saved, but Sampaati's wings were burnt off. Unable to fly, he fell down on a hill. Since then he could not move but stayed in the same place ever hungry for meal and just alive.

"Who brings sad news of my dear brother Jataayu?" he cried in agony. "Oh, *Vaanaras*, is beloved Jataayu dead indeed? Why did Raama, son of King Dasaratha, go to the forest? Why did he lose his wife? Was Jataayu killed by Raavana? Tell me all."

The *Vaanaras* had resolved to end their lives. The wingless, old vulture had desired to make an easy meal of them. But now things turned out otherwise. The *Vaanaras* got up, went to Sampaati and gently led him down from the hill. Then they talked and exchanged information. Sampaati recounted his story. Angada related all that had happened in Kishkindha and asked old Sampaati how Raama could be helped. Sampaati was old and weak, but his eyes had not lost their keenness. He could see things very far off. He could see Seeta captive in Lanka and described in detail the wealth of Raavana's kingdom. He saw and described how Seeta sat surrounded by *raakshasis* in Lanka.

The *Vaanaras* were wild with joy. They jumped about saying, "Now we know all about Seeta. There is no need for us to die. Raama's purpose will be achieved."

Sampaati's troubles were also over. The boon he had received that when he helped Raama he would get back his wings came true and even as they were talking, young feathers began to spring and grow on his sides. Sampaati now shone with fresh beauty and he found satisfaction in performing the funeral obsequies of Jataayu.

CHAPTER XLVII

SON OF VAAYU

FROM Sampaati the *Vaanaras* learnt the place where Seeta was kept a prisoner in the land of the *Raakshasa*, a hundred *yojanas* across the ocean. But of course it would not do to return to Sugreeva at once with this second-hand information. They had outstayed the allotted time and only outstanding success could save them from punishment. They could not stop their search till they saw with their own eyes what Sampaati had described. Only then could they fulfil Raama's purpose.

But then they had to cross the sea.

They went to the edge of the water and discussed matters. "How can we cross the sea, enter Lanka, see Seeta and return?" Anxiety and fear overwhelmed them.

Angada said: "No matter how hard the task, one should never lose courage. Courage is the key to success. To lose heart is to lose everything."

Then he asked each one of his followers to state truly the maximum length that he could jump.

"Oh *Vaanara* warriors!" he said, "much have I heard from Sugreeva of your prowess. Your strength and your enterprise are beyond dispute. We should fulfil this task. We cannot return to Kishkindha without seeing Seeta. That is certain. It is better for us to end our lives here than to be slain in disgrace by the king. Therefore, tell me, one by one, the longest jump you have the strength and courage to attempt."

Gaja said modestly, "I can jump ten *yojanas*."
Gavaaksha said: "I can do twenty." Another *Vaanara*
leader claimed he could do thirty.

And so each improved on the figure of the other.
At last Jaambavaan, the oldest of the warriors,
spoke:

"I am now old and infirm. Yet I would gladly
spend myself to fulfil our king's command. But what
will mere devotion avail if not seconded by strength?
I think I can manage ninety *yojanas*, but this is not
enough to cross the sea and reach Lanka. I can only
regret my lost youth."

The *Yuvaraaja* himself said: "I can do a
hundred yojanas and reach Lanka, I have no doubt.
But I wonder whether I shall have the strength for
another jump of equal length for the return journey."

Jaambavaan answered, "O Prince, you need not
doubt your strength. Your prowess is as great as
Vaali's. Yet it is not proper for the Crown Prince to
undertake this task while there are others to do it
under his orders. It is neither statesmanlike nor safe
for a king to act directly."

Then Jaambavaan cast an appraising and
admiring look at Hanumaan, who had sat apart,
listening to the talk, but saying nothing.

"I feel that the son of Vaayu, sitting there in
silence is the one best fitted by strength and skill to
do this deed," said the old *Vaanara* and walked up to
Hanumaan and brought him to their midst.

Addressing Hanumaan in the hearing of the
myriads of gloomy *Vaanaras*, Jaambavaan said: "O
Warrior, learned in all branches of knowledge, why
are you sitting silent and apart? You are the equal of
King Sugreeva, are you not? In strength and

splendour do you not surpass all the rest of us? Why, are you not the equal of Raama and Lakshmana themselves? I have seen Garuda, the king of birds crossing the sea. The might of your shoulders is not less than that of Garuda's wings. You are not inferior to the son of Vinata in strength or speed, but you are not aware of your own prowess and intelligence. There is no equal to you in the whole world. Anjanaa, your mother, was a maiden among the goddesses above. By the curse of a *rishi* she was born as a *Vaanari*. One day, while she was wandering care-free on a mountain slope, Vaayu saw her beauty and fell in love with her and embraced her. She was wroth. 'Who are you, O wicked one,' she asked, 'who dares insult me?' The Wind-God answered, 'Be not angry, your body is not tainted by my touch and loses not its virgin purity. Not in body but in my heart's desire did I embrace you and out of this ethereal embrace, a child will be born to you, equal to me in strength and vigour. He will be the mightiest and most intelligent amongst the *Vaanaras*.' Thus did the Wind-God pacify Anjanaa.

"When you were a little child, O Hanumaan, you imagined the rising sun to be a fruit and flew towards it in order to pluck it. Seeing your effortless and fearless flight Indra, king of the gods, became concerned for the sun's safety and hurled his thunderbolt at you. Struck down by it, you fell on a mountain and your right jaw was broken. Enraged by this, your father the Wind-God stopped his movements and stood still. All living creatures became breathless and felt strangled in the stillness. The gods begged Vaayu to lay aside his anger and showered blessings on you. Brahma and Indra gave you boons. No weapon can slay you. Death can only come to you at your will and not otherwise. You are immortal. Born of Anjanaa and begotten of the spirit of the Wind-God, you are equal to him in splendour, intelligence and power.

"But, for all your strength, you are virtuous and modest. You alone can help us to fulfil Raama's purpose. Crossing the sea is no hard task to you. This great army of *Vaanaras*, struggling in a sea of distress, you should rescue. You, who can cross the sea, should not leave your power unused.

"Increase your stature. You are the equal of Garuda. Once I too was strong like you and traversed the globe twenty-one times. At the churning of the ocean of milk, I fetched herbs from the four quarters at the bidding of the gods. But now I am old and weak. You are the sole hope of the *Vaanaras*.

"O, Son of Anjanaa, we beg you, noble one! With your heritage of divine strength, delay no further. Realise your true strength and spring forward. Like Trivikrama, you can cross the sea at a single jump. Do it and end our troubles."

The aged Jaambavaan thus praised Hanumaan, reminded him of his strength and roused his dormant courage. At once Hanumaan's form began to swell like the sea in high tide. Even as the *Vaanaras* were watching him, the son of Vaayu grew in size. The radiance of his body filled Angada and his companions with wonder and joy.

From now on, Hanumaan is the hero of the *Raamaayana*. The devotees of Vishnu lovingly call him the 'Junior Servant of Hari.' The Senior Servant is Garuda who is always with Vishnu in personal attendance.

How the Junior Servant of Hari ended the grief of Seeta, destroyed by fire the city of Raavana and returned to the Lord and told him: "Found I have Seeta"—we shall now proceed to relate.

Reminded of his might by Jaambavaan, Hanumaan was now determined to fulfil Raama's purpose. And with fervour he uttered his faith:

"May your words come true. Flying through the sky and alighting in Lanka, I shall see Jaanaki, I have no doubt. I shall return and bring you good news. To take the jump I must press my foot hard against the earth. This hill may stand it," he said and climbed up the Mahendra hill.

There for a while he threw his whole strength into his foot and walked a few steps. The creatures in the hill could not endure it and came out.

Standing on the hill, Hanumaan looked at the sea and directed his *yoga*-concentrated mind towards Lanka. He said to himself: "I shall search and find Seeta. I shall fly in the sky and cross the sea."

With this resolve he offered worship and prayer to Soorya, Indra, Vaayu, Brahma, and all creation. Then facing east, he made obeisance to his father Vaayu and, magnifying his frame still further, turned towards the south.

He pressed the hill with his feet and struck it with his hands. At this impact the flowers fell from the trees and covered the hill. Squeezed irresistibly by the pressure of his feet the hill threw out springs of water, like the rut flowing down the cheeks of the elephant. Many coloured veins of ore burst out of the rock. From the caves the beasts emerged with panic-stricken outcries. Hooded serpents emitting venom bit the rock and sparks flew out.

The hair of Hanumaan's body stood on end and he roared and lashed his tail on the ground. He contracted his hind parts, held his breath, pressed down his feet, folded his ears and stiffened his muscles. Then with a roar of triumph he rose into the sky and like Garuda flew with the speed of Raama's arrow. With the momentum of his speed, many trees were uprooted and followed in his wake. Like friends who speed a parting guest, they accompanied him a little way, showering down their flowers, and dropped. One by one the trees that followed Hanumaan fell into the sea, like the mountains which of old were pursued by Indra and denuded of their wings. Covered with bright-coloured flowers the sea shone like the sky with its stars. Hanumaana's arms with their outspread hands as he flew through the sky appeared like two five-headed cobras. He seemed to swallow the sky as he flew forward. His eyes glistened like mountain forests on fire. His red nose shone like the evening sun. His huge frame spanned the sky like an enormous comet. The air roared as he sped fast. Beneath him his shadow travelled like a ship on the sea. It looked as though a huge mountain with wings was flying in the sky. Hidden at times by clouds and again emerging from them, he shone like the moon sailing across the sky. The *Gandharvas* showered flowers. The *Devarishis* blessed him.

With courage equal to every occasion, with foresight, skill and resolution, Hanumaan met and survived the trials on the way. Shooting up suddenly from the sea, a mighty mountain rose and stood, in his way. Hanumaan struck it with his chest and the

Mynaaka mountain yielded, like a cloud struck by the wind.

The mountain said: "My son, I am mount Mynaaka. The king Ocean bade me help Sri Raama, the descendant of the Sagara race. The Ocean is an old friend of that race. In honour of that ancient association, stay here on me for a while. You will fulfil Ramaa's purpose all the better for this rest. When Indra struck with his thunder all the hills, I fled from his persecution and hid myself in the ocean and survived. The Ocean who gave me shelter now bids me help you. The sons of Sagara dug and deepened the ocean. Did not your father Vaayu help me to escape from Indra's thunder-bolt and find sanctuary in the sea? Both the Ocean and myself will be pleased if you will accept my hospitality and rest here for a while."

But Hanumaan could not yield to Mynaaka's importunity and said politely: "I cannot stop, my friend. I have no time to lose. My vow to fulfil Raama's purpose permits no delay. Your kind words are enough to please me."

He stroked the mountain affectionately with his hand and took its leave.

Later, a huge form stood in his way and said: "Enter my mouth. I have been without food for a long time and am eagerly waiting for you," and the monster opened its mouth wide like a cave.

Hanumaan answered: "I am bent on doing Raama's purpose. Do not stop me."

"Impossible!" said the monster. "You must enter my mouth."

Hanumaan thought quickly and decided what to do. Step by step he made his body grow bigger and bigger. The *Raakshasa* form (which had been assumed by Surasa, the Naaga maiden) opened its mouth correspondingly wider and wider.

When the mouth was thus enormously wide, all of a sudden Hanumaan contracted his body into a speck and, darting through the demon's mouth and body, came out again and resumed his former normal shape.

He then laughed and said: "You have had your wish, mother. I have entered your mouth. What more do you need?"

And the Naaga goddess blessed him saying: "Your effort will be crowned with success. I did this at the bidding of the gods who wanted to test you. Raama's purpose, which you seek to serve, will assuredly triumph."

This was not the last of his trials. As he was flying in the sky, for no reason which he could discover, he found his speed obstructed and he suffered like a ship against a contrary wind. Some mightly force, he felt, was holding him and dragging him down.

He looked up and down and on all four sides. Then he discovered the cause. It was a huge she-demon in the sea holding him by his shadow below, arresting his speed and dragging him down.

The demon, holding him by his shadow, said: "Come, come! Long have I been waiting for you. No longer can I bear my hunger," and she opened her mouth like a cave.

At once Hanumaan entered her mouth and ripped a way out through her entrails and emerged. The demon died and sank down in the water. Like the full moon emerging from an eclipse, Hanumaan shone in the sky and resumed his journey.

Thus surviving many trials with the help of his subtle wit, courage and strength, he flew across the ocean and approached the coast of Lanka covered with plantain and coconut trees.

On the shore of the island he saw groves and mountains and forests and the mouths of rivers.

Hanumaan saw the wealth of Raavana's kingdom and the beauty of the fortified city.

"I have reached the destination," said Hanumaan to himself. "Now without letting the *Raakshasas* know who or what I am, I must search the place and find out where Seeta is kept."

He reduced his huge form to the size of a normal monkey and alighted on a hill-top in Lanka.

CHAPTER XLVIII

THE SEARCH IN LANKA

FULL of hope, Hanumaan alighted and set foot in Lanka. But soon the flush of triumph at the accomplishment of the journey gave place to sober thinking.

"True I have crossed the sea, but that is only the beginning of my mission. There, on mount Trikoota, stands Raavana's magnificent city, as if suspended in the sky. How beautiful, how wealthy, how well secured it is! The city and the fortress are not inferior to Amaraavati or Bhagavati. The lovely groves, the elegant buildings, the engines of defence, deep moats, these fill me with much admiration but also with greater concern.

"Who can attack and vanquish this Raavana? How can an army cross the sea which I have just crossed? Even if it crosses the sea and reaches this shore, how can it attack and bring down this fortress defended by bulwarks manned by well-armed warriors? Neither guile nor force can bring it down.

"But first I must find out whether Seeta is alive or not. Other questions can wait. When and how can I best enter this well-guarded city? I have to search it thoroughly, if I am to discover the place where Seeta is kept. If thoughtlessly I do something wrong now, this error would be irretrievable and a great purpose would fail because of haste or negligence on my part. If I enter the city by day, it will be noticed by the *Raakshasas*. It is best I go in at night. But in what shape shall I go? To ward off suspicion, I must put on a trivial, inconspicuous shape."

Accordingly he shrank to the size of a little monkey, no bigger than a cat. To enter and search the palaces and parks of this vast city, this would be most convenient. His present form was as much smaller than his usual size as the latter was than the mighty proportions he had assumed as he crossed the sea.

By now the sun had set. The little *Vaanara* walked towards the fortress gate. The moon shone brightly. Hanumaan was glad and grateful for this help in his search.

Even on a distant view Hanumaan wondered at the wealth and beauty displayed in Raavana's capital. The streets and mansions were bright with flags and festoons and glittered with gold and precious gems. The breeze blew gently from the sea. Like Indra's Amaraavati and Kubera's Alakaapuri, Raavana's capital had attained the peak of prosperity. The messenger of Raama was filled with wonder and anxiety how to overcome the master of such wealth and military power.

As he was walking along in amazement and anxiety, he was rudely accosted by the terrible-looking Guardian goddess of the city.

"Who are you, little monkey? How did you manage to come here and why are you here at all? Speak the truth."

"Yes, I am indeed a little monkey and I have come here to look at this beautiful city. I shall go back after I have gone round and seen everything and satisfied my curiosity."

The deity struck an angry blow at the monkey.

Hanumaan returned the blow carelessly with his left hand. It doubled her up with agony on the ground.

But soon she got up and remembered the prophecy that, when a monkey should strike and throw her down, the city she guarded would be destroyed.

She said to herself: "Raavana's sins are many and grievous. The end of Lanka is approaching. The word of the gods is about to be fulfilled." And she stood aside. The goddess of Lanka was not a servant of Raavana. She was the spirit of the city.

Hanumaan climbed over the wall and jumped into the city. It was part of the ancient code of warfare that one should not enter the enemy's fortress through the regular gate, but should make his entry in an out-of-the-way manner

Vowing that the *Raakshasas* should be destroyed he entered the fortress of Lanka with his left foot foremost, for that meant defeat for the enemy.

He went along the royal street which was strewn with beautiful flowers. Like lightning shining through the clouds the buildings shone against the sky. Clambering up the mansions and going along on their roofs he admired the beauty of the city. The *Raakshasas'* mansions and streets and their decorations shone with ineffable beauty. The sounds of cultivated and correct music were heard. Lovely women moved about to the accompaniment of tinkling anklets. The city was filled with sounds indicating a full and joyous life.

In some houses *mantras* were being chanted. In some others *Vedic* chants were heard. In others songs celebrating the heroic exploits and glory of Raavana were being sung. Soldiers and scouts were everywhere. In the streets were people dedicated to particular religious practices and vows. There were others cruel in looks and ugly. The guards were armed with bows, swords, cudgels, slings, lances and other weapons. All the warriors were clad in armour. Some were handsome, some ugly, complexions varied from fair through brown to black. Some figures were very tall, others very short. Thus Hanumaan saw that the population had been drawn from a wide area with varying climates and that the army had been recruited from the pick of many nations.

He examined mansion after mansion. He saw women of exquisite beauty, some of them in the company of their husbands and others by themselves. He saw many young damsels, bright and beautiful like images of molten gold. Some were seated on the terraces, others were sleeping in their beds. Some were playing, others singing.

Innumerable beautiful women he saw, but not Seeta pining for Raama. The sight of so much beauty only filled Hanumaan's heart with disappointment and sadness.

He entered and examined the homes of many *Raakshasas*. There were war elephants, pure-bred horses, chariots and armouries. Soldiers stood fully armed.

After passing through many mansions and gardens filled with merriment and music, he came to a great palace rising aloft in a nobility of splendour far transcending all the magnificent buildings around.

Looking at the elephants, horses and foot-soldiers in front, the high walls surrounding it and the beauty of its structure and the richness of its decorations, he concluded that this was Raavana's own palace, the central glory of splendid Lanka. He entered this palace. It was in every way a heaven on earth worthy of Raavana's peerless power and glory. The park, the birds sporting there, the shrines scattered here and there, filled Hanumaan with wonder.

He said to himself: "What wealth, what beauty and what bliss!"

He was for a while lost in amazement. But soon he recollected that he had not yet found Seeta. Admiration gave place to concern over the yet unfulfilled purpose for which he had come.

Passing through many mansions, he entered the innermost private apartment of Raavana and was almost overcome with the luxury and richness of its apartments which made it look a very abode of the gods. Everywhere was gold and silver, ivory and gems and pearls, and beautiful carpets and furniture and in their midst he saw the *Pushpaka Vimaana*.

It was a magic vehicle obtained from Brahma by Kubera. Vanquishing Kubera, Raavana brought it to Lanka as his booty. As from Vasishtha's cow, in the *Pushpaka* car one could get anything one desired.

Raavana's chamber, which Hanumaan now entered, was a very ocean of delight. Countless lovely women lay sleeping in the spacious chamber, some linked arm in arm and all in dishabille and the careless attitudes of sleep, making the place look like a garden of bright, flower-laden creepers.

With his spirit controlled by *dharma,* Hanumaan looked at all these sleeping women, each more beautiful than the other and all filled with joy and love, to see if any of them could be Seeta. Raavana's power to take what shape he would and to please all women was evident from the sight of these lovely women.

Hanumaan pulled himself together reproachfully at his own folly in supposing for a moment that Seeta could be in that sensual paradise of happy damsels. "It is certain that Seeta is not in this crowd. What a fool am I to search for her in this company! This is no place for her."

Then he went elsewhere. In another chamber he saw many beds. He saw one more gorgeous than the rest, covered with gold and diamonds and Raavana stretched on it, like another Mount Meru. His form and majestic splendour made even Hanumaan tremble for a moment.

He stood on one side and scanned the sleeping figure unable for a time to take his eyes off the majestic and virile beauty of that mighty form—the great muscles now in repose, the symmetrical grace of limbs which made the *Raakshasa* King at once beautiful and terrible.

Then Hanumaan looked at the women in the beds around and on the carpets. Some, who had fallen asleep while singing, were still hugging their musical instruments.

His eyes finally fell on a figure lying on a divinely beautiful cot. The shapeliness of her limbs and the beauty of her features made Hanumaan imagine it might be Seeta. He leaped up with joy.

The next instant he cursed himself for his folly. "Fie, fie," he said to himself, "how foolish have I been! Could Seeta sleep thus carelessly, covered with jewels, in a stranger's chamber? The very thought is a sin." And he was overwhelmed with shame and sorrow at his error.

Then he said to himself: "Because she would not yield to him, this *Raakshasa* must have killed her. What use is there in continuing the search?"

He had now searched the inner apartments of Raavana's palace. The bed room, the dining room, the hall of drink, the music room, all places had been searched and Seeta was nowhere found. "I have entered every nook and corner. Against all the rules of propriety, I have even looked at every one in the women's chambers. But all in vain."

Saying this he left the hall of drink and went to the garden and looked into the little shrines and the arbours made of creepers. But all in vain.

"I have seen all Lanka," he thought with irrepressible grief. "I have seen every inch of Raavana's palace. What more could I do here? Am I to return without seeing Seeta? No. I shall rather end my life here. Yes, that is the only thing for me to do."

But again he said to himself, "Fie, fie on me for yielding to such despondency unworthy and dishonourable."

He sprang up again and searched once again every inch of the places he had been through. He opened every door and window and looked in. There were ugly women, beautiful human and Naaga maidens, all captured by the *Raakshasa,* but not Seeta.

Once again his heart sank. He did not know what to do. He said to himself: "If I return to Kishkindha failing in my mission, with what face shall I meet my friends? If Raama loses all hopes of recovering Seeta, what would happen to him? He would surely die. And after that, what would happen to others? Instead of going back to Sugreeva and telling him that all my labours have been wasted, it would be far better to stay here and spend the rest of my days in the forest and sea-shore of Lanka. But why live on? Is it not best to end my life?

"But, then, was Sampaati wrong in saying that Seeta was in Lanka? Or has she been killed by the *Raakshasa* since Sampaati sighted her in this island? She might well have been devoured by the *Raakshasis*. Nothing is clear, everything is enveloped in doubt. What shall I do?"

Thus was Hanumaan lost in anxiety and thought. Just then his eyes lighted on what he had so far left unexplored—a park attached to a shrine and surrounded by high walls. "Oh, here is a park, I have not seen or searched so far. Here surely I shall find Seeta."

With these words as the son of Vaayu meditated on Raama, hope sprang within his breast. The secluded park was well protected by high walls. "Yes, Seeta must be here," he said to himself. Again he bowed to the gods. He jumped up and sat on the wall of the *Asoka Vana* and surveyed the beautiful park.

CHAPTER XLIX

SEETA IN THE ASOKA PARK

AS HANUMAAN stood on the high wall, he did not know why, a thrill of joy passed through his frame. It was the invisible atmosphere which envelops an accomplished mission and influences subtly the devoted heart. As he had at last reached the spot where Seeta was, his whole being throbbed with exulting expectation without any apparent reason.

It was an early spring night. Trees and plants were in flowers, Hanumaan jumped to a place where there was a thick cluster of trees. This disturbed the birds that rested there and they flew out with sweet noises. Deer and other animals moved about. Flowers dropped from the branches and covered the body of Hanumaan.

The creatures in the park, looking at the lovely figure of Hanumaan covered all over with flowers, thought that the God of Spring was visiting the grove in the early dawn.

The garden was entrancingly beautiful. Lovely tanks, terraces decorated with gold, silver, ivory, pearl and coral, crystal steps, artificial hills and waterfalls—the sight filled Hanumaan's heart with joy. Around some trees were platforms overlaid with gold and silver. Little bells suspended from the trees made music in the breeze.

Hanumaan climbed up and sat hidden among the leaves of a tall, spreading tree with a golden platform around its stem.

"If she be alive and in Lanka," said Hanumaan to himself, "Seeta would surely visit this garden. She

would choose this place above all others for solitude
and contemplation of Raama. They said, did they
not, that she loved groves and trees? She would
surely come here at dawn to offer worship to the
Universal Mother."

He gazed all round, hiding himself among the
leaves. He sat on a branch and looked below. He
beheld a female figure seated on that platform,
blindingly beautiful and divinely pure.

Thin and pale, she shone like the streak of the
moon in the beginning of the bright half of the
month. Her beauty glowed fitfully through deepest
dejection like flame through enveloping smoke.
Wrapped in a soiled upper garment she resembled a
lovely lotus obscured by miry moss. Her face was
bathed in tears, and she was wan and thin for want
of food. She had no thoughts but of sorrow, no
glimpse of friends or hope. There were only
Raakshasis wherever she turned her eyes, and she
felt like a doe which had lost its herd and found itself
beset by a pack of wild dogs. A single snake-like
braid of hair wandered unregarded down to her hip.
She seemed to Hanumaan at once adorable and
pitiful, like the holy word torn from its context by
infidels, like prosperity sunk in unmerited ruin, like
shattered hope and faith betrayed, like frustrated
fulfilment, like intellect muddied by insanity, like
blameless purity besmirched by foul slander.

Hanumaan said to himself with conviction:
"This image of beautiful despair is surely Seeta. For,
behold, hanging unregarded on the branches of the
tree are the jewels decribed by Raama as having
been on her when she was carried away—all except
those which she dropped during the flight and which
were picked up by us on the hill. And see, the scarf

she wears, though soiled and crumpled, is the fellow to the one we found. Surely this sublimely beautiful lady, who seems like one steadfast in true love in a tempest-tossed sea of troubles, is Raama's beloved queen. It is for her that Raama is consumed by a three-fold agony—grief for her suffering, wrath for the insult to her and heart-broken pangs at separation from her. Surely he is ever in her heart and she in his, and in truth they are not parted or they could not live."

And as he continued to see her, his heart leapt back across the ocean and sought Ramaa's feet in adoration. And again he looked at Seeta and said to himself: "It was for the sake of this divine lady that the mighty Vaali, the peer of Raavana in prowess, was slain; for her that Kabandha and Viraadha met their death, and fourteen thousands fierce *Raakshasas* with Khara, Dooshana and Trisiras crimsoned with their gore the glades of Janasthaana. It was for her that the splendid sovereignty of the *Vaanaras* was wrested from the heroic Vaali and given to Sugreeva. It is to do her service that I crossed the sea, the lord of rivers, and am now here in Lanka. All this seems much—but verily, if for her sake Raama should transform or even destroy the universe, I would say from my soul—It is well done! She is worth it all and more!"

And again Hanumaan's heart crossed the sea back and dwelt on Raama far away.

Just then, as on the clear surface of a lake a swan might glide, so in the blue sky the moon swam into sight and shone brightly as if on purpose to help the son of Vaayu.

Peering between the leaves and not knowing what to do, Hanumaan took another long look at the face of Seeta, a face that disclosed a sea of care like a heavily-laden ship caught in a storm. The *Raakshasis* who guarded her were intolerably ugly. One had only one eye, another only one ear. Some were without ears and some without noses. Some had noses turned steeply upward. Some were bald, while some had done their hair in grotesque styles. Some had pendant stomachs and some had camel's lips. Some were hunch-backs. Some were dwarfs and some tall like palmyrah trees. Swine-face, tiger-face, buffalo-face, goat-face—all were to be seen. These unsightly creatures were holding spears and other weapons in their hands.

And in their midst, the pale-faced princess sat trembling, befriended only by her virtue, like an unsupported beautiful creeper fallen on the ground.

It was still dark and not yet dawn. Raavana was roused from his slumber by the chanting of the Vedas and the morning songs of the court bards. The moment he awoke, he thought of Seeta and started towards the park where she was kept.

With all his retinue, he entered the palace park, accompanied by scented torches and the royal umbrella, surrounded by maidens, covered all over with brilliant ornaments and clad in spotless white clothes. Raavana appeared charming like another Manmatha.

As the procession entered the gate, Hanumaan could hear the noise of the crowd and the tinkling of women's anklets. Soon he saw the *Raakshasa* king approaching. At once Hanumaan hid himself more effectively than before among thick leaves.

As Raavana came towards Seeta, his strength and splendour were wonderful to behold. At this sight Seeta's body shrank and trembled like a plantain tree in a storm.

As one reads or listens to this sacred story, one should form a mental image of Seeta in her present state. One can imagine the agony of depair of any good woman who has by misfortune fallen into the power of a lustful man. What must be the state of Seeta, daughter of Janaka and wife of Raamachandra, in such a predicament? To appreciate Vaalmeeki's metaphors and similes in this context, one should purify one's heart and fire it with piety.

One feels unequal to rendering into another language the beautiful similes by which Vaalmeeki illustrates her condition. Only a few are cited here to give some idea of them.

Raavana approached Seeta still in the hope of obtaining her consent. Seeta was covered with dust and had no jewels on her person but she shone as if wearing all the jewels that a princess must wear. She looked like a beautiful tree felled down and lying low. Her face was covered by light and shadow, like a lotus flower stained by mire. She swayed like a cobra bound by charms. Her state was like one surrounded by raging fires on all four sides, like an army which had lost its chief warriors, like a river which had run dry, like a vessel for sacrificial fire that suffered desecration, like a lovely lotus tank destroyed by elephants, like a flowering creeper uprooted and cast aside, like a cow elephant separated from the leader of the herd, captured and tied as a prisoner.

Seeta sat trembling, overwhelmed with grief and fear. When she perceived Raavana's approach, that very instant her heart travelled to Raama like a chariot drawn by swift steeds. With faded face and wasted form, she thought of her protectors far away.

"When will they come? Will they ever come?" she asked herself and meditated on God.

Raavana approached and spoke to her. Hidden in the branches of the tree, Hanumaan watched what went on below.

CHAPTER L

RAAVANA'S SOLICITATION

TO SEETA, plunged in a sea of sorrow and clinging to *dharma* and to the thought of her lord, Raavana spoke these words:

"O beautiful one! Why do you shrink from me? Do you not see how much I care for you? Though it is lawful for a *Raakshasa* to take another's wife and possess her by force, I am a beggar for your love. There is no need to fear me. I shall never touch you till your heart turns towards me. Do not be afraid. My one wish is that you should care for me as I do for you. You must accept me with affection. Why do you make your body a prey to unavailing sorrow?

"O beautiful one! There is none like you in loveliness, none in all the world. It is not right for you to reject beautiful jewels and clothes, to sleep on the ground and leave your hair unkempt. O gem among women, do not thus waste your youth and beauty. Now you have come under my protection, you should lack nothing. All pleasures are suitors for your selection.

"I cannot take my eyes away from your face bright like the full moon. Wherever on your body I set my eyes, there they remain fixed and immovable. Why should one with so much beauty suffer so much sorrow? Accept me and enjoy all the pleasures of the world. I will conquer the world and give it to Janaka for your sake. What will I not do for you? You will be my sovereign consort. All the queens and women in the palace will be ruled by you. My wealth, my kingdom, all shall be yours to enjoy. Lanka and myself, why, the whole earth, shall belong to you. My strength and courage are known to the *Devas* and *Asuras*. Vanquished by me, they stand with bowed heads.

"With jewels and garments fit for you my hand-maidens will adorn you. I long to see you splendidly decked. And you will be free to give away generous gifts in charity. Your authority will extend over all mankind. My subjects and kinsfolk will deem it a joy to serve you.

"Why do you waste your thoughts on wretched Raama, wandering in the forest? How can you love, how can you trust one who has been deprived of his rights and driven out of his kingdom and is roaming about clad in bark garments? What can this helpless fellow do? The Goddess of Wealth, she that presides over Power and she who rules over Success, have all abandoned him, and you know it. It is even doubtful whether he is alive today. Anyhow, you may take it, he will never set eyes on you again, much less come near you. Like Garuda seizing a serpent, you have captivated my heart. I am unable to escape. Even in your present state, devoid of jewels or good clothes, you have drawn me away from my other wives. What can I do now? In my apartments are innumerable lovely women. But after seeing you, I can bear the sight of none of them. You will be the Queen over all of them and receive their humble service.

"In what sense can Raama equal me? Do you not see that in severe austerities gone through, in strength, wealth and glory, in every way I am superior to him? Shake off your fear. We shall wander over the whole world, happy in each other's company. With me you will enjoy limitless wealth and pleasure. Life will be one continuous joy. O beautiful one, have pity on me. Let us sport together in the parks and groves by the sea. Only say 'yes'."

Thus Raavana uttered his impassioned appeal for love and pity.

When Raavana had finished speaking, Seeta plucked a little blade of grass and, placing it between them, laughed in derision and gently spoke:

"Raavana, lay aside all such vain thoughts concerning me. It is altogether improper for you to desire me. Turn your heart to your wives. Never can I agree to what you say. Think of the family I was born in. Think of the family I was married into. How can you ever hope to persuade me? Do not give room for such foolish and impossible desires and make sorrow for yourself!"

Then she turned her face away and continued:

"How can I become your wife, when I am the wife of another? Do not violate *dharma*. Do not tread the path of sin. Listen to me. Think how carefully you watch over your wives to keep them safe from the touch of others. Would not other husbands do the same by their wives? Remember other men are like you. Do not cast your eyes on another's wife. To be happy with your own is the way of true happiness. But if you allow your mind to dwell on another's wife, sorrow and dishonour will be your portion.

"Is there none in the world to advise you aright? Why do you do evil and bring destruction on yourself and on your people? When a king loses self-control, his kingdom and wealth will all be destroyed. Be sure, this Lanka and its great wealth will be utterly destroyed if you persist in your sin and the foes whom you have conquered and humiliated will rejoice. I have no use for the wealth and the pleasures that you promise. They do not tempt me. I have married Raama and I cannot take my mind and heart away from him. I, who held his hand, can never touch another, never. I am his, the Prince's, entirely and for ever. I belong to him, as the *Veda* belongs to one who has reverently mastered it. It is not right for anyone else to look on me with longing eyes. Listen to me who speaks for your good. Beg Raama humbly for forgiveness and escape from his anger. Do not go in search of your own ruin. Raama is generous and will surely forgive you if you seek his mercy. Seek forgiveness and safety. Do not seek death and destruction.

"There, I hear even now the twang of Raama's bow. You cannot escape. Yama stands very near, ready to carry you away. The arrows of Raama and Lakshmana will soon be here in Lanka and your city will be in flames. Did not Raama utterly destroy the *Raakshasas* at Janasthaana? Did you not, knowing his strength, come like a thief to our hut, when Raama and Lakshmana were away, to steal me? Can you for a moment stand before them face to face? Can a dog approach a tiger? Will it not flee from the very scent? As the sun sucks up moisture from the wet earth, Raama and Lakshmana will drink your life. Will you run to hide yourself among the mountains? Will you try to escape under the sea? Even then, as at the appointed hour the tree is struck by lightning, so will you perish at their hands. You cannot escape."

Thus Seeta ended with a stern warning. Raavana controlled his anger and spoke:

"O Seeta, doting on this spurious ascetic Raama, you talk foolishly and repay my loving words with insult and contumely. Because of my love for

you, I have refrained, else you would be dead by now.
Of the time I had allowed you, two months more
remain. Change your mind before they pass. Be my
wife and come to my bed. If you refuse, you will be
sent to my kitchen and cooked for my meal. Beware!"

It was well-known that the food of the
Raakshasas included human flesh. Hence this threat
of Raavana was no exaggeration, but conveyed a
clear possibility. Yet Seeta was unafraid, and
answered:

"Alas! Alas! Is there none to give you good
advice? Have you no friend to save you from this sin
and put you on the path of virtue? You cannot escape
Raama's punishment. Like a rabbit antagonising a
wild elephant you have incurred the wrath of
Raama. O wretch who stole me in his absence, are
you not ashamed? Your destruction is certain. Your
evil fate has driven you to this act. And yet you are
the brother of Kubera; you are famous as a warrior;
you are the master of a complete four-limbed army.
Why should you do this mean deed in this mean
way?"

Raavana's eyes rolled in anger and he looked
fiercely at Seeta, hissing like a snake.

Seeing his mounting anger, one of his young
wives, Dhaanyamaali, walked up to his side and,
embracing him, said:

"King! Why do you vex yourself over this mean
human creature who does not seem to care for you?
She has not the good fortune to be your wife: that is
all. And what is there so attractive about her? Why
do you waste your thoughts on this puny creature?
Come away. Let us enjoy ourselves."

She drew him away affectionately and the *Raakshasa* went with her, laughing.

Before he went, Raavana ordered the *raakshasis* who guarded Seeta to bring her round somehow, and with resounding steps left the Asoka park, followed by his retinue. As soon as he turned his back, the *raakshasis* surrounded Seeta.

The Princess, who had been bold up till now, trembled when she looked at these ugly creatures that began speaking to her.

"When Raavana, scion of a noble family, a world-famous warrior, desires you," said one, "how can you refuse him, O foolish girl? Who do you think Raavana is? Know that he is a direct descendant of Brahma. He is the grandson of Pulastya Prajaapati, son of Brahma, a hero who has won many battles and vanquished many foes. How foolish to slight him!"

"Let not pride ruin you," said another. "Raavana is the son of *rishi* Visravas. Do not think he is a nobody. Accept him and be happy."

"The king of the *Raakshasas*, who defeated in battle and put to flight the gods of heaven, invites you to be his wife," said another. "You must yield, poor girl, or you must die."

"Slighting all his other wives," said another, "Raavana wants you and promises to make you chief among his queens. Forsaking all his noble wives, the King, bewitched by your beauty, begs for your love and offers to make you first among his consorts. Why are you foolishly obstinate?"

"None in all the world can equal Lord Raavana," said another. "Good fortune comes seeking you and you spurn it. How foolish!"

"The Sun and the Wind gods are afraid of the *Raakshasa* king. And he comes seeking you and wants to make you his favourite wife! Do not let your pride betray you. Do not reject the fortune that comes to you unsought."

And another concluded: "We have given you good advice. We have done our best and we leave the rest to you. If you reject his offer, you must surely die."

CHAPTER LI

FIRST AMONG THE ASTUTE

THE boldest and most strong-minded woman may, if kept in captivity for a long period, lose heart and become depressed.

Seeta hoped month after month that her lord would discover her whereabouts and come to her rescue. Sick with disappointed hope, alone in the midst of enemies, she clung to life only from an abiding faith in the love of Raama which made her feel that he would surely come.

The *raakshasis* plied her with what from their point of view was well-meant counsel. "Won't you listen to our advice? You are a human and so lack sense. You still hold on to this wretched man-husband of yours.

"Your proper place is our King's bed-chamber. That is the place for every kind of pleasure. But spurning his offer, you are for ever thinking of your worthless husband. Why are you still fond of this luck-less wretch driven out of his kingdom? You will never see him again. Yield to Raavana and be happy."

Seeta, hearing these words, could only shed tears.

"What sinful words you utter!" she said. "Never can I do what you say. You tell me that Raama is poor, and wretched and an exile from his home. All this I know. But among us of the race of men, no wife would think of giving up her husband on such grounds. It is wicked for the *Raakshasa* king to desire me for his wife. As the sun's brightness belongs inseparably to the sun so do I belong to

Raama. As Sachi is faithful to Indra, or Arundhati to Vasishtha, so am I ever to Raama."

The *raakshasis* gave up all hopes of persuading her and said to one another: "What can one do with a stubborn fool like this? It is best to eat her before she gets too thin with brooding!"

"I am in the family way," said one. "I have a great longing for human flesh. I shall tear her out and make a meal of her soft body."

"We shall strangle her and report to Raavana that she died of grief," said another. "The King is lost in unavailing grief because of this obstinate woman. Once he knows that she is dead, he will forget all about her and sleep soundly."

Another said: "I long to eat her liver. It must be very tasty."

Another added decisively: "Let us kill her and share her limbs. Fetch some sauce and strong liquor. Let us feast on her and drink and dance in the temple of Nikumbhila."

Hearing these horrible words and seeing these terrible forms, Seeta broke down and cried aloud. Her physical courage failed and nature had its way. She sobbed like a child; but even in her sobs her mind was clear and it was fixed on Raama.

"In Janasthaana Raama destroyed thousands of *Raakshasas*. Why does not Raama come yet to redeem me? The warrior princes who killed Viraadha in Dandaka, why are they still indifferent to my fate? It could only be that they do not yet know where I am! Jataayu, the vulture king, was slain by the *Raakshasa*. If he at least were alive, he would have told them the news that he saw the *Raakshasa* carrying me. But he gave up his life in trying to save me.

"But how long will Raama remain ignorant of my being here? How long can Lanka and the *Raakshasas* survive? It is certain that, in every house in this city, *Raakshasa* widows will soon be lamenting loudly. It is certain that this city of Raavana and the whole *Raakshasa* race will perish."

Thus she thought within herself and slowly recovered courage. But soon again other thoughts came to her and filled her with gloom.

"Could it be that Raama gave up his life, unable to bear my loss? It might well be so. Otherwise, could he neglect me and leave me all alone these so many days? Indeed he is happy now and with the Gods.

"I must have been guilty of many sins to be thus left to suffer. My heart must be made of stone. How else can I suffer all this and yet survive? Yet something tells me that Raama is alive — else I should be dead!"

Then again another thought occurred to her. "Perhaps he has resolved to spend his life in penance and has laid aside all thought of me. No, no. How could a warrior forsake his duty and, leaving his wife in the hands of his foe, take up the life of *sanyasa*? How foolish of me even to think of this! The fact is that they do not know where I am.

"Could it be that Raama has lost his love for me? 'Out of sight, out of mind,' they say. Could it be that he has forgotten me? Fie, fie! What a sinful thought! How can my Raama forget me? He never can. And what wrong have I committed that he should cease to think of me? This cannot be the reason. Perhaps Raavana has played some trick and treacherously slain the Prince."

Thus her mind wandered from one sad thought to another and sank even deeper in the sea of sorrow. She decided that it was best by hanging herself. She could hang herself with her long braid of hair round her neck and jump down from a branch of the Simsupa tree.

Having failed in their attempt to persuade Seeta, the *Raakshasis* did not know what to do next. Some went to inform Raavana of their failure. Some stayed behind to look after Seeta.

Appearing among them Trijata, a *Raakshasi,* reprimanded them, saying: "O foolish ones, you are talking nonsense! Listen to me, I shall tell you of a dream that I dreamt. The time has come when Lanka shall be destroyed."

Then she proceeded to recount in detail the terrible dream that she had dreamt:

"I saw in my dream Raama, shining like a sun, come to Lanka to find Seeta. I saw Raavana entering the abode of Yama. I saw Raama mounting Seeta on his elephant and carrying her home. I saw Raavana and all the *Raakshasas*, clad in soiled garments and dragged away by Yama."

Relating this dream to the *Raakshasis*, Trijata warned them: "Don't persecute this saintly woman. Don't seek your own destruction. Fall at her feet and beg for grace."

Even as Trijata was speaking to her companions, Seeta, who resolved to slay herself, suddenly began to see many good omens.

Her left eye-lids, hand and foot throbbed auspiciously. A vague courage once again came into her heart. All ideas of self-destruction disappeared.

Hanumaan, sitting hidden above and watching all that happened in the grove, wondered what he should do next.

One might imagine that, having reached Lanka and seen Seeta, Hanumaan had nothing more to do. But he was not so easily satisfied. He thought within himself.

"I have done something which no one else could do, I have crossed the sea and discovered Seeta. I have seen the city of the *Raakshasas* and noted its defences. All that a spy can do without revealing himself to the foe, I have done. But the situation here is fraught with danger. If I go back now to report what I have seen to Raama and my king, who knows what meanwhile will happen here? Before Raama, Lakshmana and the *vaanara* host arrive here, Seeta, unable to bear her suffering, might put an end to her life. All my labours would then be lost. It is not enough to have seen Seeta. I must talk to her, give her news of Raama and put hope and courage into her heart, so that she may hold with life in spite of all.

"How would Raama receive me if I return without speaking to Seeta? I must find some way of speaking to Seeta."

In the rosary of Hanumaan's name occurs the title, *Buddhimataam Varishtham*, 'First among the Astute.' It is a true description.

"In what form should I appear before Seeta? In what language should I speak to her? If suddenly a monkey came and spoke to her in this Asoka grove,

Seeta would surely suspect foul play and imagine that Raavana was playing some new trick on her. If I appeared suddenly before her, she might cry out in fear. In her present condition this is most likely to happen. The *Raakshasis* guarding her, who have now fallen asleep, will be startled awake and discover me. They would know that I have come from their enemy and in disguise, and they would bring the *Raakshasas* to attack me. A great battle would ensue. Of course I shall slay most of them, but the task of comforting Seeta and bearing news of her to Raama would be jeopardised if I were to be captured and held a prisoner here. This would never do. Even if I escape being caught and come out successful in the struggle, I might be wounded and lose strength and be unable to cross the sea. What then would I have gained having seen Seeta? One should never do things in a hurry. One should keep in mind one's main business. King Sugreeva and Raama are confidently awaiting my return. Even a little fault on my part now may lead to great disaster.

"The first thing to do is to get speech with Seeta and put joy and hope in her heart. I must approach her in such a way that she can never for a moment entertain a doubt about my good faith.

"Well, I shall recite in a sweet low tone, and for her hearing only, the story and virtues of Raama. Her heart would then be filled with joy and trust, displacing suspicion. Only thus can I proceed."

So he thought and, still hidden by the branches of the tree, he began to utter in a low voice, the sweet words, "Raama," "Raama."

CHAPTER LII

SEETA COMFORTED

HIDDEN by the branches, Hanumaan sang in a sweet and gentle voice the story of Raama so that it fell on Seeta's ears:

"King Dasaratha ruled his kingdom well. His army was mighty and comprised of chariots, elephants and horses. He was virtuous and a doer of great deeds. He kept his word and was foremost among the famous kings of the world. He was equal to the *rishis* in virtue and to Indra in statesmanship. He hated no one and harmed no one. All his endeavours were crowned with success. Therefore men called him *Satya-paraakrama*, truly valiant. The richest of the Ikshvaaku race, a king of kings, the ruler of the world, he enjoyed and communicated happiness. The eldest of his four sons was Raamachandra, whose face was like the full moon. Wise, virtuous and a master of the bow, Raama was beloved of all. And he was full of kindness for all the people in the kingdom, a warrior wedded to *dharma*. He was the heir to the throne. And yet, to preserve the honour of his father, he left the kingdom with his wife Seeta and his brother Lakshmana and lived in the forest.

"There he vanquished the *Raakshasas* and protected the *rishis*. He destroyed Khara and Dooshana and their mighty army. Coming to hear of this, Raavana, bent on revenge, induced a *Raakshasa* to assume the form of a deer and beguile the princes in pursuit and, in their absence, carried off Seeta by force.

"Grief-struck Raama went in search of Seeta. He met Sugreeva, the *Vaanara*, and made friends with him. Raama slew Vaali, the *Vaanara* king, and secured to his brother Sugreeva the *Vaanara* kingdom. And Sugreeva sent his *Vaanara* warriors to all the quarters of the globe to find out where Seeta was.

"These *Vaanara* warriors, who could assume what shape they would, searched the whole world for the missing Seeta. Following a clue given by Sampaati, I crossed the sea a hundred *yojanaas* broad, and have come here. And now I see one whose form, complexion and qualities are those described to me by Raama as his royal spouse's."

Having said this, Hanumaan paused.

These sweet words, uttered by some one from somewhere, filled Seeta with wonder and delight. She looked around in all directions to discover who conveyed such sweet matter in so sweet a voice and in such exquisite language.

She looked round, and up and down but found no human form to match this perfect speech. She only saw a lovely little monkey seated on the branch above her.

Seeta saw the son of Vaayu, the wise minister of the *Vaanara* king, in the form of a little monkey, radiant like the rising sun.

The reader should imagine for himself the joy of Raama's messenger, as Seeta's eyes fell on him. The reader who experiences this joy will find God in his heart. Naaraayana, who is waiting eagerly to enter and take possession of our hearts, would leave the great and boundless ocean of milk and come to dwell within us, when we cleanse ourselves of sinful thoughts.

Seeing Hanumaan, Seeta said to herself: "The words I heard, the form I see, — they cannot be real. I am only dreaming. One sees in one's dream what one is constantly brooding over. How often has my mind dwelt on the story of my Lord! Is it any wonder then that I seem to hear the tale as told by some one? It is not real, it is only a dream.

"They say that if one sees a monkey in a dream, it forebodes evil to one's kinsfolk. May God protect Raama from harm! May God keep all harm away from Lakshmana! May God bless all my kinsfolk in Mithila!

"No, no, this is no dream. My eyes are open and I see the same form still seated above me. There it is, clear and solid. No, this is no dream. And I am not asleep. How can one dream without sleeping? This is no dream. All this is real. Oh Gods! Could this indeed be a messenger from my dear Lord? Oh grant that it be so! Oh Vaachaspati! master of speech, I salute you. Oh Agni! I salute you. Oh Swayambhu! I salute you. Oh Gods! protect me. May this be Raama's messenger!"

Hanumaan, radiant with the joy of seeing Seeta, descended to the ground and stood before her, palms joined and head bent in salutation.

And he said in a deep soothing voice: "Mother, tears are falling from your eyes like drops from lotus petals. May I know who you are, who stands there, leaning on the tree trunk, face clouded with sorrow and eyes wet with tears? Are you a goddess or a *Naaga* maiden? The radiance of your body makes me question whether you could be of merely terrestrial

birth! Are you Rohini separated for a while from the
Moon-god? Or are you Arundhati parted from sage
Vasishtha?

"No, on closer observation, you seem to be a
human woman, — may be a princess adorable in
your distress. Please tell me who indeed you are.
May God bless you! Are you the princess Seeta
carried off by Raavana from Janasthaana? Is mine
the bliss of seeing Seeta, the beloved of Raama?"

Seeta was beside herself with joy. "My child,"
she said, "indeed I am Seeta, daughter of the king of
Videha and Sree Raamachandra's spouse. For
twelve years I enjoyed all happiness with him in
Ayodhya. In the thirteenth year, King Dasaratha
made preparations to crown my husband. Then
Kaikeyi, his youngest wife, reminded him of boons
he had granted long ago, and demanded that in
redemption of his word he should crown her son
Bharata king, and exile Raama to the forest. She
threatened to kill herself if this was not done. Bound
by promise the king had to yield to her insistence. At
his bidding Raama relinquished the crown and
betook himself to the forest not only without regret
but happy that it was given to him to enable his
father to keep his plighted word. I refused to be left
behind and insisted on going with my lord into the
forest. Even before me, Lakshmana had put on
bark-garments, determined to accompany his
brother to the forest and serve him. The three of us
entered the forest and were living in Dandaka. One
day the evil-hearted Raavana carried me off by force.
And he has kept me a prisoner here in this Asoka
garden. Of the time-limit of twelve months he has set
for me, only two more months remain. When they
are over I shall end my life."

Thus spoke the helpless princess in her sorrow.

The speeches of Hanumaan and of Jaanaki are sung by Vaalmeeki in two brief chapters. As Hari appeared before the emperor Bali in the form of Vaamana and measured the universe in two steps, so Vaalmeeki has given the tale of Raama in a short recital by Hanumaan and another by Seeta. What greater joy can we have than reading Hanumaan and Seeta telling the divine story themselves? As Vaamana got the better of Bali and saved him from his *ahankaara*, may this tale of Raama as told by Hanumaan and Seeta rid us of the sense of 'I' and 'my'.

Seeta concluded her story with the statement that two more months remained of the allotted twelve-month term and that her life would then end. To Seeta overwhelmed by grief, Hanumaan spoke words of comfort.

"O princess of Videha! Raama, the noblest of men and the mightiest of warriors, has sent me to you with good news. His beloved brother Lakshmana, ever anxious for your welfare, sends through me his salutations to you.

"Ah! what happiness is mine!" she exclaimed. "I now see the truth of the common saying that so long as life lasts there is hope."

Thus between these two utter strangers a profound confidence and affection sprang up like the sudden blossoming of the *paarijaata* in Indra's garden. Yet when, in his joyful eagerness to console and encourage Seeta, Hanumaan took a nearer step towards her, Seeta lost the confidence inspired by his words and again grew suspicious. She shut her eyes and moved away further from the tree. Hanumaan, noticing this, withdrew respectfully and stood with hands clasped in obeisance.

"I have been deceived," she cried. "You are no other than Raavana. Once you came disguised as an ascetic and imposed on me. Now you have come again in another disguise and speak sweet words. All this will bring you no good. Why do you torture me, O Raavana? I am weary and full of sorrow. You call yourself a warrior. Is it a warrior's part to persecute a helpless woman?"

Then she opened her eyes and thought again, "No, no. This cannot be Raavana. Trust and friendship spring in my heart at the sight of him. He can be no enemy of mine. It is wrong to suspect him."

She addressed him saying: "O *Vaanara*! Are you indeed a messenger sent by Raama? May God bless you. Tell me more concerning Raama. Let my ears hear and my heart rejoice."

Then once again doubts assailed her. "Am I a victim of delusion, imagining good news? Is this a dream that mocks me with the illusion of joy to make my despair blacker when I am awake? Am I in my right senses? Of course, I am. My thoughts, my words are all normal. I am sane and sensible. But then he says that he crossed the sea a hundred *yojanaas* broad. No, no. This cannot be true. He is Raavana and none else."

So she concluded in her mind and without lifting her eyes to look at Hanumaan sat apart in silence.

Hanumaan understood her doubts and fears. They were natural in one who had been deceived by the *Raakshasa*. He thought for a while and realised that the only approach to her confidence was to awaken hope and joy in her sorely tired heart by extolling Raama and harping on the certainty of her rescue, and his victory.

And he began: "Raama has sent me, Raama radiant like the Sun, Raama pleasant to look at like the moon, Raama praised by all the rulers of the earth, Raama valiant like Vishnu, Raama wise like Brihaspati, Raama handsome like Manmatha the god of love, Raama whose words are ever sweet and true, Raama whose indignation is ever righteous and well directed, Raama peerless warrior, Raama has sent me.

"While a *Raakshasa* in the shape of a deer beguiled Raama and drew him away in the forest, you were left alone and Raavana carried you off by force. Soon he will pay dearly for this evil deed. You will see it with your own eyes. Soon the shafts of Raama and Lakshmana will strike Lanka and destroy it along with Raavana and all his race. At Raama's bidding have I come to you to learn about your safety which is his constant concern. On Lakshmana's behalf I place at your feet his respectful salutations. And so too homage from Sugreeva, the *Vaanara* king. Raama, Lakshmana and Sugreeva are ever thinking of you. It is my good fortune to have seen you alive. Now there will be no more of loss of time. Soon Raama, Lakshmana and Sugreeva, accompanied by the whole *Vaanara* army, will descend on Lanka. I am Sugreeva's minister. My name is Hanumaan. I crossed the sea and reached Lanka. You may take it that my foot is already on the head of the evil-minded Raavana. By Raama's grace, even more than by my own prowess have I, his servant, crossed the sea to behold you. Do not suspect me. Have faith in my words, mother." So said Hanumaan with tears in his eyes.

These sweet words of Hanumaan acting on her great love for Raama and confidence in him, put an end to Seeta's fears and gave her courage and faith.

"Forgive my suspicion, O *Vaanara* friend," she said. "Deceived by the *Raakshasa* and surrounded by this artifices, I am prone to needless fear. O friend and messenger of Raama! How did you first meet Raama? How did the Prince make friends with the *Vaanaras*? Tell me all."

To confirm her faith, Hanumaan recounted once again the virtues and attractive qualities of Raama and Lakshmana.

He said: "What wonder is there in Raama becoming friends with me and my king and the *Vaanaras* when the whole world lives and finds bliss by his loving kindness?"

He proceeded to describe fully how the quarrel arose between Vaali and Sugreeva, how the latter first met Raama and Lakshmana, how they became friends, how Raama promised to slay Vaali and secure the *Vaanara* kingdom for Sugreeva, how the *Vaanaras* had picked up and preserved the jewels dropped by Seeta, how with mounting sorrow Raama recognised them, how Vaali was slain and Sugreeva crowned, how after the rainy season was over the *Vaanara* hosts searched the whole world for Seeta, how the party led by Angada and proceeding south having failed to find her, decided to fast to death, how they met Sampaati and received a clue from him, how he, Hanumaan, crossed the sea and searched the inner apartments of Raavana— all this he recounted.

At the end of the narration he placed in her hand Raama's signet ring that he had brought.

Seeta received the ring and pressed it to her eyes with joy. Now all fear of Raavana's deceit and *Raakshasa* magic was over. She had complete faith in Hanumaan and infinite affection for him.

"My child!" she said, "How foolish was my error! How could I suspect one like you?"

The son of Vaayu explained to her who he was and who his father was and what his own might was.

"Though I, who enjoy the grace of my father Vaayu, should not sing my own praises, I do so now to end your sorrow. Soon the *Vaanara* warriors will be here to destroy the *Raakshasas* and their kingdom. I must first return and tell them where you are."

And then he described Raama's desolation in being parted from Seeta, and the ascetic life he led, and Seeta's heart melted in loving sorrow.

Seeta forgot her own suffering thinking of Raama's grief.

CHAPTER LIII

SEETA AND HANUMAAN

"DEAR, dear *Vaanara* friend," said Seeta, "I do not know whether to rejoice or grieve at the news you have brought. Your words are like nectar mixed with poison. My lord's love for me is sweetest nectar, and his grief over my plight is bitterest poison." Thus Seeta spoke what she felt and found comfort in putting in words her love and her grief.

Pleasure and pain, happiness and misery alternately impel human beings. Seeta was consoled but also pained by the thought that Raama had not forgotten her, but was thinking of her, grieving and searching for her.

"We are puppets manipulated by the twin strings of joy and sorrow," said Seeta. "None of us can escape their pull. My lord and Lakshmana and myself are all subject to this law. You say my lord suffers like a sailing ship caught in a storm on the high seas. O! When will he come here? Dear *Vaanara* friend, when will he destroy Lanka and Raavana and the other *Raakshasas*? All this must take place within the two months' time still left. Please explain this to my lord. Only two months remain to me. Vibheeshana, the younger brother of Raavana, tried his best to persuade the latter to change his ways. 'Return Seeta, he said to Raavana', and save Lanka and the *Raakshasa* race.' All his words have gone in vain. My heart is strong within me. I know Raavana is on the road to the abode of Yama. Soon my lord will vanquish his foes and redeem me. I have no doubt about this. My innocent heart tells me this and it cannot prove false."

Thus Seeta went on speaking with tears in her eyes. Hanumaan could not bear the sight of her suffering.

"Mother!" he exclaimed, "I shall go at once and bring back Raama. He will descend on Lanka with a mighty army. But why should you suffer any longer? If you are agreeable, sit on my back. I shall carry you across the ocean and restore you in a moment to Raama. Do not for a moment doubt my ability to do this. As Agni carries the sacred offerings to Indra, so shall I transport you to my Lord Raama. Permit me, O pure of heart, to do this service. I can not only carry you and restore you to Raama, but I have the power to wrench Lanka from its foundations and throw it and its ruler at Raama's feet! Sit on my back now and, like Rohini rejoining the Moon, you will rejoin Raama. As I sprang and came here, so shall I spring and reach the other shore with you."

Thus Hanumaan went on speaking out of his affection and enthusiasm. And Seeta wondered how the little monkey before her could hope to carry her across the ocean.

Hanumaan saw her doubt and so, to demonstrate his powers, he jumped off from the platform and began to grow big in size. Seeta was pleased.

But she said: "O Son of Vaayu! I realise your strength and yet it is not right that you should carry me. On the way the *Raakshasas* are sure to intercept and challenge you. They will hurl their weapons at you. Your care will be to guard me. You will not be able to fix all your mind on the battle and that may be a serious set-back to the strongest warrior. In a battle, one cannot be certain of victory and what would be my fate if you should fall? And besides, in the violent convulsions of a heady fight, how could I

be sure of maintaining my position on your back? I
may slip and fall into the sea. It is clear, therefore,
that you should not try to cross the sea with me.
Apart from that, Hanumaan, if you snatch me away
stealthily from the *Raakshasas* it would be no credit
to the valour of my lord. The honour of the Kshatriya
race demands that he should come and fight and
vanquish Raavana and redeem me as the prize of
victory. Would Raama have me stolen back even as
Raavana stole me from him? No, my son, return and
quickly bring Raama here with Lakshmana and the
Vaanara army. Let my lord's arrows destroy Lanka
and send Raavana to Yama's abode. His victory is
certain. Like the fierce sun at the hour of doom,
Raama's arrows will burn the *Raakshasa* people to
ashes."

"You are right," said Hanumaan, "I shall return
alone. But what shall I tell Raama? What sign shall
I carry of my having met you and talked with you?"

Hearing these words, all her happy life with
Raama came like a flood to her memory and her eyes
were filled with tears. If she told Hanumaan and
Hanumaan told Raama some intimate happenings
known only to herself and her lord, it would be proof
of Hanumaan having seen her and also make Raama
see her present disconsolate state. With flowing
tears, she recounted incidents of their forest life.

"Once in Chitrakoota my lord and I wandered
about in the grove beside the river and became
weary and rested on the ground. He laid his head
upon my lap and fell asleep. While thus, a crow came
down and hungrily pecked at my bosom, I drove it
off, but again and again it returned and troubled me.
I then flung a pebble at it. But even that had no
effect. Raama was roused from slumber and saw me

thus troubled and weeping in pain. At first when he saw what the matter was and found it was but a crow, he was inclined to laugh at my discomfiture. But he saw the bruise the crow had made and discovered that the bird was really an *Asura*. The bird flew for its life, but Raama sped a dart at it which pursued it wherever it went, till at last the crow-*Asura* sought Raama's feet for refuge and found pardon there.

"Tell him of this incident. O Hanumaan, I cannot wait for many more days. Tell him to come quickly and save me."

Again she was in tears as she said: "On another occasion we were both wandering all alone in the forest. I was tired. Perspiration had washed off the *tilaka* on my forehead. My lord playfully plucked a pinch of red mineral from the rock and applied it between my brows with his own sweet hands. Ask him if he remembers this incident."

As she went on recalling happy memories of the past the weight of her present sorrow overwhelmed her and she wept and said:

"What should I tell Raama? What is there that he does not know? Does he need my words to rouse his indignation? Only tell my lord that I embrace his feet. That is enough. There is Lakshmana beside him, the brother born to serve him and of unrivalled skill in arms. Looking at his sweet face, my Lord even forgot his grief for the father's death. The pure-hearted hero, dear Lakshmana, parted from his own mother and came away with us and regarded me as his mother. Tell him he should come and end my suffering."

As she thought of Lakshmana's heroism and devoted loyalty, Seeta's eyes were filled with tears. When Raama had gone chasing the golden deer, did she not insult him and fling burning words at the selfless and devoted friend? The thought of this injustice filled her repentant heart with insufferable pain.

She was unwilling to part from Hanumaan, who had come to her and consoled her just as she was about to put an end to her life. At the same time, she wanted him to return quickly to Raama and give him the news concerning her.

At last she said: "My child, here is the jewel given by my mother at my wedding and fixed on my forehead by the late Emperor. Take it and give it to my husband as a sign from me."

So saying she untied a knot at the corner of her sari, took out the divine jewel and handed it to Hanumaan who received it with humble reverence.

When Hanumaan had the jewel in his hand, pride and joy filled his mind.

His heart was far away with Raama. Mentally he had recalled Raama's presence and conveyed the glad message of his discovery. Only his body now stayed in Lanka.

"Dear friend," said Seeta, "you must tell Raama all you have learnt here, and it will be your good fortune to help him to achieve victory."

As Hanumaan was about to leave, Seeta spoke again: "Dear Hanumaan, convey my affection to the Prince and also to king Sugreeva and the other *Vaanara* leaders. Tell them from me that I implore them to give help to Raama to save me from this sea of sorrow. You, more than anyone else, I hope, will encourage and show the way to the Prince in all matters."

Hanumaan answered: "Lay aside your sorrow, dear princess. Raama, Lakshmana and the *Vaanara* army will descend on Lanka, destroy the *Raakshasas* and redeem you. Have no doubt."

As he was about to go, Seeta said again: "Should you not stay here somewhere, for a while, and rest? Should you return at once? Your visit has given me such great consolation and made me forget my grief for a while. When you leave, I shall sink again in my sea of sorrow. You came here crossing the great ocean. How will Raama and the big army cross it? Have you thought of that?" Doubts assailed her once again.

"Have no doubt, my queen!" said Hanumaan. "Do you think I am the only *Vaanara* that could cross the sea? There is not a *Vaanara* but has more power and skill than I. Not only Sugreeva, but many in his army can fly round the world. What is this narrow sea to them? There are thousands among us who can roam in the sky. Have no doubt whatever. Do you think they would send the best among them as a mere messenger? Dear lady, have done with sorrow, for you will soon see me with the two mighty princes on my back. They will lay waste this city with the arrows. They will destroy Raavana and all his race. You have as good as crossed the ocean of sorrow and reached the other shore.

"God bless you. In a few days you will see the two princes standing, bow in hand, at the gates of Lanka, destroying the *Raakshasa* host. You will see the *Vaanara* army leaping with joy over the ruined city.

"Once they hear the news from me, they will not delay a moment. I have only to tell them and they will start at once. Do not lose heart." Saying this and bowing profoundly, Hanumaan prepared to go.

"Tell Raama and Lakshmana that I am alive," cried Seeta. "See that no time is lost. May God bless you.'"

And Hanumaan left. Let us meditate with reverence on the heroic son of Anjana, the wise messenger who gave consolation to Seeta and quenched her grief.

CHAPTER LIV

INVITING BATTLE

AFTER taking leave of Seeta, Hanumaan sat for a while on the top of the garden wall and began to think:

"What can I do to put courage into Seeta and some fear into Raavana and his friends to shake their arrogant confidence? It would be good to leave them some souvenir of my visit, some indication of what the future has in store for them.

"It is clear I must instil some fear into Raavana to prevent him from troubling Seeta in the meantime; fear is the only argument they understand. Raavana has untold wealth and one cannot part his friends from him. Hence *Saama* (conciliation), *daana* (buying over) and *bheda* (sowing discord) are useless in this case. I should therefore do something terrible to frighten them, and warn them not to ill-treat Seeta. Yes, I must do this before I go away."

At once he began to grow and assumed a huge form and began to lay waste the grove. Trees fell cracking to the ground, bowers collapsed, tanks and artificial hills were disfigured and destroyed. The beautiful Asoka park soon became a mass of ruin from which the deer and the birds fled in fear. The slumbering *raakshasis* woke up and were bewildered to see this unaccountable sight.

Hanumaan sat on the top of the wall of the garden, a huge figure of wrathful menace, waiting for the answer to his challenge. The *Raakshasis* quaked with terror at the sight of this stranger and some ran to tell Raavana the news. Some

approached Seeta and asked: "How did this huge
monkey come here? You should know who he is. Did
he say anything to you? Tell us the truth. Do not be
afraid to speak out.".

"How do I know what can happen in this
charmed world of *Raakshasas*? Seeta answered,
parrying the question. "This monkey is probably one
of the *Raakshasas* and you are likely to know more
about him than I."

The *Raakshasis* fled in fear from the park and
reported to Raavana what had happened.

"O king! A huge monkey terrible to look at has
laid waste the royal garden. It was in secret talk
with Seeta."

Of course they omitted to add that they had
fallen asleep and given a chance for Seeta to talk to
the monkey.

"We tried our best to get some information from
Seeta," they added. "We asked her who he was, and
how he came there, and what he told her. But she
refuses to answer. You should seize and slay this
creature. Do send a strong foe. The beautiful grove is
completely devastated except for the *Simsupa* tree
under which Seeta is seated. Its spreading branches
have suffered no damage. The monkey which laid
waste the tanks and bowers has spared the
habitation of Seeta. There must be a reason for this.
We suspect that this is not an ordinary wild animal.
It must have been sent by some enemy of yours,
either Indra or Kubera. Or could it have anything to
do with Raama? How did this monkey dare to talk to
Seeta? He must be a messenger from Raama. Do
send your warriors to capture this terrible beast."

Raavana was furious on hearing that his favourite park, set apart for his queens, had been destroyed. His eyes glowed like twin torches and hot tears rolled down from them like drops of burning oil.

He turned to the bodyguards standing beside him ever eager to do his bidding and ordered them at once to go and destroy the monster-monkey. A strong force started to execute the king's commands, armed with maces and spears and other weapons.

CHAPTER LV

THE TERRIBLE ENVOY

THE *Raakshasa* warriors saw with amazement a mighty *Vaanara* seated on the garden gate, who at their approach grew to still bigger size and formidable menace.

"Oh! You have come, have you?" he said and, jumping down, brandished his tail, and striking the ground with it, roared till the four quarters shook. He snatched the huge iron bar from the gate and, armed with this weapon, began to attack them all.

He sprang and leaped in all directions and, whirling the iron rod, struck the *Raakshasas* down, one by one. After finishing them thus, he resumed his seat on the top of the pillared entrance, and roared once again.

"Long live Raama! Long live Lakshmana!" he loudly proclaimed. "Long live King Sugreeva! Oh ! Ye *Raakshasas* of Lanka, your doom is near. The great warriors Raama and Lakshmana and King Sugreeva have sent me here to destroy you. Come on in your thousands. I stand here ready to hurl you to destruction. I have saluted Seeta and received her blessings. And now I am going to destroy your city!"

All Lanka heard the thunder of his words and quaked in terror. When the news reached Raavana that the warriors sent against Hanumaan were all slain, he opened wide his fierce eyes in amazement and wrath.

"What is it you say?" he yelled, and called Jambumaali, the matchless warrior, son of Prahasta. And he said to him, "Go at once! Punish this monkey and report to me."

The *Raakshasa* Jambumaali took some time to put on armour and to take up weapons and get ready to meet his foe. Meanwhile, Hanumaan was not sitting still. He climbed to the top of a temple in the park and stood there, shining against the horizon like a second sun suddenly risen in the sky. He magnified his body still further and looked like a golden mountain range up in the heavens.

His roar filled the city of Lanka and raised echoes from all the eight quarters. The hearts of the *Raakshasas* trembled in fear.

"Long live Raama! Long live Lakshmana! Long live King Sugreeva! I have come as an envoy of the King of Kosala. I have come to destroy Lanka. I am Hanumaan, son of Vaayu, come here to utterly destroy the enemies of Raama. I have vowed before Seeta and received her blessings. Know that I possess the strength to vanquish a thousand Raavanas. Big boulders and uprooted trees I shall aim at the *Raakshasas* and destroy them. That is what I have come here for!"

The sentries in the temple took up various weapons and attacked him. Hanumaan jumped down and plucked up a big pillar, supporting the temple, and stood there like the Destroyer. Whirling his massive weapon easily as though it were a willow wand, Hanumaan struck down and slew the sentries. The temple, from which the pillar had been removed, collapsed. As Hanumaan struck the ground with the pillar, sparks of fire flew all around.

"In Sugreeva's army there are monkeys much mightier than I and they will soon be here," he roared. "You and your king and your city will be destroyed by them, root and branch. Your king has incurred the enmity of the Lord of the Ikshvaaku race, has he not? Lanka is nearing its end. Destruction awaits the *Raakshasas*. The God of Death is approaching Raavana."

Jambumaali arrived at last. With wide, glaring eyes and ugly, irregular teeth, dressed in scarlet, with large golden rings in his ears, bow in hand, garland round his neck, sword at his hip, he came in a chariot rattling like thunder.

Hanumaan set eyes on the chariot dragged by enormous mules. And he got ready.

Seated in his chariot, Jambumaali bent his bow and aimed a few arrows at Maaruti who was seated on the wall. They wounded his face and drew blood, which added to the beauty of his face. It was as if a red lotus had suddenly blossomed in the heavens. The wounds enraged Hanumaan, who picked up a big boulder and flung it at the chariot.

He uprooted a *sal* tree and, twirling it, flung it at Jambumaali. Then he plucked out a huge iron rod from the temple and aimed it at the chariot and reduced it to splinters and crushed the huge body of Jambumaali into a shapeless mass, in which neither head nor limbs could be distinguished.

The issue of this battle was duly reported to Raavana. He was struck with wonder. "This is indeed something strange," he said to himself. "This murderous brute is not an animal, certainly not a mere monkey. It is some new creature devised by my old enemies the gods to annoy me."

And he ordered mighty commanders to go with a great army to capture the creature and produce it before him.

The *Raakshasa* chiefs went forth in a great array of chariots. In full force they attacked

Hanumaan, who was as before stationed on top of the entrance and was laughing aloud in disdainful unconcern. They showered missiles on him which mostly glanced harmlessly off his adamantine frame; with each dart or arrow that struck him, he grew in stature and fierceness, and ranging all round with energy pelted them with rocks and huge tree boles, till all the leaders lay crushed and slain, and the survivors fled in panic and despair.

Having killed or put to fight the entire contingent of *Raakshasas*, Hanumaan roared in triumph and Lanka trembled at the roar. He resumed his seat on the stone-battlement on the top of the garden-gate.

Hearing of the defeat of the force sent to capture Hanumaan and the slaughter of five of his best commanders, fear for the first time entered Raavana's heart.

"It is extraordinary that a solitary monkey should have this devastating valour and purposeful malevolence," Raavana thought with anxiety. "This is clearly a conspiracy of the gods."

But he kept his concern to himself and laughed derisively.

He looked round at all the members of his great council. His son the heroic Aksha stood foremost, eager for battle, and the proud father bade him go forth to battle against the tremendous foe.

Radiant with youth and health and glowing with high courage at this opportunity of distinguishing himself, Aksha went forth in a shining chariot, confident of victory.

CHAPTER LVI

HANUMAAN BOUND

VAALMEEKI describes in beautiful verses how the youthful warrior Aksha, the equal of the gods, rode to battle in a chariot drawn by eight horses.

Who can put up in a different tongue Vaalmeeki's poetry describing the beauty of forests and the terrible fury of encounters between warriors? The rhythm and grandeur of his words convey the terror and majesty of what he describes. This power is Vaalmeeki's special gift. We can only summarise in pedestrian prose his glowing account, of the battle between Aksha, the beloved son of Raavana, and Hanumaan.

In a golden chariot acquired through *tapasya* rode Raavana's young son. When he saw Hanumaan, seated on the stone battlement above the gateway, and noted approvingly the beautiful symmetry of his mighty limbs, and the majestic intrepidity of his look, Aksha felt that here was a foe worthy of his steel, and summoned all his strength and resolution to do him honour.

The young warrior aimed three sharp arrows at Hanumaan. They struck his body and drew blood. But Maaruti's strength increased and his face shone with new splendour. He too was pleased with the prowess of the youthful *Raakshasa*.

Fierce grew the battle between the two. Hundreds of arrows rose in clouds into the sky and hit Maaruti. Like rain falling on a rock, they fell on Hanumaan's body. Rising in the air Hanumaan dodged about evading the arrows—slipping as it were through the meshes of that deadly network of missiles—and finding a favourable opening closed with Aksha. Hanumaan admired Aksha's youthful promise and heroism, and was sorry to have to slay him, but there was no help for it for the prince seemed to get more and more formidable as the fight went on, and it was unwise to take chances with him. At last Hanumaan hardened his heart and decided to destroy the youth.

He rushed against Aksha's chariot and broke it to pieces. The horses fell dead. The *Raakshasa* prince stood on the ground chariotless. Nothing daunted, he rose in the air with bow and sword and attacked Hanumaan. A great battle took place in the air. In the end Aksha's bones were crushed and splintered and he fell down dead.

Hearing that the prince had been killed by Hanumaan, Raavana shook with rage, but controlling himself he called his son Indrajit, the conqueror of Indra.

"You have mastered all weapons," he said. "You have vanquished the *Devas* and *Asuras* in battle. You have by your austerities called Brahma down and secured from him the *Brahmaastra*. There is none in the world who can oppose you. Fatigue cannot approach you. Your knowledge of battle is unique. You have attained strength through *tapasya*. Nothing is impossible for you. None can equal you in foresight. The *kinkaras* I sent and Jambumaali and the five generals of our army, and your dear brother Aksha have all been slain by a terrible foe who has raided us in the form of a monkey and it is yours now to avenge them. Do not underrate him. It seems he cannot be vanquished by weapons. He cannot be brought down in wrestling. Consider well therefore what needs to be done. Do it and return victorious. The *astras* you have secured through *tapasya* can serve you at this moment. Without allowing your mind to wander, fight with concentration and return triumphant."

Indrajit, bright like the gods, accepted his father's command with reverence and receiving his blessings went with courage and eagerness towards the *Asoka Vana*.

Standing in a chariot drawn by four fierce lions and twanging his bow-string, Indrajit proceeded towards Hanumaan. His chariot sounded like the wind off the monsoon. His lotus-like eyes shone victory.

As Hanumaan saw the chariot coming towards him, he was filled with joy. Indrajit too, skilful in battle, bent his bow and got his sharp arrows ready for Hanumaan. Knowing that a great battle was at hand, the *Naagas, Yakshas* and *Siddhas* assembled in the sky to see.

At the sight of Indrajit, Hanumaan roared and increased his stature still further. Silently the *Raakshasa* warrior dispatched his darts. Showers of arrows began to descend as in the battle of the gods and their cousins, the *Asuras*. Hanumaan rose in the sky and, moving with speed like lightning, struck down the sharp arrows. His roar made the quarters echo, drowning the drum beats and the bow-twangs of the *Raakshasa*.

The battle raged with increasing fury and filled all beholders with amazement. In skill and strength the two warriors were perfect equals. No matter how often he was wounded, Hanumaan's strength showed no signs of lessening. Indrajit therefore resolved, 'My arrows cannot vanquish this monkey.

What my father said is true. He can be bound only by using the *Brahmaastra*.'

The *Raakshasa* Prince sent forth the *Brahmaastra*. At its touch the *Vaanara* warrior lay bound and helpless.

Hanumaan realised what had happened. He said to himself, 'I have been bound by the *Brahmaastra*'.

Hanumaan too had secured a boon from Brahma, and this he now remembered.

'This will keep me bound for only one *muhoorta* (four-fifths of an hour)', he said to himself. 'I run no real risk. Let me see what the *Raakshasas* do to me while I lie bound and helpless. I might find here a further opportunity to function as a messenger.'

As instructed by Brahma when he gave him the gift of immortality, he surrendered himself to the *Brahmaastra* and lay down on the ground, inactive but in full possession of his faculties.

When they saw Hanumaan thus lying helpless on the ground the *Raakshasas* who till then stood at a distance in fear, surrounded him and danced with joy and called him insulting names and praised their prince.

"We shall cut you to pieces!" they shouted. "Let us eat him up." "We shall drag him to the throne of our Raavana." Thus and in many other ways they shouted.

A few among them feared and said, "This fellow is only pretending. He may get up suddenly and attack us." So they brought ropes of jute and coconut fibre and bound him hard and shouted exultingly: "Now we have bound him, let us drag him to the Lord of the *Raakshasas*."

Indrajit, who discovered too late and could not prevent this foolish mistake of the *Rakshasas*, felt sad.

'Alas!' he thought with sorrow. 'They have undone all my work. These fools do not know the secrets of supernatural weapons. When they have thus used ropes and jute for binding him, the *astra* withdraws its power. The bound of *mantra* is undone when physical bonds are added. Hanumaan is now held only by the ropes which he can burst asunder and the *Brahmaastra* cannot be used a second time.'

Hanumaan too understood this, and knew he could spring up free if he liked, but he welcomed the opportunity to meet and talk to Raavana and allowed himself to be dragged to the king, patiently bearing all their insults and cruelties in seeming helplessness. They belaboured and foully abused him, and dragged him through the streets and women and children came out to look at him and jeer.

CHAPTER LVII

LANKA IN FLAMES

HIS captors took him to the court of Raavana and placed him in front of the King. Forgetting the pain and insults he had borne, Hanumaan gazed with wrathful curiosity at the giant monarch. As he gazed at him resplendent on his throne a sort of pitying admiration of the doomed *Raakshasa* entered his thoughts.

Clad in silk of golden hue, with the royal crown on his head, the jewels inlaid in it shining brilliantly, Raavana sat there, a figure of dazzling splendour. The whole court was brilliant with shining gold and gems, pearls and silk. His dark body, lit up by the marks of royalty, looked like a great radiant hill.

"Alas!" thought Hanumaan full of anger, wonder and pity. "If only this great one had not swerved from the path of *dharma*, not even Indra could equal him. What a form, what radiance, what strength! Trusting to the boon he had secured, he took to wicked ways and has lost his happiness and forfeited his greatness."

As Hanumaan was lost in thought thus, Raavana addressed his ministers: "Find out from this wicked fellow who he is, where he has come from, who has sent him here and why he entered Lanka. Tell him to speak truthfully."

As ordered by the king, Prahasta questioned Hanumaan. "Do not be afraid, monkey! If you speak the truth, you will escape punishment. Did Indra send you here? Or are you Kubera's servant? Whose orders are you carrying out? Speak the truth and

save yourself. Why have you come here thus
disguised? Take care you hide nothing!"

Hanumaan, facing Raavana directly, said:

"Neither Indra, nor Kubera has sent me here. I
am a *Vaanara*. I came here to have a look at the
Raakshasa king. That was why I laid waste the
garden. Otherwise I could not get to the king's
presence. And because they attacked me and tried to
kill me, I killed them in self-defence. I have come
here as the messenger of Sugreeva, the *Vaanara*
king. O *Raakshasa* king, my lord looks on you as a
brother and sends you his greetings. Raamachandra,
the famous son of king Dasaratha of Ayodhya, has
become a friend of Sugreeva and slaying Vaali has
made Sugreeva king. When Raamachandra, heir to
the throne of Ayodhya, was living in the Dandaka
forest to fulfil his father's word, his consort who had
been left alone for a while was lost and at the behest
of Raama and Lakshmana, Sugreeva has sent his
servant to look for her throughout the world. I came
to Lanka on this search and here I saw the good
princess. O lord of the *Raakshasas,* I speak to you
with respect due from the messenger of a brother
king. I speak to you also as a devoted servant of the
Prince of Ayodhya. You know well it was a cowardly
act and totally contrary to *dharma* to carry off the
princess Seeta. This is sure to end in the destruction
of your race if you persist in your wicked folly.
Restore Seeta to the Prince and seek his forgiveness.
Know that death has come to you in the form of
Seeta. Do not mistake poison for food. It is not
wisdom to oppose *dharma* and run into deadly
danger. You know well enough that the sin of
desiring another's wife will consume utterly the
merit you have earned through *tapas* and destroy

you inevitably. Your only recourse now is to seek refuge at Raama's feet. Do not make Raama your enemy and bring about your own destruction. The boons you have secured will avail you nothing against the Prince of the Raghu race. Consider well and realise the danger you are in. Pay heed to the words of this humble messenger of the *Vaanara* king. Turn to the right path and find safety. These words from a brother king are true and meant for your welfare."

Hanumaan uttered this bitter warning in a loud and clear voice. When the *Raakshasa* king heard it, his eyes grew red with anger, and he ordered that Hanumaan should be killed forthwith.

But Vibheeshana pointed out that it would be improper to kill a king's envoy.

"According to the law of kings it is not permitted on any account to kill envoys and messengers. You can have him mutilated, whipped or branded, but not killed," so counselled Vibheeshana.

"What is wrong," asked Raavana, "in killing one who has sinned so greatly?"

Answered Vibheeshana with due politeness: "No matter how grievous his offence, it was done at the bidding of others. To leave his royal masters alone and to slay their instrument, a mere messenger—what use or sense is there in it? Let us by all means seek ways of punishing those that sent him here. They must be brought here and given due punishment. If he is slain now, what chance is there of our real enemies being brought here? If, on the other hand, he is sent back alive to them, they will come here and attack us. Then they will receive proper punishment at your hands."

Raavana agreed. "Very well," he said, "a monkey's most cherished possession is his tail. Set fire to his tail, flog him soundly and turn him out."

At these words of the *Raakshasa* king, his servants took Hanumaan out. They wrapped his tail in rags of all kinds. His tail grew in size and, as it grew, they brought more and more old rags and wrapped them round. They soaked the whole in oil and set it ablaze like a huge flaming torch.

Thus bound by ropes and with tail ablaze, Hanumaan was taken through the streets of Lanka.

"Here goes the thief that entered our city!" cried the women and children. They jeered at him as he was taken round by the exulting *Raakshasas* to the accompaniment of pipes and drums through all the highways and byways of Lanka.

In the *Asoka Vana* the *raakshasis* told Seeta: "The monkey with whom you had secret talk, do you know what has happened to him? They have wrapped his tail in cloth soaked in oil and have set fire to it. His tail is ablaze. They are taking him in procession through the town."

They told Seeta the tale and laughed in scorn.

She kindled a fire and offered a prayer to the god of Fire: "O Agni! If there be any goodness in me, any purity, be cool to Hanumaan; do not hurt him."

Hanumaan endured the blows and the insults heaped upon him, and proceeded from street to street quietly observing everything. The *Raakshasas*, to amuse their women and children took him through all the streets and bylanes of the city. And he noted in silence, for future, use, all the secrets of that fortified city.

"But what is this miracle?" he thought. "The rags soaked in oil burn brightly but the fire does not hurt and is cool on my tail. The elements themselves seem kind to one engaged on Raama's purpose. Did not the mountain rise above the sea and offer me hospitality? Even so the god of Fire is gracious to me now and does not harm me. Or may be, Agni being a friend of my father Vaayu, is gentle with me. Now, I think I should not let slip this opportunity which has come to me unsought to put the fear of God into these *Raakshasas*."

Suddenly he shrank in size and shook off the ropes that bound him and, resuming his huge shape, jumped with his blazing tail to the top of a tall building. He plucked a pillar there and whirled it round, striking terror in all beholders.

Then he jumped from mansion to mansion, setting fire to them. In a little while a strong breeze began to blow and the whole city was in flames. The *Raakshasas* and their women and children shouted in terror and ran hither and thither.

"This monkey is no other than Yama," said some. "No, he must be the god Agni," said others. And they all fled from their burning houses.

Recalling the insults he had suffered, Hanumaan was pleased when he saw the flames rise. He sat on the summit of the Trikoota hill and contemplated with satisfaction the red glow of the burning city.

Then he went to the sea and, plunging in, put out the fire in his tail and came ashore.

"Alas! Alas! What have I done?" he said with uncontrollable grief. "I have lost my senses in my rage. What is the use of strength and skill and all other gifts, if one cannot control one's anger? Seeta too must have perished in this great conflagration I have raised. My angry deed has led to the utter ruin of my whole purpose. Alas, there is no fool, no sinner, like me on earth. My rage against the *Raakshasas* has ended in the death of Seeta. Here and now I must put an end to my life and to my shame!"

Then he heard some voices in the sky. The *Chaaranas* and *Yakshas* were rejoicing and saying, "What a miracle! Glory be to Hanumaan's prowess! Except the spot where Seeta is, all Lanka is in flames!"

Hearing this ethereal conversation, Hanumaan was relieved. "Seeta has saved herself. She saved me, for it was her purity and power that kept the fire from harming me. How can fire help paying homage to the goddess of Chastity? What can fire do to fire? This fire that I started could not go near Seeta. And is not all this Raama's purpose? Did not the ocean king and Mynaaka mountain come to my help?

Thinking thus, Hanumaan went straight to the Asoka park again. There, under the Simsupa tree, he saw Seeta who was greatly relieved to see him alive and cheerful.

Rejoicing, he bowed before her and said, "Oh mother! I have seen you safe and sound. This is your power and my good fortune. Now give me leave to go."

And Seeta said, "You are indeed a hero. For you there is nothing impossible. See that my lord comes here soon and lays low the *Raakshasas* and redeems me. I depend on you. You alone can achieve this."

"Be assured," said Hanumaan. "Sugreeva will soon be here with Raama and Lakshmana and the myriads of *Vaanaras*. Raavana and his wicked hordes will perish. The happy Prince will return with you to Ayodhya. Grieve no more. God bless you."

Thus consoling her, Hanumaan took leave of Seeta. He went to the shore of the sea and, climbing up the beautiful hill called Arishta, rose into the sky.

On the way he saw Mynaaka eagerly awaiting him. He affectionately stroked it with his hand, but did not stop. He flew straight like an arrow shot from a bow. At sight of the Mahendra hill he knew that he was near the other shore and he roared.

The *Vaanaras*, meanwhile, who saw Hanumaan flying towards them like a great eagle across the sky, shouted, "He is come! he is come!"

Till now their hearts had been full of care and their eyes wet. Now they jumped in their joy.

"It is certain he is returning in triumph," said Jaambavaan. "Else he would not roar in this manner."

They climbed up trees and hills and stood watching with joy the approach of Hanumaan returning from Lanka.

And Hanumaan rejoiced to see the mountains and trees all covered with his friends. Amid their glad uproar, he alighted on the Mahendra hill.

CHAPTER LVIII

A CARNIVAL

BESIDE themselves with joy at the sight of Hanumaan, the *Vaanaras* asssembled on the Mahendra peak; and the veteran Jaambavaan welcoming the son of Vaayu with great affection, spoke on behalf of all.

"We are eager to hear a full account of your journey and its triumphant conclusion. More particularly, we are anxious to know how you discovered Seeta. How is she now? What is the state of her mind and body? And dear son of Anjana, tell us about Raavana's state and behaviour. After knowing everything we shall be in a position to consider and decide what needs to be done next."

Hanumaan tendered mental salutations to Seeta and began his story.

"You know how I sprang into the sky from this peak. As I was flying over the sea, a golden mountain rose suddenly above the surface of the water. I thought it was something rising up to obstruct me and I gave it a flick with my tail. Meekly receiving the blow, the mountain said in a sweet voice, 'My son, I am no enemy. I was saved by your father from the dire wrath of Indra and am ever grateful to him. I now live in safety sheltered by the sea. In olden days, we mountains had wings and flew hither and thither in the sky and the world was in dread of us. Then Indra, to rid the world of this terror, relentlessly pursued us and cut off our wings. It was from this common fate that your father rescued me. You are engaged in the most fatiguing task of flying across the sea. I have come up here to offer you some rest. Stay here for a while and then fulfil Raama's purpose.' I declined the offer for lack of time and, taking leave of him, went on my way."

Thus, in proper sequence and without omission, Hanumaan recounted all that happened during the passage and in the city of Lanka; how he searched for Seeta in vain in Raavana's palace, how he found her at last in the *Asoka Vana*, how there Raavana sought and importuned her and was spurned by her, what dire threats he held out, how the *raakshasis* teased her and drove her to think of putting an end to her own life, and how it was at this juncture he approached and gave her the news of Raama and hope and interest in life.

With tears in his eyes he told them what a divinely precious soul Seeta was and how nobly she had borne herself. Then he narrated how he destroyed the park and killed the *Raakshasa* warriors, how he was finally bound by Indrajit and produced before Raavana. He described what took place at the interview, and how as a punishment for his boldness of speech they set fire to his tail, furnishing him thereby with a great torch with which he set their city ablaze.

On such occasions, when a character has to recapitulate past events, we can see Vaalmeeki's skill in retelling the story in beautiful words. This is a source of special pleasure to those who read the *Raamaayana* as a religious exercise. They do not dislike such repetitions. Indeed it is one of the special charms in a large epic. But I have abridged the recital to suit the general reader who has no time or taste for an oft-repeated tale however edifying.

Those who wish to avert some calamity or desire success in some great undertaking usually make a *Paaraayana* (devotional reading exercise) of the whole of the *Sundarakaanda*, the canto dealing with Hanumaan's expedition to Lanka. It is believed that the same result can be obtained even by a *Paaraayana* of only this chapter where Hanumaan relates to the *Vaanara* warriors all that happened between his crossing and recrossing the sea.

After this full narration of the happenings, Hanumaan proceeded: "Our efforts have been successful so far because of the power of chastity of Seeta who is chastity incarnate. When I think of her I wonder how the *Raakshasa* could seize and carry her away and yet escape being burnt to ashes. But Raavana too had accumulated great power through his *tapas*. Even so, Seeta could have reduced him to ashes if she had chosen, but she patiently endured all this, because she wanted the punishment to proceed from her lord. And now what is your advice? Shall we go straight to Lanka, destroy Raavana and the *Raakshasa* hordes, recover Seeta and restore her to Raama? It is not as if we have not the strength to do this. Single-handed I can destroy them and leave not a trace behind. And Jaambaavan too, all by himself, can utterly destroy the *Raakshasas*. And so can our Prince Angada; and so can Panasa or Neela; so can Mainda and Dwivida, the sons of Asvini. Yes, there are many among us who can slay Raavana and the *Raakshasa* hordes. Indeed I proclaimed aloud in Lanka: 'I, the messenger of Raama and the minister of Sugreeva, am come to destroy you.' But while we are talking, Vaidehi, the Goddess of purity, is there under the Simsupa tree a closely guarded prisoner pining with aching heart for rescue. In her hour of despair, I showed myself to her, and comforted her with the assurance of her lord's speedy arrival. Consider well and decide what should now be done."

Angada, listening to all this, full of indignation jumped up, saying: "I can do it all alone. And there are so many of us here, eager warriors thirsting for battle. It would be improper, after all these days, to go to Raama empty-handed and without Seeta. Let us go straight to Lanka, destroy Raavana and the *Raakshasa* army and return to Kishkindha with Seeta in our midst."

Jaambavaan, old and wise, uttered a gentle protest. "No, it is not right, dear prince," he said. "We should report everything to Raama and Lakshmana and then do what they desire. Raama's purpose should be fulfilled in the manner that he desires. That alone is proper."

All the *Vaanaras*, including Hanumaan and Angada, agreed that this was the right thing to do. They then rose into the sky and flew towards Kishkindha.

They alighted near the protected park of the *Vaanara* king. They made their way into it, drank honey and ate fruit, regardless of the warnings of the guards. They indulged in unrestrained revelry and ruined the beautiful park.

Unable to stand the riotous behaviour of the mirth-makers, Dadhimukha, Sugreeva's uncle and keeper of the royal park, hurried to the king and complained.

"Your protected park has been laid waste. The *Vaanaras* that went south have returned and, alighting in the garden, are behaving outrageously. They pay no heed to my words. On the contrary, they assaulted and insulted me, drank up and ruined all

the honeycombs and plucked and ate fruit as they
liked and are now lying senseless as a result of their
revelry. The trees and plants are all in ruins. The
king should forthwith inflict condign punishment on
these undisciplined *Vaanaras*."

Sugreeva understood the position at once.
"Lakshmana, it is clear that Hanumaan, Jaambavaan and Angada have succeeded in their search and
are celebrating their triumph in this manner."

Saying this he turned to Dadhimukha and said
to him, "Send them all here at once."

Dadhimukha now understood the real state of
affairs and, hastening to the *Vaanaras*, conveyed to
them the king's command.

CHAPTER LIX

THE TIDINGS CONVEYED

SUGREEVA'S conjecture was like nectar to Raama's ears. They eagerly awaited the arrival of the *Vaanaras*. In a short while a great clamour was in the air and the *Vaanara* hordes alighted with cries of triumph.

Hanumaan and Angada leading, the *Vaanaras* marched to the presence of their king who with Raama and Lakshmana was awaiting their coming.

Hanumaan bowed and said: "Seen have I the Goddess of purity, your queen. She is safe and well in Lanka. I salute her from here across space." And he turned southwards and offered worshipful salutation.

Thus succinctly did Hanumaan convey to the Prince the glad news that Seeta was found and was well in body and mind. Sugreeva and Lakshmana, beside themselves with joy, embraced Raama.

"Dear *Vaanara* friends," exclaimed the Prince of Ayodhya, "tell me where exactly Seeta is. How is she? How did you manage to see her? Tell me everything in detail." His eager enquiries came quick upon one another.

The other *Vaanaras* turned to Hanumaan who stood behind, and asked him to narrate all that he had seen and done. Hanumaan began to tell the tale. With his unrivalled courage and strength and single-handed, he had performed a mighty task; and yet he did not push himself forward into the presence of Prince Raama or King Sugreeva, but gave precedence to Angada and the aged Jaambavaan and the others, and was silent until they asked him to speak.

Indeed, generally, great men who dare and do mighty deeds are disinclined to speak about their exploits. In painting this scene the poet brings out this law of natural conduct.

Another thing to note here is Hanumaan's reverence for Seeta. From the time he first saw her his reverence for her appeared to surpass even his devotion to Raama, if the two could be distinguished. This is the case with all pious devotees who regard and worship the Supreme as Mother. When that aspect of the All-immanent Power is before true devotees, their reverence becomes ecstatic like the child's joy in the mother's lap.

"Crossing the hundred *yojanaas* of water, I reached the city of the wicked Raavana on the southern shore. There, in a park attached to the palace, I saw Seeta held prisoner and closely guarded. It was wonderful to see her emaciated form. She maintained life only in the thought of her lord and repetition of his name. Cruel and ugly *Raakshasis* surrounded her. I saw her lying on the ground, her hair unkempt and her face clouded by sorrow and care. When I reached there, she had resolved to put an end to her life to escape from the *Raakshasa* king's importunities and threats. I began uttering praises of your glory in a low voice. Unknown to her, and a mere monkey, I had to secure her confidence first. Then I spoke to her. I told her of the alliance between King Sugreeva and yourself. I told her of your great grief and unchanging love. This filled her with sweet sorrow and awakened hope in her and the desire to live. Asked for a token which I might convey to you, the angel of purity gave me this jewel to be given to you.

"She also told me how once a crow had troubled her while you were asleep and how you were grieved about it; she asked me to remind you of the incident. She wanted me to remind you of another occasion when, roaming among the hills, perspiration had made the *tilak* trickle down her forehead and you replaced it with red ochre rubbed out of a rock.

"She bade me tell you that she would struggle and keep alive for a month, but then she would perish at the hands of Raavana, or she would seek her own release of death. She bade me convey her respects to the *Vaanara* King. Now let us think and make preparations at once for proceeding to Lanka to redeem the princess."

Saying this, he handed the *sikhaa-mani*, crest-jewel, of Seeta to the Prince.

Raama took the jewel from Hanumaan's hand and at the sight of it fainted, racked beyond bearing between extremes of joy and grief.

He pressed the jewel to his bosom and cried, "O Lakshmana!" Again he embraced Hanumaan and said, "Heroic son of *Vaayu*, blessed are you who have seen Seeta. I too see her now before me. You have, indeed, brought her to me."

"Dear hero, my heart's friend!" he cried "tell me everything again in full. Tell me once again what Seeta said. Let me hear her words which are sweet like water to parched lips."

Hanumaan narrated the whole story to the eager listeners and Raama wept when Hanumaan repeated these words of Seeta:

"Many *Raakshasas* has my Raama slain, but why has he not come here yet to slay Raavana and save me from my sufferings? Why has he not sent brave Lakshmana to slay the wretch? It cannot be that my lord has grown indifferent towards me! For I know of no wrong I have ever committed in thought or word or deed to lose his love."

Hanumaan said: "I tried to console her saying, 'Raama is ever thinking of you and grieving for you. He knows no rest. Do not imagine that Raama and Lakshmana have forgotten you. No words of mine could describe their grief. Now that I am going to tell them you are here, it will not be long before they come and destroy Raavana and return with you in triumph to Ayodhya.' It was then she untied the jewel from a knot in a corner of her sari and gave it to me. I placed it on my head in reverence and, securing it, started to return. She stopped me and uttered a benediction again and said: 'Friend Hanumaan! Convey the news of my welfare to the lions, my lord and his brother, to king Sugreeva and his ministers. Devise your plans and help him to come here and redeem me. I trust in you, Hanumaan, absolutely. May God bless you."

"Lay aside your grief, my Lord," continued Hanumaan, "and think out now what has to be done. Seeta doubted how you and the *Vaanara* army could cross the sea. I assured her that she need have no fear or doubt on that score, since, by no means the strongest among the *Vaanaras*, I myself had crossed it as she could see. I said to her that I myself could carry Raama and Lakshmana on my shoulders and cross the sea and bring them there."

CHAPTER LX

THE ARMY MOVES FORWARD

RAAMA heard Hanumaan with heart and eyes overflowing and, when he had come to the end of his narrative, said:

"The deed done by Hanumaan none else in the world could even conceive of attempting — crossing the sea, entering Lanka protected by Raavana and his formidable hosts and accomplishing the task set him by his king not only fully but beyond the fondest hopes of all."

And it saddened him to think that it was not in his power to reward Hanumaan at all adequately for the supreme joy he had brought. "O Hanumaan, let this embrace of mine stand as an acknowledgment of all that my heart feels of gratitude for your great service to me."

So saying while his whole being thrilled with grateful love, he took Hanumaan into his arms and clasped him to his breast.

"Sugreeva," he said, "Hanumaan has indeed wrought a wonder. He entered Lanka so strongly guarded by the *Raakshasas*. He has discovered Seeta and, by consoling her, preserved her life. Bringing back good news of her, he has saved my life also.

"But how are we now going to cross the sea? How can our huge army reach the other shore? Before we can attack Raavana's city and the *Raakshasa's* army, we have first to cross the sea. I see no way of doing it. Our joy in Hanumaan's achievement and the good news he has brought is overlaid by anxiety about our future course."

But the *Vaanara* king said: "What is this, my Lord Raama? What need is there for dejection? Here are my warriors, ready to lay down their lives for you and let it be our joy to transport you and Lakshmana to Lanka. Have no doubt that we can do it. The moment Hanumaan saw Lanka, you may take it the fortress has fallen. Doubt only makes the warrior weak and afraid and should be cast aside. Our victory is certain. The feeling of confidence in my heart at this moment is a good enough omen for me."

Thus Sugreeva reassured Raama, and inspired him to action. Then Raama and Hanumaan discussed matters about Lanka, the town, the fort, the moat and other defences. Understanding nothing, Hanumaan described the wealth of Lanka, the happy lives of the *Raakshasas*, their confidence in Raavana and their affection for him. He told Raama of the might and size of Raavana's army; the strength and structure of the fortress; the alertness of the sentry; the moats, walls and gates, catapults and drawbridges, the care and thoroughness of all the arrangements for defence. He also explained how the coast too was carefully guarded so that no enemy ship could approach it.

"And yet you may be certain," he said, "our *Vaanara* army is fully equal to the conquest of Lanka. We have with us peerless warriors like Angada, Dwivida, Mainda, Jaambavaan, Panasa, Nala and Neela. We have an enormous army. We shall fly in the sky and without touching the ground destroy Lanka. Its mountains and forest defences are nothing to us. We shall raze the city to the ground. Fix the auspicious time and give us the order to start."

Under the star of triumph, Uttara Phalguni, at high noon, the army set forward towards the southern sea. Good omens greeted them.

As they marched, Raama, Sugreeva and Lakshmana went conversing with one another. "If only Seeta could know that we have set out," said Raama, "it would encourage her to keep life going."

Scouts who knew the way went ahead, looking out for enemies lying in ambush. They led the army through regions that could provide food and drink for the huge army. With speed the army crossed mountains and forests.

The *Vaanaras* sometimes carried Raama and Lakshmana on their shoulders so that the march might be speedy. Every moment the enthusiasm of the *Vaanaras* increased. They jumped and roared and sported. Raama could hear them saying to one another, "I shall kill Raavana! I shall meet and kill Raavana!"

Neela and Kumuda went ahead reconnoitering in front of the army. Strong warriors were kept in the rear, guarding it from behind. King Sugreeva, Raama and Lakshmana were in the middle. Raama gave strict orders that the army should inflict no harm or hardship on the towns and villages on the way. The noise of the marching army was like the roar of the sea and filled the eight quarters. The dust they raised covered the sky.

When they came to the Mahendra mountain, Raama climbed the peak and surveyed the sea.

"We should now think and decide," he said, "how the army can cross the sea. Till then let it camp and rest in the forest." And Sugreeva passed the order to the commanders. The *Vaanaras* camped in the forest by the seashore.

When Sugreeva, Raama and Lakshmana had satisfied themselves that the whole army had settled in comfort, the two brothers retired apart.

Raama said: "If a person loses a dear thing, people say that time will enable him to forget about it and he will cease to grieve. But Lakshmana, this is not what I find.'

Dejection again seized Raama for the thought of Seeta and her condition preyed on his mind now more than ever before.

"When Raavana seized Seeta and carried her off," Raama said, breaking down with fresh grief, "she must have cried aloud 'Ha my Lord! Ha Raama! Ha Lakshmana!' But she saw no one coming. We failed to go to her help. Every time I think of the suffering she then must have gone through, my grief swells up afresh. What am I to do? Like the limbs of one who has drunk poison, my whole body burns with pain. She is held in the grip of the cruel *raakshasis* and she is in great anguish. Janaka's daughter, the bride who entered the home of great Dasaratha, she lies on the bare ground, a prisoner surrounded by *raakshasis!*"

"Raama!" said Lakshmana, "cease from sorrow. Soon we shall destroy Raavana and rescue Seeta and take her home to Ayodhya. She will enter the city like the goddess of chastity. Give up your grief. Arm yourself with courage."

CHAPTER LXI

ANXIETY IN LANKA

NOW let us leave Raama and his host here and go back to Raavana. Great poets in all languages delineate with sympathy even their bad characters allowing gleams of goodness to shine through occasionally, for nature has not made anybody wholly and unredeemably evil.

The poet's aim is to direct the reader's mind into the path of Good, the *saatvik* way. For this purpose they use all their skill and power in developing even their *raajasik* and *taamasik* characters.

The reader who is held by *raajasik* and *taamasik* qualities, naturally tends to sympathise with such characters; much more so readers below the average who are untouched by the *saatvik* element. They would regard the deeds of the hero and other *saatvik* characters as mere fiction invented for blind worship, and identify themselves with the *raajasik* and *taamasik* characters and even claim these as their own kith and kin. They would find themselves attracted by such characters and follow their doings with considerable interest.

Paradise Lost, the English epic on a Biblical theme, is famous throughout the world. In this poem Milton delineates the Almighty and Jesus, His spiritual son and human incarnation, as well as several orders of angels. But the most impressive character in the great epic is Satan who rebelled against God and brought sin and death into this world. Critics of English poetry admire Milton's wonderful success in the characterisation of Satan.

Similarly, the great dramatic poet Shakespeare has created a wonderful character in Shylock, the usurer and miser. Even such embodiments of despicable qualities are presented by the poets as possessing courage, determination, energy and other good qualities which attract us and serve as a bright background to their blackness. In Vaalmeeki's portraits of Raavana and Kumbhakarna too, we notice the same artistic skill. The cook who meets all tastes shows his skill in making out of bitter vegetables an attractive dish. So does the poet show his skill in portraying evil.

The *Raakshasa* king was somewhat ashamed and afraid at the thought of what Hanumaan had achieved in Lanka. He summoned his ministers and took counsel with them.

He began in an apologetic tone. "What has happened is something strange and unexpected. No one has till now been known to enter our city, but this envoy of Raama has not only entered Lanka, he has met and talked with the imprisoned Seeta. He has destroyed temples and palaces. He has slain some of our best warriors. He has filled our people with fear. And this thing is not likely to stop here. Hence we have to consider what should be done. You know that the king should decide his course of action only after consulting his loyal ministers of clear vision and well-versed in statecraft. And so I have summoned this Council. Raama has become an inveterate enemy. Let us consider what we should do about it.

"The king has no use for ministers who are not straightforward or who not knowing their own minds wobble in their advice. The matter before us is most important. Raama is strong, and so is his army. It is certain that they will contrive somehow to cross the sea. It would be unwise to trust to that single defence. Consider well and tell me how we can strengthen and secure our city and army and what steps we should take to defend ourselves."

After listening to the king, the members of the Assembly spoke with one voice.

"Great king! Knowing well that our army and our weapons are the strongest in the world, why need you be anxious? Where is the enemy who dares to attack your fortress and who can oppose your army with any hope of success? The world knows your might. Did you not invade the city of Bhogavati and defeat the Naaga king? Did you not attack powerful Kubera and defeat him and his *Yakshas* and capture his *Pushpaka Vimaana* as well as this island of Lanka? Did not Maya in fear of you sue for your favour and friendship and give you his daughter in marriage? How many cities in the nether region have you not attacked and taken? You fought and defeated the Kaalakeyas. The sons of Varuna, yea, and Yama himself have been suppliants for your mercy. And who is this Raama? Your son Indrajit by himself can destroy Raama and his *Vaanara* army. Did he not seize and imprison Indra himself and afterwards let him go? How can Raama and his *Vaanaras* stand against such a warrior? You have only to bid Indrajit destroy this *Vaanara* crowd and all will be over. Why should you, great king, be anxious?"

Thus they spoke in praise of their king.

The Commander-in-chief Prahasta rose like a great black cloud. "You, who subdued in battle the *Devas, Daanavas* and *Gandharvas*, why should you, oh King of kings, feel anxious because of these little creatures? It is true that the monkey came here and caught us napping and did some mischief. But this sort of thing will never happen again. If he comes again, I know how to manage him. I alone can destroy the whole *Vaanara* race, if only you will order it. You need not fear any danger from this small indiscretion of yours, the abduction of Seeta."

Next Durmukha rose and roared: "We shall not let this monkey's bravado and undeserved good luck go unavenged. I shall go this very instant and destroy the *Vaanara* army, root and branch, and return."

Vajradamshtra stood with a terrible iron club in his hand and cried: "Here is my weapon unwashed and still covered with the blood and flesh of my foes. Why waste your time talking about this monkey? Are not Raama and Lakshmana our enemies? I shall slay them first and then destroy the *Vaanara* army and return immediately. Only let me go. I have a piece of advice to give you, King, if you would listen. Let us order some *Raakshasa* warriors to put on human form and approach Raama, telling him, 'Bharata has sent us in advance. A great army is coming behind to help you.' While Raama is thus fooled into negligence, our *Raakshasa* army can travel through the sky and destroy him and his followers on the other shore. This is my advice."

Nikumbha, son of Kumbhakarna, rose and said, "All of you may stay here with the King. I shall go alone and meet and destroy the enemy and bring you the news."

Another *Raakshasa*, licking his lips, said with gusto: "I shall go alone and kill and feast on the flesh of these two men, Raama and Lakshmana. Please let me go."

Thus one after another they got up and spoke brave words to please Raavana and then all of them stood up together and, raising their weapons, roared aloud.

At that Vibheeshana, the younger brother of Raavana, made them all sit down, and said to the king with folded hands: "Brother, what these people say is sweet to hear but not true or good to act upon. Anything done in violation of *Neeti shaastra* (the Science of Politics) can only lead to grief and ruin. It is only after trying *saama* (conciliation), *daana* (buying off the enemy) and *bheda* (sowing discord) that one should think of using *danda* (force of arms) against a foe. If you take the advice of these people and start a war now, it would mean the destruction of Lanka and all of us. We should also consider the demands of *dharma*. It was not right, it was indeed a great sin for you, to have seized and brought Raama's wife here. We should first cleanse ourselves of this sin. What harm did Raama do to us? What Raama did in the Dandaka forest was in pure self-defence and the defence of those that looked to him for protection. He fought with and slew only those that went out to slay him. His actions surely do not justify your carrying away his wife. And even if we had any just complaint against him, we should have met in battle. Instead of that, to contrive his absence and seize his wife was very wrong and sinful. When the fault is on your side, it is morally not right that we should think of battle. Further, warcraft requires that before fighting we should take some measure of Raama's strength and that of his army. We have had some taste of Hanumaan's strength and skill. It is pointless to talk lightly to him. Did he not do remarkable things? Though our

own strength may be great, we should weigh it
against the enemy's strength and then decide
whether we should seek war or avoid it. But first it is
essential that we should restore Seeta. My advice is
this, before Raama and the *Vaanaras* attack Lanka,
let us restore Seeta. Dear brother, I am saying all
this for your good. Pray, do not be angry with me. We
should first set right our own fault and then think of
other things."

Thus with folded hands Vibheeshana besought
Raavana.

Though Raavana was pleased with the
vain-glorious words of his ministers and generals,
there was doubt lurking in his mind. Hence, after
listening to Vibheeshana, he said: "Let us meet again
tomorrow and consider this matter."

He adjourned the Council and retired.

CHAPTER LXII

RAAVANA CALLS A COUNCIL AGAIN

AS soon as the day dawned, Vibheeshana went to the king. He had thought deeply over the matter and had come to a decision. His brother's welfare demanded that he should seek somehow to convert and save him.

Vibheeshana entered the royal palace and stood with folded hands before the king. Raavana sent away all but the principal Ministers and asked his brother to speak.

"My brother and my lord," began Vibheeshana, "forgive me if what I say is not pleasing to your ears. My desire is not to flatter but to save you from a great danger while there is yet time. I beg of you to listen to me, consider well what I say and then decide on your course of action.

"Ever since you brought Seeta to Lanka we see only evil omens. Even when the libation is poured with the correct *mantra*, the flame does not spring to receive it. One finds snakes in places of worship. Ants infest food offerings. The udders of cows are dry and yield no milk. Elephants, horses, camels and monkeys fall sick, reject food and behave strangely. Medicines have lost their efficacy. Crows perch in numbers on the house-tops making hideous noises. Vultures circling overhead fill the augurs with anxiety. Foxes boldly enter the city and howl at unusual hours. Wild beasts haunt the streets. These portents should not be disregarded. I beg of you, restore Seeta to her husband. It is only since her coming here that these omens are noticed as you can verify by asking others. Why should we, who have so much to lose, needlessly incur any one's enmity? Let us restore Seeta to her people and live happily."

Thus did Vibheeshana plead earnestly with his brother.

"Never, never!" exclaimed Raavana. "Let there be no talk here of Seeta being returned to her people. I do not think much of this enemy. I see nothing to be afraid of. Now, you may go."

Though he spoke thus and was obstinate, Raavana had no peace of mind. Seeta had not yielded to him and his own near kinsmen disapproved of his conduct. He was agitated, but putting on an air of confidence and unconcern he summoned the Council again. Lust and injured vanity kept him from the straight path, but he found some consolation in taking counsel from others.

From the palace to the hall of Council he drove through the street in a golden chariot drawn by noble steeds. Warriors, holding swords and shields and wearing brilliant uniforms, marched in front, behind and on the sides. Others mounted on elephants and horses and armed with axes, spears and other terrible weapons, followed the chariot. Trumpets were blown and drums beaten.

As the Lord of Lanka, accompanied by his retinue, passed majestically through the royal street, his people bent low their heads and folded their hands and invoked victory for him. As he entered the hall, drums and trumpets sounded loudly and filled the eight quarters.

Raavana took his seat on an agate throne in the great hall constructed by Maya which shone in all the splendour of gold and silver and precious carpets.

Hundreds of demons stood sentry without. Obedient to the call of the King, thousands of *Raakshasa* warriors had assembled in the chamber. Long rows of vehicles stood in the streets. Within the chamber each was assigned a seat appropriate to his rank.

Priests and chanters of the Vedas came in hundreds and after receiving tokens of respect from the king were seated in the hall.

Vibheeshana, Suka, Prahasta and others bowed before the king and sat in their respective places. Devoted officers thronged the hall, all brave and efficient and waiting to fulfil the commands of their king.

The air was heavy with rich perfume. The assembly equalled Indra's in splendour and everyone felt that momentous decisions were to be taken. Raavana broke the hushed expectant silence of the great assembly in a voice deep and resonant as thunder. He said:

"You are strong, brave and skilled in the arts of peace and war. You can find a way out of every difficulty. Never so far has your advice miscarried. And so, once again, I seek your counsel. You know well what I have done. I have brought here Seeta who was living in the Dandaka forest. My desire for her so entirely possesses me that sending her back is to me unthinkable. She has not so far submitted to my wishes and entertains a foolish hope that Raama will come here and redeem her. I have told her that it is an impossible wish and a vain hope. Finally, she asked for a year's time and I gave it to her. I now seek your counsel. My desire is unfulfilled. I can never agree to sending Seeta back and begging forgiveness from Raama. Till now neither you, my great warriors, nor I have known defeat in battle. True, a big monkey somehow contrived to cross the sea and wrought some mischief here. But hard indeed will it be for Raama and the *Vaanara* army to cross the sea and come here. And even if they did come, what need we fear? What chance have they against us?

"On the other side of the sea, Raama, Lakshmana, Sugreeva and the *Vaanaras* are encamped. Think how we can slay Raama and Lakshmana.

"I should have summoned the Council earlier. But Kumbhakarna was in his period of sleep and I waited till he work up."

Thus spoke Raavana, blinded by lust, hiding his real anxiety and mixing a little falsehood with truth. For Seeta had not asked for a year's time. She had absolutely rejected his advances, but he asked her to reconsider and gave her a year's time.

CHAPTER LXIII

VIBHEESHANA

KUMBHAKARNA, the younger brother of Raavana, spoke in the assembly:

"Great King! Ignoring the principles of state-craft, you have run into a great danger. If you had any grievance against Raama and Lakshmana, you should have met them face to face and defeated and slain them before carrying off Seeta. If you had acted thus, even Seeta would have admired you and there would then have been a possibility of her accepting you. As waters flow down a mountain, she would have followed a victorious warrior.

"You did not consult us before committing the offence and incurred the enmity of Raama, but now, when it is too late, you seek our counsel. This is not the right way of doing things that a king should follow."

Having spoken thus harshly, Kumbhakarna looked at the king and saw he was pained. Affectionate as he was brave, he could not endure the sadness in his brother's face.

"Let by-gones be by-gones," he thought, "one cannot forsake one's honour." Kumbhakarna was under no delusion as to the consequences, but his generous spirit accepted them for the sake of the brother he idolised. He knew that Raama was a peerless warrior. He knew the power of his bow and also the limitations of the boons that Raavana had received from the gods. But it was no good taking the heart out of others in the face of unavoidable peril and so he also began to speak vaunting words like the rest:

"What you did may be wrong, and so too the way you chose to do it. You have done first what you should have done last. And yet, it does not matter. I shall slay Raama. Do not be afraid. One or two of his arrows may touch me. In spite of it, I shall kill him and drink his blood and victory will be yours. My brother, lay aside your care, and think of other things."

Some people suggest that Kumbhakarna was dull and so he thus contradicted himself; but it was not stupidity, it was due to generous affection that he accepted the inevitable fearlessly. He was a proud warrior who loved his brother and his people and he decided on honourable death with them.

Prahasta was Raavana's chief counsellor. He spoke of the King's invincible strength and cheered him up.

Raavana now grew enthusiastic and said: "Didn't I vanquish Kubera? Didn't I drive him out and make Lanka my own? Who dare come here and oppose me? Let us see!"

The assembly applauded these words.

Vibheeshana alone did not join the applause. He did not mind the wrath of his royal brother. He felt it was his duty to warn him of the danger and the error of his ways.

He felt bound to make his utmost effort to save him and the *Raakshasa* face from doom. He stood up and spoke:

"You have brought Seeta and with her, death for yourself and your race. Your first duty to yourself and your people is to restore her to Raama. If you fail in this, we shall all assuredly perish. This is certain."

He went on describing Raama's strength and skill and his mastery of weapons. He spoke frankly and without fear.

"If we oppose Raama," he said, "defeat is inevitable. Our fortune is sinking. Let us restore Seeta, seek Raama's pardon and thus save our kingdom, our lives and possessions and honour."

At this importunity of Vibheeshana, Indrajit, Raavana's son, lost patience and burst out:

"My uncle's words fill me with shame. What race are we? What is our strength? I marvel that a descendant of Pulastya should talk in this strain and that the assembly should meekly sit and listen. My uncle has only betrayed his evil intentions. We can never agree to his proposal. Are we to be afraid of two petty humans? Did I not beat Indra down in battle and his hordes of gods? Does not the whole world tremble even now in terror before us? Vibheeshana's counsel is an insult to our race!"

Vibheeshana answered gently: "Boy, you lack experience. That is why you talk thus. You are the king's son and should be his best friend; but I am afraid you are proving yourself his worst enemy. And you, ministers who ought to give good advice, you are leading the king to ruin. My Lord of Lanka! Do not reject what I say. Return Seeta honourably to Raama and seek his forgiveness. This is the only way; there is no other. Failing to pursue the only available course, we shall all perish."

Raavana's rage was now uncontrollable. "I put up with your talk thus far," he shouted in anger, "because you are my brother. Else you would by now be dead. A brother, I see, is one's worst enemy. All the world knows that the envy of brothers brings

dishonour and discomfiture to the brave. They hide
their real desire and wait for their time and, when it
comes, do not hesitate to practise their treachery.
How true is the complaint of the wild elephants in
the story! We are not afraid of the burning fire. 'We
do not mind the hunters and their long spears. The
noosed ropes and the chains can do little harm to us.
But the elephants which join the hunters and give us
trouble, these brothers and cousins who turn against
us, they are our terror!' Yes. So long as one is safe
and prosperous, the brother smiles and talks
pleasantly. But when danger comes, he is ready to
leave. The bee does not stay with the flower after the
honey has been sucked. It goes in search of another
flower. Brothers and cousins are no better than
these bees. One cannot trust them in adversity. If
any one else should have spoken as you have done,
Vibheeshana, I would have slain him here and now.
Base fellow! You are a disgrace to our race!"

Unable to bear the insult, Vibheeshana rose
and said: "My brother, you may speak as you please.
Though you have wandered from the way of *dharma*,
you are still my brother and I warn you that, drawn
by the noose of Yama, you are going along the path of
destruction. My advice, salutary but unpleasant, you
reject. It is easy to speak sweet words; your
ministers are doing it. I spoke for your good, but
truth is bitter and you hate it.

"The terrible vision of Raama's darts destroying
you is before my mind's eye and makes me speak as
I do. You call me your enemy. Defend your city and
your life as well as you can. God bless you! I am
going. May you be happy! I thought I could serve you
in your need, but you will not let me. You imagine

that I envy you and your possessions. Good counsel is rejected by one whose end is near."

Having spoken thus, and realising that there was no place for him in Lanka thereafter, Vibheeshana renounced all his possessions and, rising into the sky, proceeded straight to the spot where Raama and Lakshmana were encamped. Four good *Raakshasa* friends went along with him.

CHAPTER LXIV

THE VAANARA'S DOUBT

HAVING committed a sin and run into danger, Raavana did not see how to extricate himself. Like other kings in a quandary, he called a council for consultation. Many spoke flattering words. Only two spoke harshly.

One said: "You have committed a fault. But I will give up my life for you." This was Kumbhakarna.

The other, Vibheeshana, said: "You have committed a sin, but there is still time for repentance and escape from consequences. If you take this right and wise course, we shall all escape destruction and live happily. Restore Seeta and seek pardon of Raama."

"Never," said Raavana.

"Then our ways part and I leave you," said Vibheeshana.

In a conflict of duties, each one follows his own nature. All cannot follow one and the same path.

Raavana's self-indulgent vanity would not let him admit his error or retrace his steps. Very rarely does one who has committed a sin confess defeat. It requires some courage of a bad sort to commit a sin; but it requires much greater courage of a noble kind to confess it.

It was this noble courage that Raavana lacked. When an evil is being perpetrated, the friends of the evil-doer face a difficult problem. Some are constrained against their better judgment to espouse the wrong cause through gratitude for past

kindness, a sense of loyalty, or affinities of blood.
Others think it their duty to try and reform the
sinner. Regardless of his anger and hatred and
consequent danger to themselves and if their efforts
fail they part company from the sinner, rather than
abandon *dharma* and give their support to the
sinner who persists in crime. They hold that it can
never be one's duty to support or co-operate with
adharma. It would indeed be *adharma* to refrain
from doing one's best to reform the sinner or to
co-operate in his sin.

In the *Raamaayana*, Kumbhakarna and
Vibheeshana represent these two different types. If
Raavana had told Vibheeshana: "Come, let us go to
the Dandaka forest and carry off Seeta," it is
inconceivable that Vibheeshana could have com-
plied. That is why we respect Vibheeshana.

"At least now restore Seeta and be happy,"
Vibheeshana said and tried to persuade Raavana.
"Raama will surely forgive you. Take the way of
dharma." But Raavana would not listen, and
Vibheeshana, as an enemy of sin, had no alternative
but to part company from the perverse wickedness of
Raavana. Hence it would be wrong to find fault with
Vibheeshana. And if we find fault with him, it
because our concern for *dharma* is weak.

But can we find fault with Kumbhakarna? We
cannot do this either. He is one of those noble
soldiers of lost causes whose faults we forgive for
their selfless loyalty, and sublime acceptance of
death.

But. because we cannot condemn Kumbhakarna, it does not follow that we must condemn
Vibheeshana. There are some people today who
rejoice in arguing against *dharma* and against

Vibheeshana; hence his elaboration of a simple point.

Men are restrained from evil by the wholesome fear that if they commit sin they would forfeit the affection and goodwill of their friends and kinsmen. This fear is a strong incentive to good behaviour and its removal would be a serious loss in society. All this is forgotten by those who argue that Vibheeshana was a 'traitor'. Raavana was the first, unfortunately by no means the last, to dub him by that name. Those who are anxious to retain the support of kinsfolk while pursuing evil ways disapprove of Vibheeshana's conduct. But Vibheeshana was not afraid of being a traitor. He would have nothing to do with *adharma*. His course was, however, not easy as we shall see.

The *Vaanara* chieftains standing on the northern seashore saw all of a sudden the sky lit up with a golden glow like summit of Mount Meru. It was too steady to be a flash of lightning.

In the brightness could be distinguished the forms of five big *Raakshasas*. Sugreeva, the king and commander of the *Vaanaras*, looking at them said: "There is no doubt these are *Raakshasas* come from Lanka with hostile designs."

On hearing this, the *Vaanara* warriors armed themselves with trees and boulders and said: "Let us go. We shall intercept and slay them and bring them down to earth."

Vibheeshana, hearing these words of the *Vaanaras*, showed no signs of fear but from above with calm courage spoke out in a clear voice:

"Vibheeshana stands here before you, the brother of Raavana, the wicked king of the

Raakshasas. I am here before you, none other than brother to Raavana, who killed Jataayu and carried off Seeta by force and is now keeping here a prisoner in Lanka.

"In vain I strove to turn him from his wicked designs and counselled him to restore Seeta and seek Raama's forgiveness. All the response I got was disdain and public insult. Hence I am standing here before you. Renouncing kingdom, wife and children, I seek service and sanctuary at Raama's feet. I pray you, convey this information to Raama."

Sugreeva mistrusted the good faith of the *Raakshasa* king's brother and reported thus to Raama: "Vibheeshana, the brother of Raavana, has come here with four *Raakshasa* friends seeking sanctuary at your feet. They are standing there in the sky. Consider well, you who are skilled in affairs, what should be done now. These *Raakshasas* are adepts in duplicity. They can make themselves invisible and do many other tricks. They have all the skill and courage of the wicked. One cannot trust them. I believe that these *Raakshasas* have been sent by Raavana himself.

"They have come here to mix with us for subversive purposes. Or else they intend seeking an opportunity to assassinate the leaders in our camp. Whatever Vibheeshana may say, we cannot forget that he is the brother of our foe. By birth he belongs to the wicked *Raakshasa* race. How can we trust him? This is some trick of Raavana, I have no doubt. It is best to kill Vibheeshana and his companions right now. If we admit him into our camp, he will betray us at the first opportunity and return to his own people. Permit us, therefore, to destroy forthwith Raavana's brother and his followers."

Having thus frankly expressed his feelings at the sight of the *Raakshasa*, Sugreeva stood in silence, awaiting Raama's reply.

Raama listened and turned to Hanumaan and other leaders and said:

"You have heard the words of the King who is well-versed in policy. Raavana's brother has come and waits there for our pleasure. I wish to know your opinion on this matter. In times of crisis, one should ask for the advice of friends. Tell me without reservation what you feel in your hearts."

Angada, the *Vaanara* prince said: "He has come from our enemy's camp. We do not know whether he has come of his own accord or was sent by our foe. While perhaps it would not be right to reject him out of hand, it would be dangerous to accept him without testing him. Let us at least watch his behaviour carefully without giving him any opening for mischief. If his movements are suspicious, we can throw him out. If they are friendly and show good faith, we shall accept him." Thus spoke the son of Vaali.

Sarabha said: "I do not think it safe to admit him now, to decide later what to do with him. Even now, let us test him through skilful questioners and decide once for all what to do with him."

Jaambavaan said: "Nothing can be discovered by testing such persons. If he is come here hiding treacherous intentions, no test can discover the truth. Raavana is our inveterate foe. His brother says that he has all of a sudden broken with him and come over to us. Thus sudden rupture with a brother is hard to believe.

"We have not yet crossed the sea. What is his motive in seeking safety with us while we are on this hither shore? All this is very suspicious. They are a deceitful race. I think we should not admit him."

Mainda said: "How can we reject a man on mere suspicion? Only after careful examination can we decide how to deal with him. He say that he has forsaken Raavana and come over to us. We can find out the truth of this statement. Some of us should talk to him and then decide. Surely we have enough ability to do this."

Then Raama turned to Hanumaan the wise.

CHAPTER LXV

THE DOCTRINE OF SURRENDER AND GRACE

IN response to Raama's invitation, Hanumaan expressed his opinion in clear, sweet and pregnant words:

"Why should you ask for our advice? Not even Brihaspati has anything to tell you that you do not already know. If it is dangerous to admit Vibheeshana, how is the danger met by delay and trial? Where is the time or opportunity for a test? Moreover, Vibheeshana has not approached us stealthily. He has come to us with frank openness and a clear object. What is there for scouts to discover about him? It has been said by some that his sudden advent is suspicious. But why? What wonder is there if Vibheeshana became disgusted with Raavana and foresaw his certain disgrace and a defeat? What wonder is there if he recognised your heroic virtues and nobility and the certainty of your victory?

"To me the time and manner of his coming give no room for suspicion. It has been suggested that before admitting him our leaders should put him questions and examine his answers. But one who knows that he is suspected would cease to speak or behave naturally. He would be afraid that we are out to find only faults in him. And thus his real nature will not be revealed.

"I see no cause for suspicion in the face or speech of this *Raakshasa* suppliant. His care-free looks disclose a guiltless heart. The wise say that the face is a perfect mirror of the heart. I think that

Vibheeshana has come here honestly to seek sanctuary at your feet. And there is nothing strange in his action. He knows Raavana's real weakness. He knows that the lord of Lanka is fated to fall. He knows too that you have slain Vaali and given his kingdom to Sugreeva. Granting that his real motive is to secure for himself the sovereignty of Lanka, there is nothing wrong in it and certainly it is a guarantee that he will be loyal to us. Hence I feel that we should admit him."

The *Vaanara* chiefs thus differed in their views.

Kumbhakarna acted according to ordinary morality. This was a simple thing which everybody could understand. But Vibheeshana followed a higher morality. The path he chose was more difficult and likely to be blamed. He knew (how could anyone else know?) his inward suffering at the thought of Raavana's evil doings. Ordinary people could not sympathise with his situation. Hence the *Vaanaras* failed to understand the conflict in his mind. Even today people find it hard, without elaborate explanation, to appreciate Vibheeshana aright.

Patiently, Raama listened to the various views of the *Vaanara* chiefs. When at last he heard Hanumaan's words he was filled with joy.

Raama, steadfast in his own *dharma*, found satisfaction in Hanumaan's utterance. A good man is glad when a friend's opinion supports his decision on a question of duty.

"If a man comes as a friend," said Raama, "how can I reject him? It is against the law of my life. All of you, my friends and helpers, should know this.

Once a man surrenders himself, one should overlook all his faults."

But Sugreeva was not satisfied. He said:

"This *Raakshasa* has on his own showing deserted his brother whose cause he considers lost. How can put faith in a person who forsakes his own brother in his need?"

Vaalmeeki records that on hearing these words of Sugreeva, Raama turned to Lakshmana with a smile. Probably the smile was provoked by Sugreeva's forgetfulness of his own fraternal conduct in his indignant condemnation of Vibheeshana!

Raama said to Sugreeva: "I see what you mean. But listen. It is natural for kings to suspect brothers and neighbour-kings. Good kings who entertain no such suspicion are exceptions. Most kings imagine that brothers envy them. What wonder then if Raavana suspected and insulted Vibheeshana? It follows that Vibheeshana feared danger to himself if he stayed on in Lanka. I conclude therefore that he has no sinister motive against us in coming here for refuge. Let us go further and grant that he has eyes on the kingdom, expecting Raavana's defeat at our hands. Even in this ambition there is nothing wrong. Well, Lakshmana, can we expect all people to be like our Bharata?"

Having said this, Raama was silent for a moment, lost in remembrance of Bharata's selfless love.

Then he spoke: "Who in the world is as lucky as I am? Who has a bother like Bharata? And what a father I had! His love for me was so great that his life fled when I came away to the forest. And my friends, who else is blessed like me with friends such as you?"

Having spoken thus he wiped the tears in his eyes, and went back to the subject on hand.

"I see no point in the argument that Vibheeshana will forsake us, as he has forsaken his brother. He had cause for forsaking his brother, and can have none for leaving us. We do not want Lanka, and if, as is natural, he wants it, he can get it only through our victory. From the point of view of policy, it would be a mistake to reject Vibheeshana.

"But there is a stronger reason. When one comes to me for refuge, I cannot reject him. This is my *dharma*. It does not matter if as a result of this I suffer. Even at the cost of life I must do this duty of mine. Never can I deviate from it. Verily, I tell you, even if Raavana himself came to me for sanctuary, I would accept him without hesitation. How then can I reject his brother who has done me no wrong? Go and fetch Vibheeshana."

"My Lord Raama! It is wonderful how clearly the right stands out demonstrated when you speak!" said Sugreeva. "I see things clearly now. I shall go and bring Vibheeshana. May he too become a loving friend of yours, even like us!" And Sugreeva went to fetch Vibheeshana.

In the Vaishnava tradition, this episode, in which Vibheeshana is taken by the Prince into his camp and innermost council, is held to be as important as the *Bhagavad Gita* episode in the *Mahaabhaarata*.

It illustrates the doctrine that the Lord accepts all who in absolute surrender seek shelter at his feet, regardless of their merits or defects. Their sins are burnt out by the mere act of surrender. This is a message of hope to erring humanity. It is the heart of the Vaishnava faith that there is hope for the worst of us if only we surrender ourselves to the Lord.

But why should I restrict this doctrine to the Vaishnava tradition? Is not this the heart of all the religious traditions in our land, yes, and of all the religions in the world? Every world teacher stresses this certainty of relief and redemption. It is not to Arjuna only that Krishna said: "Have no fear, cast off all doubt, I shall destroy all your sins." Wherever in the world God has spoken to mankind in a human voice, He has given this assurance.

There are two ways in which we can regard Vaalmeeki's account of Raama's acceptance of Raavana's brother. The poet describes the rules of policy, the matters to be examined before one can accept a visitor from the enemy's camp. This is shown in the speeches of the *Vaanara* king, the cultured and accomplished Hanumaan and Raama, the firm upholder of *dharma*. But in addition to right policy, we see here Raama's character and personality due to nature and nurture.

He said: "I cannot reject anyone who comes to me for protection. This is my *dharma*. If Raavana himself came to me, I would not reject him."

Those who look on Raama as an *avataar* of God find in this utterance the essence of scripture. The solemn assurance which Krishna gives to Arjuna later in the *Gita*, that assurance the Prince of Ayodhya declares in the presence of Sugreeva and others in this Vibheeshana episode of the *Raamaayana*.

This divine assurance is the life and light that a world filled with sin and darkness, needs.

CHAPTER LXVI

THE GREAT CAUSEWAY

MEANWHILE Raavana did something foolish. He sent a scout to seduce Sugreeva from his loyalty to Raama. This *Raakshasa*, Suka by name, flew across and in disguise met Sugreeva in secret and with every appearance of benevolent solicitude spoke to him thus:

"Raavana, the king of Lanka, has sent me because of his affection and regard for you. He sends you his fraternal greetings. You are a king and he is another and there is no sense in your staking your high heritage and making common cause with a disinherited prince against an all-powerful king.

"If Raavana desired Raama's wife and carried her off, how does it concern you? What do you lose by it? Consider well and choose your course with discretion. It is most expedient that you and your army should return forthwith to Kishkindha."

But Sugreeva's response was scornful and definite:

"Base fellow! Go and tell your king that he is no brother of mine. He is wicked and, being an enemy of my friend Raama, he is my enemy too and we are out to rid the world of him and his wicked gang. He is a fool to imagine that he can offend Raama and still survive. Tell him that there is no escape for him. Tell him all this as from me."

When Sugreeva delivered this message to the *Raakshasa* spy, the *Vaanaras* caught hold of him and began to handle him roughly but Raama sternly forbade it and set him free to go the way he came.

The spy rushed back to Lanka and conveyed the result of his adventure to Raavana.

As soon as Vibheeshana's adherence was accepted by Raama, Lakshmana and Sugreeva crowned Vibheeshana king of Lanka and performed the *abhisheka* with sea water. Vibheeshana pledged unchanging friendship to Raama and Raama in turn gave his word that he would not return to Ayodhya without slaying Raavana.

Then Sugreeva, Vibheeshana and Lakshmana deliberated on how to cross the sea. They thought it best to begin with a prayer to the ocean-god and submitted their opinion to Raama.

Raama accepted their counsel and, spreading *darbha* grass on the seashore and laying himself on it, began a fast, addressing his request for a passage across, to the king of the sea.

For three days he prayed to the god of the sea but received no response. Then Raama, his eyes glowing with anger at the sea-god's arrogance, turned to Lakshmana and said:

"The low-minded mistake courtesy and gentleness for want of strength. Mildness is simply wasted on them. See now how I shall bring this misproud sea to its senses with my arrows which shall not only choke it with the carcasses of mighty fish but even dry it up with their fierce odour. Bring me my bow and quiver, O Soumitra!"

Then bow in hand and blazing with wrath like the destroying fire at the end of the world he shot arrows irresistible as thunderbolts into the bosom of the sea. These missiles of power disturbed the sea to its depths carrying death and dismay to all it contained and presently the tortured waters began to exhale steam in their agony. It looked as though Raama in his wrath would convert the sea with its infinitude of waters into a desert of blazing dust bereft of all life. The sea-god could stand it no longer. Shining like the rising sun behind Mount Meru, he appeared and stood before Raama.

With folded hands he said:

"My Lord Raamachandra! I am subject to the laws of nature like the earth, the air, space, light, and all constituents of the universe. How can I depart from my nature, which is to be vast, deep, wave-filled, impassable? But this I can do. Ask the *Vaanaras* to bring boulders and trees to build a causeway. I shall permit it. I shall help you by receiving and keeping in place the rocks and trees. This is all that I can do and I shall also show the most favourable place for this causeway.

"There is Nala, son of Viswakarma, with you, who has the ability to build this path. May victory be yours."

Raama, true to his nature, graciously accepted the sea god's apology and offer of help. And then, ordered by Raama, they all began to work. Thousands of *Vaanaras* went at it with enthusiasm and soon finished building the causeway.

Vaalmeeki describes the work at length. He sings with gusto of the noise and confusion of the gigantic project. The *Vaanaras* went to the mountains and forests and, plucking rocks and trees, dragged them to the shore. The bigger *Vaanaras* brought big boulders and threw them into the sea. As they fell down, the water splashed up sky-high. Nala stood and supervised their labours. The leaders in charge of companies kept them active. On top of the rocks and trees, when the base was firm, a dressing of grass and little pieces of wood was given to produce a level surface. The noise raised by the dam-builders drowned the roar of the ocean.

The construction was complete. The new path shone across the sea like the milky way in the sky. Hosts of gods above rejoiced, as hosts of *Vaanaras* shouted below in exultation. The gods and the *rishis* uttered benedictions.

Then they went on the causeway. Hanumaan carried Raama on his shoulders and Angada carried Lakshmana on his. The *Vaanara* army crossed the sea.

There is a principle expounded here. As Raama stood bow in hand, the ocean-god bowed before him with clasped hands and said:

"Dear Raamachandra! Earth, air, ether, water, fire — these five elements must follow the eternal laws of their nature. Tempted by pleasure or reward or frightened of punishment, can I ever swerve from my nature? Can water harden and become stone? Or can I reduce my depths into a shallow pond for your easy crossing?"

Thus the ocean king protested with all politeness to Sri Raama.

Vaalmeeki puts into the mouth of the ocean king a fundamental of our religious philosophy. He explains the primordial relationship between God and Nature. God's law operates in and through Nature. The laws of nature were created so that the universe may proceed by itself. So too the law of *Karma*. The five elements, all objects without life as well as all living creatures, must follow their own permanent laws.

According to the Hindu *Shaastras*, Nature itself, the sequence and chain of cause of effect, the properties of matter, and the law of *Karma*, all are ordained permanently by God.

Nature itself is a witness to God; He is not proved by a suspension of the laws of nature.

This is expounded clearly in the 9th Chapter of the *Bhagavad Gita:*

"Under my supervision Nature gives rise to all that exists — movable and immovable — and the universe evolves from this cause."

This is put briefly by Vaalmeeki in the speech of the ocean king.

Maalyavaan, the aged *Raakshasa,* tried his best to impress on Raavana the error of his ways. He said:

"Your time of good fortune is over. Your sins have begun to bear their fruit and to dim your radiance. You can trust no longer the boons you have obtained from the gods. Make peace with your enemies. Look at the army that has arrived, the terrible host of *Vaanaras* and bears. Look at this wonderful causeway so quickly built. It seems to me, this Raama is Vishnu himself come in human form."

Raavana had no patience with such talk. "Your words are wormwood in my ear," he cried. "It looks as though you too have joined my enemies. Are not human beings well known to be weaklings? Why are you afraid of this wretched man driven into the forest by his father? And he relies on the support of monkeys and bears! Of such a man you are afraid. Really I am ashamed of you. Or could it be that you cannot bear to see me happy? Why do you talk like this to me? I cannot bend before Raama. If it is wrong policy or wrong ethics, I cannot help it. You may take it that it is part of my nature and I cannot change it. I would far rather die fighting than sue before Raama for peace!"

Maalyavaan replied: "Consider well and do what you think best". And he returned home, uttering the usual benedictory words: "Victory to the King! Victory to Raavana!"

The old man was Raavana's grandfather.

Raavana carefully stationed his warriors. He posted Prahasta at the eastern entrance, Mahaapaarsva and Mahodara at the southern entrance and Indrajit, his illustrious son, accomplished in the arts of secret magic, at the western entrance, while he decided himself to guard the northern entrance. Viroopaaksha, the mighty, was appointed commander of the army within the city.

Having ordered the disposition of his forces and chief warriors, he felt he had ensured victory. As his end was approaching, he listened to no one and foolishly believed himself unconquerable. The ministers raised shouts of victory to please the King and then dispersed.

Raama, Sugreeva, Vibheeshana and others held a council of war. Vibheeshana duly laid before the council the information gathered by scouts who had gone out and watched Raavana's arrangements.

"In numbers, strength and courage", Vibheeshana said, "the army now mobilised by Raavana surpasses that with which he opposed Kubera. Still I have no doubt of Raama's victory".

Raama distributed his forces to meet Raavana's disposition and assigned to each commander the task he was to perform. He ordered Neela to meet Prahasta at the eastern gate. Angada was to meet Mahaapaarsva and Mohodara at the southern entrance. At the western entrance Hanumaan was to encounter Indrajit, the master of black magic.

"Lakshmana and I shall meet Raavana, the terror of the world, and we shall direct the assault on Lanka. Sugreeva, Jaambavaan and Vibheeshana shall stay behind with our main army".

The army rested for the night on mount Suvela. The following morning, standing on the mountain top, they took a good look at Lanka.

The beautiful city on the summit to Trikoota seemed as if suspended from the sky. Behind the thick fortress wall the *Raakshasa* army stood sentry, looking like another massive wall.

Observing the great and beautiful buildings in Lanka, Raama was moved to pity. And he said:

"Alas! Because one person, drawn by the noose of Time, has committed a sin, all this wealth and the whole *Raakshasa* race must now be destroyed. Alas that this scion of a noble race should forget his real greatness and pull death and destruction on himself and his people!"

Raama continued: "However, we should now bend all our thoughts to the task before us – to win this battle and destroy Raavana. There will be much confusion in the course of the battle. The *Raakshasas* will try to deceive us with many disguises. Let the *Vaanaras* and bears retain their own shape while fighting. Vibheeshana and his friends alone need assume human forms, like Lakshmana and myself. The *Raakshasas,* our enemies, will never take the form of man or monkey. They would think it beneath their dignity to do so. If we stand together maintaining due order we can know who is who, slay our enemies and help our friends".

CHAPTER LXVII

THE BATTLE BEGINS

THE *Vaanara* army descended from mount Suvela and entered the forest adjoining the city of Lanka. As the army burst in like a flood the frightened beasts and birds in the forest fled in all directions.

Vaalmeeki describes the scene and the event in his characteristic style. Gazing now from below at the mountain fortress and the divinely beautiful city constructed by Viswakarma, Raama was again filled with wonder and exclaimed:

"Oh what beauty! What wealth."

The *Vaanaras,* for their part, noted the *Raakshasa* warriors' strength and readiness for battle, the thick walls and mighty engines of defence.

From Lanka, all ready for war, the sounds of drums and trumpets issuing from the city increased and eagerness of the *Vaanaras* for battle. The army stood in ordered divisions as instructed by Raama.

Looking at Lanka he said, "Lakshmana! Look at the beauty of the city."

His mind turned to Seeta. She would have known by now, he thought, of his arrival with the army and her depressed heart must have revived. But he spoke nothing of this and engaged himself in the arrangements for the army.

Suddenly, and without any noise or warning to any one, Sugreeva sprang up into the sky and alighted on the terrace on top of tower in Lanka, where he saw Raavana seated clad in red royal robes like a thick black cloud seen in the red evening sky.

The scar, caused by the tusk of Indra's elephant, shone like a crescent moon on his chest.

"Raavana! You are caught!" cried Sugreeva. "I am a friend and servant of Raama. This is your last day!"

And he sprang on him, knocked off his crown and gave him a mighty blow. The two wrestled together for a long time. Both were experts in wrestling. All the tricks of that science were tried by each. Raavana was at the end of his resources and so he discarded wrestling and took to magic and Sugreeva seeing this disentangled himself and sprang back to where Raama was.

The *Vaanara* leaders, who saw the son of Soorya return, shouted praises and made a great noise of congratulations at this derring-do, rash and reckless no doubt, but such as would give the *Raakshasas* some idea of the mettle of the foes they were up against.

Raama too was glad to see that Sugreeva had returned safe. Observing bleeding wounds on his body, he said:

"Sugreeva! I am filled with wonder and joy at this, your valorous exploit. But what you did was not right. It is not for a king to rush into risks. How could you suddenly and without consulting anyone take such a dangerous course?"

Sugreeva confessed his fault.

"True, it was improper to rush into battle without consulting you. But when I saw the villain who had insulted Seeta I was overwhelmed by anger and forgot my duty."

The *Vaanara* army surrounded Lanka on all sides in the manner laid down by Raama.

Raama sent for Angada and said to him:

"Prince! Take this message from me to
Raavana. Tell him, 'Great sinner, your end is
approaching. Raama waits at your fortress gate,
ready for battle. Trusting to the boons of the gods,
you have become proud and wicked. You have
troubled the world too long and committed too many
heinous sins. The time has now come for the world to
be cleansed of you. If you come out into the open and
fight and die in battle, your sins will be washed away
and you will gain a place in the world above as a
hero. But if you love your life, humbly restore Seeta
to her lord and beg for forgiveness. Then you can
escape with life. Whatever happens, you are fit to be
king no longer. The kingdom of Lanka now belongs
to Vibheeshana. He is worthy to rule and protect his
people. If you are not willing to surrender and seek
safety, then have your obsequies performed in
advance. Bid final farewell to all your dear
possessions in Lanka. Prepare for death. Come out
and meet Raama in battle.' Go, Angada, deliver this
message to Raavana."

As instructed by Raama, bold Angada delivered
his message: "Listen, Raavana. I am the son of Vaali
whom you no doubt remember. I have come as
Raama's messenger. The time for your liberation
from sin has come. You may, if you choose, die in
battle and attain the *swarga* of brave men, cleansed
of your foul sins. But if life is dear to you, you may
beg it of Raama after humble surrender, and he
never refuses mercy to a suppliant. If what I have
heard about you is true, you will elect to fight, which
means you choose to die. I would advise you to take
last leave of your kinsfolk and complete your

obsequies yourself, for none of your race will be left to perform them. Look your last on lovely Lanka!"

Raavana's rage flared up like a flame. "Seize him, kill him, the villain!" he shouted.

At once, two *Raakshasas* caught hold of Angada. He rose in the sky carrying these two *Raakshasas* on either side of him and then flung them down.

He rose higher up and, coming down, kicked and broke off the tower of the king's palace. Then with a single leap he returned to where Raama was.

Dazed by Angada's exploit, the *Raakshasas* were filled with fear, but they did not disclose it. Raavana, too, heaved a heavy sigh at the sight of the broken turret. He looked on it as a bad omen.

As soon as Angada returned, Raama issued orders to the army to begin the assault on Lanka.

CHAPTER LXVIII

SEETA'S JOY

SUKA, the *Raakshasa* scout, went and reported to Raavana: "I did my job according to your instructions. But my efforts were fruitless. They were rough with me and made me feel thankful to be allowed to come back. Raama, to whom it was sport to slay Viraadha, Kabandha, Khara and others, has arrived with the army of Sugreeva. They have somehow come to know of the place where Seeta is held captive. The bears and monkeys have crossed the sea and are standing ready for battle before Lanka. The visible earth is covered with this army. There is nothing to be gained by discussions and debates. Their hate can only be quenched with our blood, Oh King! Consider well what needs to be done, and do it."

And then he added with fear, in a suppressed voice: "We may yet escape if Seeta is restored."

Raavana was enraged. "What did you say?" he cried. "Let no one talk to me of Seeta being restored. They do not know my strength who talk like this. I can slay the gods, the *Vaanaras,* the *Gandharvas* and the *Yakshas.* My darts can burn up Indra himself and Yama too. Wait and see how this wretched fellow Raama and his army will be destroyed."

Raavana believed what he said. He had dwelt long on his previous achievements and, filled with pride, had become foolishly obstinate.

Then he sent for two of his ministers and told them: "Scouts have come and reported that a large army has built a causeway to Lanka and has come over here. This is indeed strange news, but as yet nothing serious has happened. Go and observe the enemy and bring me a full and detailed report of their strength."

Accordingly, the spies assumed the shape of *Vaanaras* and coming to Raama's camp and mixing with the other *Vaanaras* looked all around. But Vibheeshana, discovering their disguise, caught hold of them and produced them before Raama. They pleaded that they were mere messengers sent by their king and prayed for release.

Raama said: "Show them our army. Let them have a good look around before they return. Give them free and full opportunity to see our strength. And, Oh you *Raakshasa* messengers! When you go back to Raavana, tell him, 'The strength on which you relied when you carried Seeta away is to be put now to the test. Your fortress, your city and your army will be destroyed. Raama's darts will pierce your body.' Yes, convey this message to your king."

The spies heard Raama's words and agreed to convey them to their master. Then, impelled perhaps by force of habit, they said: "Victory to thee!" The *Vaanara* army took this to be a fine omen.

The spies went back to Raavana and said: "O King! We were discovered by Vibheeshana and were in fear of death but Raama would not let them kill us and he ordered our release. King! Our enemies are determined. Raama and Lakshmana, Sugreeva the *Vaanara* king and Vibheeshana, they are all of one mind. It is difficult for us to prevail against an army led by such warriors. We have seen Raama, son of Dasaratha. He impressed us as being by himself strong enough to destroy our city and army. We have seen the courage of the *Vaanaras* and their eagerness for battle. It is not expedient to try the fortune of war with them. It seems best to restore Seeta to Raama. Do consider what should be done."

Of course the advice was sincere and well meant, but Raavana could not control his fury. He said: "Even if the whole world turns against me, I shall not yield to fear. Even if all the *Devas, Gandharvas* and *Vaanaras* join together to oppose me, I shall not return Seeta. Because you were thrashed by the enemy, you give me this cowardly advice. Faint hearts! Where is the foe who can vanquish me?"

Having said this, he went to his high tower and himself surveyed the enemy's strength. His ministers and officers were with him.

Those who had gone out to reconnoitre described at length the *Vaanara* chiefs and the army behind them. They recounted the strength of that huge army of bears and monkeys gathered together from the far-flung forests, mountains and river-valleys of the world. They spoke of their physical strength and courage, their firm devotion to Raama, their unity and eagerness to slay the *Raakshasas*. All those that had gone confirmed this.

"Look!" one of them said. "That majestic and graceful youth with matted locks and bow in hand is Raama. See how he looks round him with eyes of love and command and how his glances seem to brighten the quarters and to fill all with devotion and confidence. The mighty armed warrior near him is his brother Lakshmana, a peerless bowman and Raama's second soul. And look! Next to him is Sugreeva, wearing Vaali's garland. He is the equal of Vaali himself. There, next to him you see Vibheeshana, your brother. It is not easy to vanquish such warriors. Consider well and take all steps necessary for victory in such a situation."

As the ministers extolled the strength of the enemy, Raavana's rage grew more and more furious. This is the way of a tyrant. The wise king is never angry with those who bring him true information or with ministers who give him good advice for his welfare. But now Raavana's mind was confused. He had no use for the true facts or good advice.

His thought followed a strange line. He judged Raama by his own character. He thought that, if Seeta could be made somehow to yield to him, Raama would return home disgraced and broken-hearted. Hence he resolved to make one last attempt with a different technique. He sought the help of a *Raakshasa* sorcerer. "Oh. Lightning-Tongue!" he said (that was his name), "prepare a head which looks so exactly like Raama's that it will deceive Raama's nearest and dearest into believing it is his. When I send for you, come to the park where Seeta is incarcerated and place it before her."

The sorcerer agreed to do as he was bidden.

Then Raavana went once again to the Asoka park and tried to beguile Seeta. "Your husband and his army have been destroyed," he said. "My warriors crossed the sea and attacking Raama and his monkeys, when they were tired and asleep, killed them all. A warrior has brought the head of your husband for me to see. Why do you still persist in your obstinacy? Join my wives now and reign as their chief. Take my advice and become the queen of Lanka."

Then he ordered a *Raakshasa* to fetch Vidyut-Jihva, the sorcerer. The conjurer came and

placed before Seeta a head which looked exactly like
Raama's.

Startled by the sight, Seeta cried, "So then, is
this my fate?" and broke into hopeless lamentation.

Meanwhile, Raama's army had come close to
Lanka and the ministers and generals sent word to
Raavana desiring an immediate interview. Raavana,
therefore, had to leave Seeta at once and go to
Assembly Hall.

Raavana's presence was necessary to keep up
the sorcerer's illusion. So, when he left the place, the
apparition of Raama's head vanished like smoke.
Sarama, who was a lady of the royal household
posted as a companion of Seeta, consoled her
explaining the illusion. She said: "No one has killed
Raama. He has reached Lanka at the head of a great
army. They have built a wonderful causeway across
the sea and are all over Lanka like a submerging
sea. The *Raakshasas* are panic-stricken. Raavana is
only trying to deceive you through sorcery."

Sarama went on to inform Seeta: "Several
ministers advised Raavana to restore you and save
himself by unconditional submission. But he would
not listen to them. 'I may perish in battle,' he said,
'but I will not bow, a suppliant before Raama. I shall
never return Seeta and sue for peace.' Holy lady! No
harm can come to you, Raama will surely triumph
and this wicked one will perish."

Even as Sarama was speaking, the noise of the
drums and trumpets sounded by the *Vaanara* army
reached Seeta's ears and filled her with joy. She
knew that Raavana's end was near. The *Raakshasas*
in Lanka heard the same noise and trembled in fear.

CHAPTER LXIX

SERPENT DARTS

RAAVANA was duly informed that Raama's *Vaanara* host surrounded Lanka like a tumultuous sea. In an angry mood he went up the tower of his mansion and surveyed the scene. On every side he saw *Vaanara* warriors who had armed themselves with trees and boulders. He wondered how he could destroy this vast invading force.

At the same time, Raama saw the city of Lanka guarded by the *Raakshasas*. He could see with his mind's eye the sad figure of Seeta held captive within those walls. He ordered an immediate assault.

Shouting 'Victory to the *Vaanara* king!' 'Victory to Raama and Lakshmana!' 'Perish *Raakshasas*!,' the *Vaanara* army rushed on the doomed city. Some hurled big boulders against the fortress wall and on the city gates. Others armed with huge trees torn up by the roots rushed on the *Raakshasas*.

Then Raavana sent forth a big army. He commanded it to go out and slay at once all the *Vaanaras*. They beat their drums and blew their trumpets till the sky resounded. They fell upon the *Vaanaras*. The *Vaanaras* used boulders and trees and their own nails and fists to oppose the *Raakshasas*. Thousands fell dead on either side. The field was covered with blood and mangled bodies.

Besides this gruesome engagement, there were many duels between individual warriors. Angada encountered Indrajit like Rudra against Yama. There was a duel between the *Raakshasa* Prajangha and Sampaati, one of the companions of Vibheeshana. Hanumaan fought a duel with Jaambumaali,

Neela with Nikumbha, Lakshmana with Viroopaaksha, and so on. The chariot and horses of Indrajit
were destroyed and Angada received a blow from the
mace of Indrajit. Jaambumaali hit Hanumaan with
his weapon and Hanumaan smashed his chariot to
pieces. The *Raakshasas* concentrated their attack on
Raama, and fell in thousands under his arrows.

Vidyunmaali aimed his darts at Sushena. The
latter smashed with a rock the chariot of the
Raakshasa. Vidyunmaali jumped out with his mace
and attacked Sushena who crushed him to death
with a rock. In this way many warriors fought and
many died.

The battle raged throughout the day. And at
night the *Raakshasas* would not stop fighting. The
battle became fierce. Blood flowed in streams. There
was terrible slaughter on both sides. Angada
attacked Indrajit, slew his horses and charioteer and
smashed the chariot. The *Vaanaras* admired the
skill and strength of their prince and raised shouts of
joy. All the warriors in the army praised the
Vaanara prince's prowess. Indrajit lost his temper
along with his chariot and resorted to sorcery.
Making himself invisible he aimed many darts at
Raama and Lakshmana who were greatly harassed
at this attack from a foe whose whereabouts no one
could discover and who seemed to shower deadly
missiles from all sides.

Then Indrajit shot serpent darts at Raama and
Lakshmana. Bound by them, they could not move
and lay helpless on the battlefield. They looked at
one another, wondering what to do. Lakshmana's
grief at Raama's plight was great. As for the
Vaanaras they stood round in mournful bewilder-
ment.

Indrajit congratulated the *Raakshasa* army and
returned to the city. Exulting in his victory, he went
to his father and announced that the story of Raama
and Lakshmana was over. Raavana was beside
himself with joy. He embraced his son and praised
his prowess.

The *Vaanara* warriors, wounded and downcast,
seeing Raama and Lakshmana laid low, concluded
that all was over. Vibheeshana, who saw Sugreeva
standing helpless and forlorn, put courage in the
Vaanara king. "It is foolish to lose hope," he said.
"Look at Raama and Lakshmana. Their faces are
still bright. They are not dead. Be not afraid. Soon
they will recover from this swoon and resume
fighting."

The chief took heart and did everything to save
the army from panic. The ranks were re-formed with
their respective chiefs.

Meanwhile Raavana had it proclaimed in
Lanka that Raama and Lakshmana had been slain
by Indrajit. He sent for his women and said to them:
"Go at once and inform Seeta that Raama is no more;
that the two princes lie dead on the battle-field and
the *Vaanara* army is destroyed. Also, to convince her
finally, take her in the *Pushpaka Vimaana* and show
her the battle-field from above. Let the obstinate one
see for herself what has happened. Seeing that she
has now no one to look to besides myself, she will
turn to me."

The *Raakshasis* did as they were told. From the
Vimaana Seeta saw the field of battle. She saw
Raama and Lakshmana lying motionless on the
ground with their weapons scattered by their side.
She was filled with grief. She thought that it was
now all over and cried: "To this end has fate brought

me, giving the lie to the predictions of saints and astrologers that I would live as a happy wife and mother and a glorious queen. Poor Kausalya! Who shall console you now? Like one who, having crossed the ocean, gets drowned in a little pond, these warriors, who had done so much, lie dead now. Oh princes! How did your divine weapons fail you? Alas, all-powerful is destiny!"

When Seeta was thus in the desperation of utter sorrow, Trijata, her *raakshasi* companion, who was looking closely at the motionless figures of the princes, suddenly burst out: "Dear Seeta, there is no cause for grief. Neither your husband nor Lakshmana is dead. Look at their faces. Is this how the dead look? They are bound by a charmed weapon and are unconscious for a while. Look at the orderly array of the army. Have courage. Be not frightened." Her words fell like nectar in Seeta's ears. The *Vimaana* returned to Lanka and Seeta was taken back to the *Asoka Vana*.

In time, the force of the arrows charged with sorcery weakened. Raama opened his eyes and sat up. Though sorely wounded, he recovered his strength by an exercise of will-power and sat up. He looked at his brother lying on the ground and cried out: "Alas! What is the use of victory now for me? Why did I bring you, dear brother, with me to the forest and get you killed like this? How can I return without you to Ayodhya? You used ever to console me in my sorrow. You are silent now when I face the greatest sorrow. How can I survive you? Where in the world is a warrior like you? One can replace anything lost, but where can I find anyone to fill your place?

"Like Kaartaveeryaarjuna with his thousand hands, you with your two hands discharged showers of arrows and slew the *Raakshasas*. How could death come to you? You came with me into the forest, and now I shall repay my debt to you by joining with you to the abode of Yama. I confess defeat. The word I gave to Vibheeshana cannot be fulfilled. Oh *Vaanara* king! Return to Kishkindha with all your warriors. You have worked hard for me. You have fulfilled all the duties of friendship. You have my gratitude. But there is no use in more of you dying. Go back to your city. Let me perish here." Thus did Raama lament in helpless grief.

Then Vibheeshana arrived there, mace in hand. Seeing his huge dark form, the *Vaanaras* imagined it was Indrajit again and started to fly.

In another part of the battle-field Sugreeva and Angada were discussing. "Why are the *Vaanaras* thus beginning to scatter in fear? What has happened?" asked Sugreeva.

Angada answered, "Do you not know that Raama and Lakshmana are lying wounded?"

Sugreeva said: "It is not that. Look at the way they are running helter-skelter. There must be some other reason for it."

Then he learnt that the *Vaanaras*, who had suffered at the hands of Indrajit, mistook Vibheeshana for him and were frightened. He sent Jaambavaan to rally the troops by disabusing them of this fear. Vibheeshana looked at Raama and Lakshmana. When he saw them wounded, covered with arrows all over, and unable to fight, he broke down crying, "It is all over. What more is there to do?"

Sugreeva turned to Sushena, his uncle, and said: "Take Raama and Lakshmana to Kishkindha. I shall kill Raavana, redeem Seeta, and bring her there."

Sushena answered: "There are herbs which can heal the wounds of the princes and restore them to health. Some of us know where these herbs are to be found. Here is Hanumaan. If you send him, he will fetch the herbs."

As they were speaking, the sea and air were churned up by a mighty wind and the great bird Garuda burst into view.

When Garuda arrived, the serpent darts that covered Raama and Lakshmana disappeared instantaneously. They were all venomous serpents which had become arrows through the magic of Indrajit and had bound the princes' bodies. When their inveterate and dreaded enemy Garuda appeared, they took flight. Then Garuda gently stroked the bodies of Raama and Lakshmana and restored to them their full strength. The wounds were all healed and they rose up, stronger and more radiant than before.

And Raama asked: "Who are you, my benefactor?" He did not know that he was Vishnu and Garuda was his own bird on which he always rode.

Garuda answered, "I am your good friend, and old companion. Glory be yours! Let me go now. When the battle is ended, we shall know each other better." Saying thus Hans bird flew away.

Seeing Raama and Lakshmana fully recovered and ready for battle, the *Vaanaras* were enthusiastic once again and resumed attacking Raavana's fortress.

CHAPTER LXX

RAAVANA'S DEFEAT

RAAVANA from within his palace was surprised to hear, borne on the wind, the jubilant acclamations of the *Vaanaras*, who he thought must then be mourning their vanquished leaders and slaughtered comrades. He turned to the *Raakshasas* standing beside him and asked: "What has happened to make the *Vaanaras* so happy? Something strange must have occurred. Go and find out what it is."

Some *Raakshasas* climbed up and looked over the wall. Returning, they said to Raavana with fear and trembling: "King! The *Vaanara* army, led by Sugreeva, is attacking the fortress with spirit. Raama and Lakshmana are both alive. Like elephants they have broken their bonds, Raama and Lakshmana have shaken off the *naaga* darts with which Indrajit bound them and have rejoined the army and are raging about the field like hungry lions. The darts of Indrajit have proved futile."

Raavana's face fell. He was filled with anxiety and said: "I marvel at what you say. No one till now has escaped these darts. If those weapons were powerless against these men, we are indeed in danger."

Then with an excess of anger, he shouted: "Listen, Dhoomraaksha! Why should I worry when you are here? Get together all the men you want. Go at once and destroy these two little men and return quickly."

Dhoomraaksha was indeed happy and proud to be thus singled out by the king. He took a party of warriors and, issuing out of the fort, came into contact with the group who, under Hanumaan, were attempting to enter the western gate. In the battle that ensued there was great slaughter on both sides. In the end Dhoomraaksha was slain by Hanumaan. A few *Raakshasas* escaped into the fortress, but most of them lay dead without.

News of this discomfiture filled Raavana with uncontrollable fury. He hastily summoned Vajradamshtra and said: "Oh bravest of warriors, go without delay and destroy these wicked fellows."

Vajradamshtra bowed low before the king and followed by a mighty army sallied out of the southern gate and encountered Angada.

The *Raakshasas* under the leadership of Vajradamshtra waged grim battle and slew countless *Vaanaras*. And yet the *Vaanara* army stood firm and would not withdraw. Armed with boulders and trees, they killed innumerable *Raakshasas*. On both sides the fighting was intense. In the end, Angada and the *Raakshasa* chief fought hand to hand for a long while. Vajradamshtra was slain, gallantly fighting to the last, and the *Raakshasas* fled in confusion. The *Vaanaras* surrounded Angada and shouted in exultation.

Then Raavana ordered Prahasta: "Send Akampana and let him have the most terrible *Raakshasas* to accompany him. Let them go and slay Raama, Sugreeva and the *Vaanara* army. None can resist Akampana's might and skill."

Accordingly, Prahasta sent an army of *Raakshasas* under the leadership of Akampana. True to his name, Akampana was firm and immovable in battle. He had chosen his weapons and his warriors carefully. As he advanced, bad omens met him. But neither he nor his followers regarded them. The noise of their challenge rose above that of the ocean.

A great battle ensued. Blood flowed in streams. Dust rose and cut off the sun plunging the earth in portentous gloom. The slaughter on both sides was enormous. Kumuda, Nala, Mainda and Dwivida attacked Akampana who defended himself with courage.

The battle went against the *Vaanara* warriors and they were about to take flight when Hanumaan arrived bringing courage and hope. Akampana sent forth a shower of arrows at him but Hanumaan took no notice and lifting a huge boulder and swinging it above his head hurled it at Akampana. The *Raakshasa's* darts intercepted the stone and reduced it to powder. Then Hanumaan grew in size and shone with blinding brightness like the sun and uprooting a big tree attacked the *Raakshasa* with it and slew him. The *Raakshasa* army was smashed like a forest in an earthquake and the survivors fled in panic from the fatal field that was strewn thick with the dead, and spread the dismal news in Lanka. The *Vaanaras* surrounded Hanumaan and uproariously expressed their admiration.

Raavana's spirits fell when he received the news of Akampana's death but he found strength in anger and desperation and began thinking of new plans. He went round the defences of the city again and took counsel with Prahasta, the commander-in-chief.

"We must break this *Vaanara* siege. We should issue at the head of the whole army and slay the *Vaanara* chiefs. Myself, Kumbhakarna, yourself, Indrajit or Nikumbha — one of us five — should take up the responsibility of leading the army out of the fortress. Are we to be afraid of monkeys? Why! They used to flee in terror on merely hearing the roar of a *Raakshasa*. They do not know the science of war. They are unskilled brutes. How have they managed to stand all our attacks?"

Prahasta answered humbly: "Things have happened as we foresaw. We respectfully submitted long ago that it would be best to restore Seeta and make peace. But I am bound to obey you. I am prepared to sacrifice my life, my family, my all for your sake. I shall lead this sortie, if such is your pleasure."

A huge army was collected and everything was got ready for a supreme endeavour, including the solemnisation of special rites and sacrifices.

Then Prahasta marched out to the beating of drums. Evil omens presented themselves. But he disregarded them.

Seeing the great army led by Prahasta issuing out of the eastern gate of the fortress, the *Vaanaras* roared with joy and prepared for battle.

Like moths rushing at a flame, the *Raakshasas* fell on the *Vaanara* army.

"Look," said Raama, "there comes out a *Raakshasa* at the head of an enormous army. Who is he?"

Vibheeshana replied: "It is Prahasta, the commander-in-chief of Raavana. A third of the imperial army is his to command."

Then ensued a grim battle between the *Vaanaras* armed with boulders and trees and the *Raakshasas* equipped with swords, spears, bows and axes. Exchanging showers of stones for arrows and grappling in death grips at close quarters, both sides fought fiercely, deluging the field with blood.

Prahasta's followers, Naraantaka, Mahaanaada, Kumbhahanu and others, were opposed by Dwivida, Durmukha and Jaambavaan and slain. There was a prolonged battle between Prahasta and Neela. At last Prahasta armed with a massive mace of iron rushed towards Neela. Neela, for his part, uprooted a big boulder and with it smashed Prahasta's head killing him on the spot.

The *Raakshasa* warriors fled in all directions. After this great victory, Neela went to Raama and Lakshmana and, bowing low, told them what happened. Raama and Lakshmana praised his prowess and congratulated him.

Some of those who fled from the battle carried to the *Raakshasa* King the news that Neela, son of Agni, had slain Prahasta. Raavana was beside himself with rage and grief. "My warrior chief", he said, "who could vanquish Indra and his host of gods, has been killed by these *Vaanaras*. We cannot treat this lightly. We must destroy Raama and the monkey host." So saying, Raavana got into his chariot and went forward like Rudra, the destroyer. Seated in his radiant chariot and issuing from the city, Raavana beheld the *Vaanara* army and heard their uproar which resounded like the ocean.

Seeing a new *Raakshasa* army issuing out, the *Vaanaras* stood ready to receive them with stones and trees in hand. Vibheeshana pointed out the *Raakshasa* warriors one by one to Raama. "There, seated in the chariot and shining like the rising sun, is Indrajit." And so he went on from one renowned warrior to another till he came to Raavana. "There, in the big chariot, radiant like the sun, sits the ten-headed Raavana."

Raama beheld the majestic and glowing form with interest and pity. "A great warrior no doubt," he said, "but he is so wicked that he has to be slain."

Raavana attacked innumerable *Vaanaras* and laid them low. Neela opposed Raavana gallantly but was felled by a fire-dart. Hanumaan attacked Raavana with violence and the two fought an equal battle for a while but Raavana could not be subdued and wrought great havoc in the *Vaanara* host.

There was a fight between Lakshmana and Raavana. Lakshmana fell down unconscious but Hanumaan intervened and carried Lakshmana away to Raama.

Then Raama, riding on Hanumaan's shoulders, gave battle to Raavana. The *Raakshasa* king was sorely wounded. His golden crown was broken. So was his chariot. Deprived of every weapon, he stood before Raama.

"You may go now," said Raama. "You have fought well today. Go away and rest and come back tomorrow, refreshed and with weapons." And Raavana retreated shamefacedly to the city.

CHAPTER LXXI

THE GIANT IS ROUSED

WHEN Raavana returned humbled and dejected, the gods rejoiced foreseeing the speedy end of their troubles. Raavana entered the fortress, ashamed and anxious. After deliberating a while, he recovered his courage and ordered his sleeping brother Kumbhakarna to be roused.

As the result of a curse, Kumbhakarna used to sleep for months together and he had gone to sleep just a few days before the events last narrated. Raavana asked his ministers to spare no efforts to rouse Kumbhakarna at once and get him ready for battle.

"All my penances have proved futile. It looks as though the prophecy of the *rishis* will be fulfilled," thus said Raavana to himself, but rooted in his determination to fight to the last he issued orders as if he were certain of ultimate success:

"Let the warriors guard the fortress on all sides. My brother is sound asleep. He sleeps blissfully, unaware of my anxiety. He will not wake up for months together if left alone. It is only nine days since he started sleeping. Rouse him at once. If he wakes up and goes to the battle, the enemy will be surely scattered. Who can stand before my Kumbhakarna? If he wakes up and opposes my enemies in battle, I need have no fear."

Raavana's officers and their servants accordingly went to Kumbhakarna's palace. They knew that as soon as he opened his eyes, he would be rapaciously hungry. So they first prepared and piled up mountains of food for him. Then they made a

great din beating drums and blowing conches. Many
Raakshasas exhausted themselves pushing and
shaking the huge body of the *Raakshasa*. The noise
that they made with their shouts and drums and
trumpets filled the sky and frightened all the birds
and beasts of Lanka, but Kumbhakarna in his sleep
heard nothing. The *Raakshasas* worked hard at
rousing him. They made elephants walk on his body.
They took cudgels and belaboured him.

At last his eyelids opened slightly and as one
might brush away a mosquito while still asleep he
pushed them all aside and yawned.

Kumbhakarna was thus disturbed in his sleep
which otherwise would have been months long. But
before he could find out the cause for this, he began
to eat and drink. The heaps of meat and the pots of
blood and wine kept ready for him were finished.
When his hunger was somewhat mitigated the
Raakshasas approached him to acquaint him with
the situation.

Raavana's minister Yoopaaksha said: "My
Lord, we have been defeated in battle and stand in
grave danger. You will remember the quarrel about
Seeta. The *Vaanaras* with Raama and Lakshmana
have arrived and are breaking through the fort. They
have slaughtered and defeated our army which
never knew defeat before. Lanka is surrounded by
the *Vaanara* host as by an ocean. Raavana himself
went to battle but he retired from the field having
had the worst of it. It was our good luck that he
escaped with life."

Hearing this, Kumbhakarna was beside himself
with rage. "This very instant I shall go and destroy
this enemy. I shall kill the *Vaanaras* and drink the

blood of Raama and Lakshmana. After finishing this first, I shall go and wait on the king."

The ministers were delighted to hear this furious speech but pleaded with Kumbhakarna that he should first see the King and take counsel with him as to what should be done.

Kumbhakarna agreed, washed his face and then strode in sombre majesty to the hall of the king of Lanka.

The *Raakshasas* standing on the Royal highway felt new courage and joy as they saw him pass, and bowed low before him and showered flowers on him. He entered the palace and stood in the presence of Raavana. Rejoicing at the arrival of his peerless brother, Raavana stepped down from his throne and embraced him.

"What can I do for you, brother?" asked Kumbhakarna. "Why did you get my sleep broken? What makes you afraid? Tell me who is tired of life and wants to be turned into a corpse!"

"Brother! You do not know what has happened," said Raavana. "You were lost in sleep. The man Raama has become a real menace to me. He has built a dam across the sea we considered inviolate and now the *Vaanara* army surrounds Lanka like another sea. Our warriors who sortied out and met them have been defeated and almost annihilated. It is for you now to save us from destruction and I know you can do it. You have put the gods to rout. I know your love for me. I know your keenness and your courage in battle. Go at once and annihilate these enemies and help us in our need and save Lanka."

Kumbhakarna, when he heard Raavana's words of anxiety, was moved at first to fury against

the enemy but soon he remembered the whole story
and Raavana's vain-glorious confidence in his
invincibility and that made him smile a little
bitterly. He said: "Excuse me, my brother. The
warning we gave you when you consulted us went
unheeded. Our fears have come true. You rejected
the good advice we gave you. Now, you suffer the
consequences of your error and your sin. You
brought away Seeta. What else can happen, when,
driven by lust, one acts without thinking? If you so
desired, and you had the confidence and strength, it
would have been wise first to have slain Raama and
Lakshmana and then seized her. You have done
things without due thought and in the wrong order.
When one acts without seeking or regarding the
advice of wise and faithful friends and kinsmen, it is
no wonder if he runs into danger and ruin. Did you
not know that these things must follow? Should not
a king understand who gives him good advice and
who bad?"

Raavana did not like all this lecturing. He had
no use now for lessons in ethics or politics. His face
flushed with anger but he controlled himself and
said: "Brother! The time is now past for such talk.
What I need now is not your criticism but your
prowess. What is done has been done and it is
useless discussing whether it was just or unjust,
wise or unwise. The question now is what we should
do in our present predicament. It is your duty now to
use your strength and skill and ward off the present
disasters resulting from past errors. He is a true
friend and a true kinsman who helps one out of the
trouble that has been brought on oneself, may be
because of folly. If indeed you care for me, the time is
now to show it by helping me instead of commenting

on my conduct. I depend on your strength and prowess. Out of your infinite courage, give me comfort."

Kumbhakarna was moved by this appeal. "Have no more care," he said. "I am your brother and can never forsake you. Rest assured that Raama and Lakshmana are dead. I shall scatter and slay their monkey army. I shall fling at your feet the head of Raama and you shall see the *Vaanara* King's blood flowing on the battle-field. Raama can only approach you, if he does, over my dead body and that is not possible, for no one can vanquish or slay me."

Kumbhakarna's pride swelled. "No matter who the enemy is," he cried, "I shall destroy him. Be he Yama or Soorya or Agni, I shall eat them all up." In this mood he rushed out to the field of battle.

The sudden waking from deep slumber had completely upset his temper, but when his consuming hunger and thirst had been appeased, he had recovered his balance and spoke wisdom to Raavana. Again seeing Raavana's plight, fraternal affection and pity made him forget everything else.

Raavana was pleased. "O my true warrior! O my brother! What a friend in need I have in Kumbhakarna!" he exclaimed, confident that Kumbhakarna would return triumphant and he now felt like one recovering from a mortal sickness.

Kumbhakarna armed with his great spear was about to go to battle alone, but Raavana stopped him and sent an army to aid him. He covered his brother's big body with jewels and garments and blessed him saying: "Go my hero! Destroy the enemies and return victorious."

Tall and mighty-limbed Kumbhakarna, covered
with shining jewels, was radiant like Trivikrama
himself. He circumambulated his brother, bowed
and marched out spear in hand at the head of a great
army, amidst the plaudits of the *Raakshasas*, and
under a shower of flowers and good wishes. As the
huge form of Kumbhakarna, a giant even among the
Raakshasas, was seen stepping across the fortress-
wall like Yama at the end of time or some great
natural cataclysm, the *Vaanaras* were frightened
and started fleeing in all directions. With great
difficulty their chiefs rallied them and put them in
battle formation.

CHAPTER LXXII

IS THIS NAARAAYANA HIMSELF?

RALLIED by Angada, the *Vaanaras* recovered courage, re-formed in battle order and prepared to receive Kumbhakarna. They hurled rocks at him and dealt heavy blows with trees plucked by the roots but he disregarded them all with a smile on his face went on despatching the *Vaanaras* with a methodic cruelty that was most terrifying. Some of them retreated to the newly-built dam, while others tried to save themselves by concealing on the shore of the sea and the forests.

Once again Angada had to encourage the *Vaanara* chiefs and warriors and get them to re-form and attack Kumbhakarna.

Dwivida, Hanumaan, Neela, Vrishabha, Sarabha and other chiefs attacked Kumbhakarna fiercely. But he disregarded them all and continued his ruthless slaughter of the *Vaanaras*. Angada himself received a blow, as a result of which he fainted and fell on the earth. Sugreeva was struck down. Picking up the unconscious *Vaanara* king, Kumbhakarna carried him with joy towards Lanka. The *Raakshasa* army rejoiced greatly and raised a triumphant uproar. Kumbhakarna wished to make a present of the captive *Vaanara* king to his brother Raavana.

As Kumbhakarna went through the Royal highway carrying in triumph the unconscious *Vaanara* king, the *Raakshasas* and their women-folk, standing on the terraces, showered flowers and poured sandal paste. This incidentally revived Sugreeva. He opened his eyes and wondered where he was and what had happened. He soon understood

everything. He then began to bite with his teeth and
tear with his nails the ears and nose of the
Raakshasa who was carrying him. Worried thus
Kumbhakarna threw him down intending to crush
him with his feet. But when he was once on the
ground, Sugreeva jumped and flew off across the sky
and arrived at the place where Raama was.

Hanumaan was sure that Sugreeva would
somehow come back. Foreseeing this escape of
Sugreeva, Hanumaan had rallied the *Vaanara* ranks
and prepared them again for battle.

Grim and gruesome with torn nose and ears,
Kumbhakarna, like a great blood-red evening cloud,
and raging like Death at the end of Time, returned to
the battle-field with a huge iron mace in his hand.

None could now stop Kumbhakarna. He began
to kill and devour the *Vaanaras*. The whole army
began to disappear in this way. They tried to deter
him by climbing on his mountain-like body and
tearing at it with nails and teeth but without effect
for he shook them off as if they were flies. None of
the *Vaanara* chiefs could hold him.

Lakshmana tried with his arrows to obstruct
his progress but the *Raakshasa* passed him by and
rushed forward to face Raama himself.

For a long time Raama kept aiming powerful
darts at the *Raakshasa*. The arrow that pierced the
seven *sal* trees and the adamantine body of Vaali
was powerless against Kumbhakarna.

Sending sharper and stronger arrows, Raama
wounded the arms and the feet of the *Raakshasa*,
but nothing short of death would stop him. His legs
were cut off, but legless he moved about on his

stumps and went on with demoniac ferocity, fighting his brother's battle.

At last, Raama cut off his head with an arrow.

The severed head, carried by the force of Raama's arrow, rose into the sky and red with blood fell in Lanka like a hill with its forests aflame. The news was carried to Raavana.

"Your brother Kumbhakarna, terrible like all-destroying Death at the end of Time, has entered the heaven of slaughtered heroes! He killed thousands of *Vaanaras* and for a long time kept the army of Raama and Lakshmana in fear of destruction. But at last he was slain by Raama himself, and deprived of arms and legs his mutilated body lies like a mighty tree disfigured by a forest fire. A part has fallen into the sea. Another big part blocks the entrance to the fortress. The severed head, flying across the sky, has dropped in the city and is lying there. Your beloved brother is gone to Heaven!"

When the *Raakshasas* told this tale, Raavana felt that his own life had left him. He swooned.

After recovering consciousness, he cried in grief and anger: "Ah mighty warrior! How could you go to Yama's world leaving me behind? My right hand is cut off! How did Raama kill you, you whom in the whole world no enemy dared approach? I see the gods rejoicing in their heavens at your fall. The *Vaanaras* are dancing with delight. Of what use is this kingdom to me? Why should I cling to life when my dear brother has left me? Yes, I have to torture and slay the man who killed this dear brother of mine!"

Then with sudden and futile remorse he wailed: "Alas! Why did I refuse to listen to Vibheeshana?"

Trisiras and his other sons tried to console Raavana.

"What is the use of lamentation" they argued. "You who have secured from Brahma strength and armour, why should you fear or lose yourself in grief?" And Trisiras himself set out for the battle-field. Many others eagerly followed him, riding on elephants and chariots.

A great battle ensued. Naraantaka, riding on horse-back, spear in hand, wrought havoc among the *Vaanaras* and was proceeding towards Sugreeva. Angada opposed him and killed him and his horse.

Likewise, Devaantaka and Trisiras were slain by Hanumaan, and Mahodara by Neela. Atikaaya fell a prey to Lakshmana's arrows. But before they died, these four had fought like four Yamas and caused enormous loss to the *Vaanara* forces.

When Raavana heard that Atikaaya was dead, he was bewildered.

"This is incredible! These my warriors, firm and mighty like mountains and irresistible like the ocean, have been slain one by one by these enemies. Those, who till now have never known defeat, have been defeated and lie dead in the battle-field. There stand my foes who have broken out of the serpent entanglements with which my peerless son Indrajit had bound them. I cannot explain the marvel of this man Raama's strength. May it be that he is Naaraayana himself?"

Thus bewildered, Raavana lost heart. He wanted that the enemy forces should not enter the fortress and in particular should not enter the *Asoka Vana*. He supervised the defences again and returned to the palace, downcast and forlorn.

CHAPTER LXXIII

THE DEATH OF INDRAJIT

INDRAJIT comforted his father. "Why should you worry when I am here alive?" he said and gathered an army, and with it made another sortie.

He swooped down on the *Vaanara* forces and killed and wounded thousands of them. They were helpless against his fury. The *Brahmaastra* of Indrajit was effective against even Raama and Lakshmana who were tied up by it. They lay unconscious on the ground and the *Raakshasa* prince went straight to his anxious father with the glad news of this achievement.

Vibheeshana rallied the *Vaanara* leaders who had scattered in all directions and put hope and courage into them.

Jaambavaan, who was more dead than alive, moved slowly among the *Vaanaras*, inquiring, "Is Hanumaan alive?"

"Yes, I am here," said Hanumaan, and bowed low before Jaambavaan.

"My son," said the old *Vaanara*, "proceed northwards at once across the sea to the Himaalaya range. Between the Rishabha and Kailasa peaks, there is the Hill of Herbs. In that hill-top are four medicinal plants. If you bring them here quickly, Raama and Lakshmana and the *Vaanara* army will recover consciousness. Their wounds will be healed and they will fight again. Do this without loss of time. Only you can do this."

Accordingly, Hanumaan sprang up into the air and moved fast. He reached the hill described by the venerable Jaambavaan and as he could not identify the plants, he carried the whole hill and returned with it to Lanka.

Even with the approach of the Sanjeevi hill, Raama and Lakshmana and the *Vaanaras* felt the darts slip off their bodies. Their wounds healed and they became strong and stood up.

The battle was resumed. Taking counsel with Raama, Sugreeva now chose a few *Vaanaras* and ordered them to enter Lanka and set fire to the city.

Towards midnight they entered the city with torches. They attacked and overpowered the sentry and set fire to the palaces and turrets of Lanka. Houses in their thousands were reduced to ashes. The proud city was reduced to a mass of ruin.

Vaalmeeki describes this incident in detail. It reads very much like the destruction of cities in modern battles with which we are now familiar.

Seeing Lanka being burnt down by the *Vaanaras*, Raavana was furious and sent to the battle-field Kumbha and Nikumbha, the sons of Kumbhakarna, together with Yoopaaksha and other *Raakshasa* warriors.

After another terrible battle, Kumbha was slain by Sugreeva and Nikumbha by Hanumaan. Makaraaksha, son of Khara, who opposed Raama, fell to his fiery arrows. Many more mighty *Raakshasas* perished. Then, at the bidding of Raavana, Indrajit went once again to the battle. He rose into the sky and became invisible. Thus he fought again unseen by the *Vaanaras*. Indrajit, by his necromancy, created a *maaya*-Seeta and, putting her in a chariot, took her before the *Vaanara* army and seemingly killed her in their presence.

Deceived and horrified by this, the *Vaanaras* asked themselves: "What good is it now to continue this war?" They left the field and went to Raama with the heart-rending news.

As a result of this trick, Indrajit gained time to perform an *aasuric* sacrifice. Raama and Lakshmana, like the *Vaanara* warriors, believed that Seeta was dead and were lost in grief. They were completely bewildered and helpless when Vibheeshana came and enquired what had happened.

He listened to their story. Then he said:

"You have been deceived. Never would Raavana allow Seeta to be killed. This is only a trick of sorcery. Indrajit tries to defeat you through magic. Having given up all hope of achieving success by normal means, he has gone to perform an *aasuric* sacrifice of great power. If he completes it, we cannot vanquish him. We should therefore go and obstruct the sacrifice. Let Lakshmana go at once and mar Indrajit's purpose."

Accepting this advice, Raama sent Lakshmana who was accompanied by Hanumaan and other *Vaanaras,* besides Vibheeshana. They went to the spot where Indrajit was about to offer oblations to evil spirits. The sacrifice was interrupted and a long and fierce battle ensued. Ascending his chariot, the son of Raavana sent forth his arrows. Standing on Hanumaan, Lakshamana did the same. As they were well matched in strength and skill, the battle lasted long. The chariot of Indrajit was destroyed in the course of the combat and both the heroes stood on the ground and continued the battle.

At last, Lakshmana used the *Indra-astra* spell and uttering the name of Raama discharged the fatal arrow. The head of Indrajit was severed and fell to the ground and as it fell, it shone like fire. The *Devas* and *Gandharvas* showered flowers from the heavens.

Lakshmana then went to Raama. He was wounded all over and bleeding. He walked slowly, supported by Jaambavaan and Hanumaan. Raama had already heard the news of the death of Indrajit.

"Lakshmana!" he cried, "this is the end of the *Raakshasa* race. You have achieved it."

Lakshmana modestly stood back but Raama seated him on his lap, kissed his head and gave vent to his joy.

"You have performed a mighty deed, impossible for anyone else. You have deprived Raavana of his right hand. Who in the world can equal you or Vibheeshana or Hanumaan? I have no more care. You have vanquished the conqueror of Indra. I feel I have already recovered Seeta."

The news reached Raavana that Indrajit had been slain by Lakshmana. When he heard that Vibheeshana helped Lakshmana in slaying Indrajit, his grief and anger swelled and the tears he shed burnt where they fell. And from his mouth issued fire.

"Alas, my son! O peerless warrior! O hero! Vanquisher of the great Indra! Has Death won after all? Have you entered the heaven of heroes? But I should not grieve," he said.

But the father's heart would not thus be denied, and again he cried: "What! Is Indrajit gone? The world is now empty for me. Oh son, you have left your mother Mandodari and your dear wife and myself heart-broken and disconsolate. Nothing remains to us now but revenge and despair.

"It is best to kill Seeta, the cause of all this tragedy. My son killed the *maaya*-Seeta. Now I shall kill the real Seeta herself." So saying he rushed out, sword in hand, intending to do it.

Some fierce *Raakshasas*, seeing Raavana issuing out in anger, applauded him with joy; but the minister Supaarsva was horrified and appealed to Raavana's better sense and what was due to himself as a man and a king.

"King!" he cried, "how dare you think such a thought? How can you do it? Oh, Lord of ten heads! Brother of Kubera! Are you thinking to kill a woman? Are you going to incur this shame and sin? Can you thus be tempted by anger? You have mastered the *Vedas* and all the sciences. You have performed many penances. How can you end up with such a thing as this? Who is equal to you? Let us direct our anger against Raama. It will be new moon tomorrow. Gather all your armies, issue out of Lanka, slay Raama and Lakshmana and achieve victory. Then take Seeta. Put on the armour you have secured from Brahma. Ascend your chariot and go to battle."

Raavana felt that Supaarsva was right and his words were good. Seated on this throne, he was silent for a while, lost in profound meditation. Then he addressed the commanders with folded hands, saying:

"Go now with all your strength and slay Raama. If even you fail, I shall go myself and destroy him."

Never before had he been so courteous and humble when dealing with his officers. Adversity had taught him this lesson. Mounted on chariots that shone like the hills on the evening horizon and on the back of great elephants and beautiful horses, Raavana's army went in full force for the great battle.

The *Vaanaras* tore up rocks and trees and attacked the *Raakshasas* fiercely. The *Raakshasas* returned the attack with equally grim ferocity.

The *Vaanaras* jumped about everywhere and worked havoc among the *Raakshasas*, their chariots and animals. Each of the *Raakshasas* was surrounded by many *Vaanaras* and slain.

The *Raakshasas* too did not spare the *Vaanaras* whom they killed in tens of thousands.

Raama bent his bow and sent showers of arrows against the *Raakshasas* who destroyed their army like a raging fire. Warriors only saw their companions fall. They could not see Raama because of the shower of arrows. Their fear conjured up a multitude of Raamas, who dealt death in all directions.

Countless elephants and horses perished. Thousands of chariots were broken. The *Raakshasa* army was destroyed, all but a handful who fled into Lanka.

The *Devas, Gandharvas* and *Siddhas* sang the praise of Raama from above. In Lanka, the *Raakshasa* women clung to each other and lamented loudly that Raavana's folly should have brought this great calamity on them.

CHAPTER LXXIV

END OF RAAVANA

THERE was wailing in every house in Lanka. In Raavana's breast grief, shame and anger seethed like a raging sea. He had so far sent his commanders and men in detachments, and, brave as they were, they had been destroyed in detail. This had been the result of overweening confidence in his invincibility and contempt for the enemy, most of whom fought with no better weapons than sticks and stones; but repeated reverses had brought him no wisdom. He had not even disputed the passage of the sea but allowed the enemy a lodgment in his island. But negligent and reckless as a general, he was brave and finally resolving to fight himself and with his sole strength to destroy the foe, he set out. He had full faith in his prowess and in the efficacy of the boons he had secured and he went forth with confidence mounted on his divine chariot which was drawn by eight horses and filled with all manner of weapons accompanied by a division of *Raakshasa* chariot-warriors.

As Raavana issued out of Lanka, the sun seemed obscured by an unpredicted eclipse, and foul birds and beasts of the night roared at large with weird ill-omened cries; but disregarding it all, Raavana drove out to battle accompanied by Viroopaaksha, Mahodara and Mahaapaarsva.

The mighty *Raakshasa* warriors who followed Raavana were mown down by a deadly flight of arrows and chunks of rocks and presently Raavana found himself facing Lakshmana, who tried to oppose his further progress. Forcing his way past

Lakshmana, Raavana precipitated himself against Raama with all the pent-up fury of hatred and revenge and strove to overwhelm him with a spate of arrows.

Raama easily baffled these arrows with his own and struck Raavana repeatedly, without however being able to penetrate his armour. Thus they fought, these supreme bowmen, each bent on slaying the other and using increasingly potent missiles of secret power, while the gods in heaven looked on with marvel and admiration. Neither hero had met such another opponent before and on both sides admiration was mingled with wrath.

Raama pierced with his darts every limb of Raavana. And yet he did not fall.

Then Lakshmana and Vibheeshana together attacked Raavana. Furious with his brother and determined to kill him, Raavana flung at him a powerful weapon; but intercepted by a dart of Lakshmana it broke into two and fell on the ground like a burning brand. Once again, Raavana aimed another mighty *sakti* against Vibheeshana. This too Lakshmana intercepted. Then Raavana hurled a *sakti* at Lakshmana crying, "Now you are dead!"

Under its impact Lakshmana fell down unconscious on the grund.

Not observing this, Raama went on keeping up his pressure against Raavana. While the battle raged between the two, the *Vaanara* leaders took counsel and sent Hanumaan once again to the Hill of Herbs to save the life of Lakshmana.

For the second time, Hanumaan flew north-wards and, not wasting time searching for the plants, returned with the whole mountain. Lakshmana got well again and resumed his part in the battle.

Meanwhile, Maatali brought his master Indra's chariot to the battle-field for the use of Raama.

"Indra, king of gods, has sent this for your use," said Maatali. "Be pleased to ascend this chariot and destroy Raavana, the enemy of the gods!"

Raama bowed to the gods, circumambulated the divine chariot and ascended it. Then followed a wonderful battle.

Sorely wounded, Raavana fell unconscious and, noting this, his charioteer quietly took him out of the battle-field.

When, a little later, Raavana recovered consciousness, he was highly wroth with his charioteer for taking him out of the battle-field and insisted on being taken back to face Raama. The grim battle began again. Every *astra* was met by another. In new and wonderful ways, the two chariots moved and the two warriors fought for a long time, while both armies watched the spectacle with breathless admiration and anxiety.

Maatali, the charioteer, whispered into Raama's ear: "The *Raakshasa's* end is approaching. Delay no further. May I remind you of *Brahma-astra*?"

Raama uttered the spell and sent the *Brahma-astra*. Though the *Raakshasa's* ten heads had often been cut off before, they had grown again and baffled Raama. The *Brahma-astra,* emitting flames, went towards Raavana and pierced his chest, where was enshrined the secret of his invincibility, and shattered it.

Then the bow slipped from the *Raakshasa's* hand and he fell down from the chariot and lay stretched on the battle-field.

The gods blew their trumpets. Raama and his chariot were covered by a heap of flowers showered from the heavens. Lakshmana, Vibheeshana, Jaambavaan and other warriors surrounded Raama, lost in joy and adoration.

When the first flush of triumph was over and Vibheeshana looked at his brother's body, the natural call of blood and memories of boyhood days when Raavana and he had loved and played quite overwhelmed him and he burst into lamentations over his lost brother.

"O warrior!" he cried. "O brother of heroic deeds! O scholar learned in all *Shaastras*! O valiant and famous King of kings! Your great arms are now sprawling helpless on the ground! Self-willed and self-deceived, surrounded by bad advisers, you would not heed my warning! The worst I feared has happened now! You reaped what you sowed and you lie on the bare ground, O once mighty ruler of the *Raakshasas*!"

To Vibheeshana thus lamenting, Raama spoke:

"Raavana fought like a true warrior and fell fighting like a hero! Death has washed his sins. It calls for no mourning. Raavana has entered Heaven."

Raama cleared all confusion from Vibheeshana's mind and bade him do the funeral rites for his departed brother.

Said Raama: "It is for you now, his brother, to do the rites. Death ends all enmity. I, his former foe, even I can rightly perform his obsequies. Your brother is my brother too, is he not?"

The women of Raavana's palace came to the field to mourn. They led the queen Mandodari, who looked like the goddess of Grief incarnate. The crowned Queen and beloved wife of Raavana was in utter desolation.

"Indra, King of gods, dared not face your anger," she cried. "The *Rishis* and the *Gandharvas* at the very sight of you fled in fear in all directions. And now a mere man, a wanderer in the forest, has brought you down! I do not understand how this could have happened. Truly, Fate is all-powerful! But lord, my lord, I warned you long ago. Did I not tell you that this Raama is no mere human being, but someone greater than Indra or Agni or Yama, whom you could not vanquish? This Raama is no other than Vishnu Himself in human form, God without beginning, middle or end. Even when we heard that he stood on the ground riding no car and slew your brother Khara in Janasthana, did I not say this? When Hanumaan penetrated Lanka, the impenetrable fortress, and laid it waste, I knew the truth. I begged you not to incur their enmity but you would not listen.

"Why did you cast lustful eyes on chaste Seeta? This was the madness that drove you to your death! Was it not a heinous sin to carry her off when she was alone? Death in the form of Seeta drew you to your end! Seeta and Raama are now re-united and happy after their brief separation, but me and all our race you have thrust for ever into the depths of sorrow. Alas, my husband, my lover. You lie dead. Yet how beautiful you look with your body pierced by Raama's darts, covered with blood and dust of battle!

"What should I do now? I had a lord who was the Lord of Lanka! I had a son who had vanquished Indra. They have left me and I am a mere helpless widow without friends or home!"

Lamenting thus, Mandodari fell on Raavana's body and lay unconscious.

CHAPTER LXXV

THE END

VIBHEESHANA was crowned King of Lanka in a magnificent ceremony. The new Lord of Lanka came out to the *Vaanara* camp and bowed low before Raama.

Then Raama said to Hanumaan: "With the King's permission, enter Lanka and tell Seeta what has happened." Hanumaan accordingly took permission from Vibheeshana and went to *Asoka Vana* to convey the news to Seeta.

Seeta's joy was beyond words. She was silent.

"Why, mother," asked Hanumaan, "why do you not speak?"

"What is there to say, my son?" she answered. "How can I repay my debt to you? Your wisdom, your valour, your prowess, your patience, your humility are all your own. None in the world can equal you." As she said this, her eyes filled with tears of gratitude and affection.

Hanumaan looked at the *raakshasi* women who had guarded Seeta and turning to Seeta said: "I wish to slay these cruel women who troubled you. Do give me leave!"

"No, my son," she answered. "Who in the world is blameless? It is the part of noble souls to be compassionate towards all — sinners as well as good people."

These words of Seeta are treasured like nectar by generations of pious men. The worst of sinners, clinging to the golden feet of the Mother, can gain forgiveness.

"These *Raakshasis*," she continued, "but carried out their master's orders. How are they to blame? Their king is dead and has paid for his crime. It is unjust to punish these *Raakshasis* now."

All that Hanumaan could find to say in reverent admiration was that what she said was only what was worthy of Raama's wife.

"What message am I to carry to Raama?" he asked.

"I am eager to be in his presence," she answered. "That is all."

Hanumaan returned to Raama and gave an account of his visit. For some reason Raama's face now darkened and with lack-lustre eyes he fell into a brown study. A little later he turned to Vibheeshana and said:

"Ask Seeta to bathe and bedeck herself and bring her here."

When the message reached Seeta in the *Asoka Vana,* she said "I would rather go as I am."

"Not so, my lady," said Vibheeshana, "the Prince's orders should be obeyed."

So, after a bath and bedecked with jewels and seated in a palanquin, Seeta went to the camp.

When he heard that Seeta was coming, Raama woke up from his meditation. Events of the past rose like waves and battering against his mind threw it into a wild commotion of shame, grief and joy.

As Seeta's palanquin was taken through the great concourse of *Vaanaras,* they thronged round the princess and caused confusion. It was made worse by the *Vaanara* leaders trying to push them aside and make way for the palanquin.

"Let no one be kept away," said Raama. "These dear *Vaanaras* have stood and suffered for me. Seeta will be pleased to see me surrounded by such friends. Let no one be pushed away."

Raama's face showed a strange transformation of mind. None of those around him, not even Lakshmana, could understand.

Alighting from the palanquin, Seeta, with downcast eyes, proceeded towards Raama. "*Aaryaputra*," she said and sobbed, unable to speak more.

Aaryaputra in Sanskrit means beloved and noble one and is an intimate form of address of wife to husband.

"I have slain the enemy," said Raama. "I have recovered you. I have done my duty as a Kshatriya. My vow is now fulfilled."

Incomprehensible and wholly unexpected were these words that he uttered. His face darkened for some reason. Then he spoke even harsher words.

"It was not for mere attachment to you that I waged this grim battle but in the discharge of duty as a Kshatriya. It gives me no joy now to get you back, for dubiety envelops you like a dark cloud of smoke."

"What do you wish to do now?" he continued. "You must live alone, for we cannot live together. You can stay under the protection of any of our kinsmen or friends. How can a Kshatriya take back a wife who has lived so long in a stranger's house?"

Seeta looked at Raama. Her eyes flashed fire.

"Unworthy words have you spoken!" she said. "My ears have heard them and my heart is broken. The uncultured may speak such words but not one nobly born and brought up like you. Your anger, it seems, has destroyed your understanding. My lord does not remember the family from which I come. Janaka, the great seer, was my father and he brought me up. Is it my fault that the wicked *Raakshasa* seized me by force and imprisoned me? But since this is how you look at it, there is but one course open to me."

Then turning to Lakshmana, "Fetch the faggots, Lakshmana, and kindle a fire," she said.

Lakshmana, who had been watching Raama's behaviour in dismay and indignation turned to look at Raama's face seeking his orders, but Raama did not say "No" to Seeta's request nor show any sign of softening.

Obeying Seeta, Lakshmana kindled a big fire and the princess, with eyes fixed on the ground, circumambulated her lord and exclaimed:

"Ye Gods, I bow before you. Oh *rishis*, I bow to you. Oh Agni, you at least know my purity and will take me as your own!"

With these words she jumped into the flames. And wonder of wonders! The lambent flames were crowded with celestial figures, for all the gods came and assembled there; and Brahma spoke:

"Naaraayana! Mighty God that took human form to slay Raavana! Is not this your own Lakshmi?"

Agni, God of fire, rose in his own body out of the flames and lifting Seeta in his arms with all her clothes and jewels untouched and intact, presented her to Raama.

Raama said to Brahma: "Who am I? All that I know and can tell is that I am Raama, son of

Dasaratha. You know who I am and whence I came and more; it is you who must inform me."

Saying this to Brahma, Raama accepted Seeta fire-proved.

"Think you that I did not know your irreproachable purity? This ordeal was to satisfy the people. Without it, they would say — would they not? — that Raama, blinded by love, behaved with a strange weakness and broke the rule of well-brought-up men."

So saying he drew her to his side.

Then Dasaratha descended from above and, placing the Prince on his lap, blessed him.

"My child!" he said to Seeta. "Forgive my son. Forgive him for the wrong he did you to preserve the *dharma* of the world. God bless you!"

Indra gave his boon, and the *Vaanaras* who died in battle for Raama regained their lives.

Raama and Seeta, now re-united, ascended the *Pushpaka* which carried them swiftly in the air with their friends, the *Vaanara* warriors and Vibheeshana, to Ayodhya.

As they travelled in the sky, "Look there!" he said, "that is the causeway built by Nala." Again, "Look there, that is Kishkindha," he said, "where I met and made friends with Hanumaan and Sugreeva." And Raama pointed out to Seeta the spots where he and Lakshmana had wandered disconsolate and related to her all his unforgettable experiences.

Alighting at Bharadvaaja's *aashrama*, they sent word in advance to Guha and Bharata.

The city of Ayodhya swam in a sea of joy. Raama and Bharata met. Planning for Bharata's sake, ambitious Kaikeyi and her hunchback maid had contrived and concocted plots. But now, as Bharata bowed at the feet of Raama, a joy deeper than what they had planned for him was his. What kingly crown could equal the joy one found at Raama's feet? What sovereignty could bring one the glory that was now Bharata's for ever?

The Vaishnava hymns exalt Bharata even above Raama for a spotless mind and unblemished unselfishness. For fourteen years till the return of Raama, Bharata installed Raama's *paadukas* and administered the kingdom as a devotional exercise in the service of his brother.

Now that Raama was crowned King as his father had wished, Bharata's penance was at an end and his heart was filled with joy.

Of Hanumaan, need anything be said? Receiving from Raama a pearl necklace, Seeta put it round Hanumaan's neck. He saw the smile of divine grace brightening her face as she did so. What more could Hanumaan desire?

I have re-told in brief compass the story of the Prince of Ayodhya as sung by Vaalmeeki. Those who read or listen to the tale, it is said, will be saved from sin and sorrow.

Sri Sankara, the master of wisdom, has said that, if one keeps in one's heart the son of Dasaratha and meditates on him with reverence, one's sins will all be burnt up as chaff in a fire.

After the *avataar* of Raama, the lord appeared again among men with greater *soulabhya* (easy accessibility) as Govinda. He lived among shepherds as one of them and served Arjuna as a chariot driver.

At the end of the *Gita,* the Lord says to Arjuna:

"Believe in Me as sole refuge, cast aside all doubt and come unto Me. I shall save you from all sins. This is truth, friend. Cast off your fear."

This promise of Sri Krishna is addressed to all of us. We, like Arjuna, have our doubts and fears in the Kurukshetra of life and this assurance of grace is for all of us, for we are all dear to Him.

EPILOGUE

ON one occasion Gandhiji and I were talking about a girl very dear to both of us. I said: "How did she get all these ideas and phrases of love without having read any of present-day love stories?"

Gandhiji said in answer: "But has she not read the *Raamaayana*? Is the *Raamaayana* not a love story too?" This struck me as profound. Then we turned to other matters.

Dasaratha's troubles began with love. Then the love of Raama and Seeta is the theme and substance of *Ayodhyaakaanda.*

In love that is not opposed to *dharma,* we find a manifestation of God. So was it affirmed by Sri Krishna when he explained his manifold being to Arjuna. The *Raamaayana* has, for its twin theme, love that is opposed to *dharma* also. The *Raamaayana* is undoubtedly a great love story.

Those who regard the *Raamaayana* as an allegory interpret Seeta as the individual soul and Raama as the Supreme Being. God seeks and pursues the human soul till He secures it. He is eager to save us; it is enough if we just do not obstruct or resist.

There are also other interpretations and applications of the *Raamaayana.* Seeta, the female counterpart of the Supreme Being, is the embodiment of compassion and grace. Compassion is the Supreme Mother and she is enthroned in the heart of the Lord. When she casts her merciful glance on us, we reach the feet of God. Paarvati's function in relation to Siva and Lakshmi's in relation to Hari are both identical, and are just variations of the same creed of dependence on God's grace. God as Father and God as Mother are not distinct. If the Lord were to be parted from compassion, our plight would be just that of Raavana who separated Seeta from Raama.

The quality of the Lord's compassion can be understood from the experience of true human love.

Many meanings can be read in the *Raamaayana* and its beauty appreciated in many ways as from a real diamond many glorious colours emanate. Seventeen months ago I began writing these weekly chapters not without fear and trembling. This week I close it full of thankfulness for the health of body and peace of mind which enabled me to complete this humble service. Learned men will no doubt find many faults in what I have written. But they must be glad also that it has done some good.

A word to the children who read these chapters. I have told the story of the Prince of Ayodhya mainly for your sake. Grownup people may read Vaalmeeki and Kamban. Those who know to sing can render with joy the sweet songs on Raama given to us by Tyaagaraaja. But this story that I have told can be read direct by you, children, without anyone's help.

You should look upon Raama, Lakshmana and Hanumaan like your own fathers and elder brothers who are by your side ever eager to help you. Grow to be like Bharata, Lakshmana and Hanumaan, good and brave souls, full of love and strength.

Mothers too, I know, have been reading this story with joy. This has been a great encouragement to me. They can understand why I have told the story in simple words and short sentences for the

sake of our children. Everything we do, we do for the
sake of our children, do we not? Only women can
realise and re-live the experiences and feelings of
Seeta. The story of Seeta as told by Vaalmeeki and
Kamban can be fully appreciated only by women.
Only they can fully appreciate the courage of
Jataayu and the prowess of Hanumaan. Seeta's
sorrows have not ended with the *Raamaayana*. They
go on, still, in the lives of our women.

In the Raama *avataar*, Raama did not know
that he was God incarnate. Krishna knew that he
was an *avataar* and acted accordingly. We should
read the two stories with this difference in mind. The
despair and grief that the man Raama experienced,
Krishna never knew. When he sucked at the
demon-woman's breast or was bound with a rope and
thrashed for mischief, he cared not nor grieved.
Standing weaponless in the battle-field, he led the
warrior to destroy the wicked. In every episode of
Krishna we see the difference between the two
avataars.

I have followed the story of the Prince of
Ayodhya as told by Vaalmeeki. There was a legend
current among people, I think even before
Vaalmeeki's time, that after recovering Seeta, for
fear of scandal, Raama sent her away to live in the
forest.

This pathetic episode must have sprung from
the sorrow-laden imagination of our women. It has
taken shape as the *Uttarakaanda* of *Raamaayana*.
Although there is beauty in the *Uttarakaanda*, I
must say my heart rebels against it. Vaalmeeki had
disposed of this old legend through the fire ordeal in
the battle-field. Even that ordeal does not seem to

me as consistent with Raama's character. It is painful to read it.

As the Prince returned from Mithila he met Parasuraama. I have heard it said that with that meeting Parasuraama's *avataar* came to an end. Likewise, it should be held, I think, that Raama's *avataar* came to an end with the slaying of Raavana. After that battle, Raama remained only as a King of the Ikshvaaku race.

On this theory, Raama's treatment of Seeta after the battle and in the *Uttarakaanda* can be explained simply as the behaviour of a king in accordance with the customs of the times.

But, how can we comment on a work composed thousands of years ago and coming down to us in palm-leaf manuscripts subject to corruption? If, even after the fire-ordeal in the *Yuddhakaanda*, it is said in the *Uttarakaanda* that Seeta was sent to the forest, we may take it that it mirrors the voiceless and endless suffering of our womenfolk. Sorrow and joy are both alike the play of God. God himself took with him his divine spouse, the embodiment of his own supreme compassion, into the world of men and women, and enacted with her a great drama of joy and sorrow in the *Raamaayana*.

Rain falling from the heavens flows into the rivers and flows down to join the sea. Again from the sea the water is sucked up by the sun and rises to the sky, whence it descends again as rain and flows down as rivers. Even so, feelings and values rise from the people and, touching the poet's heart, are transformed into a poem which, in turn, enlightens and inspires the people. Thus in every land the poets and their people continuously reinforce each other. The tenderness and purity and the untold sufferings of women took shape as the *Uttara Raamaayana*. Like an unflickering lamp, it throws light on the quality of their hearts. Whether the epics and songs of a nation spring from the faith and ideas of the common folk, or whether a nation's faith and ideas are produced by its literature is a question which one is free to answer as one likes. Does a plant spring from the seed or does seed issue from the plant? Was the bird or the egg the first cause? Did clouds rise from the sea or was the sea filled by the waters from the sky? All such inquiries takes us to the feet of God transcending speech and thought.

One other point. In describing how Raavana carried off Seeta, Kamban differs from Vaalmeeki. In Kamban's *Raamaayana*, Raavana does not seize and carry Seeta as Vaalmeeki describes; without touching her he lifts her with the earth on which she stands. Kamban's version is followed by most popular expositors because this version is less painful to our feelings.

It is no sin or shame to an innocent woman if a villain behaves like a brute. Yet, mistakenly, we in this country look on the violence of a brute as causing a blemish to the woman's purity. It is in deference to this wrong feeling that Kamban departed from Vaalmeeki here.

For the same reason, Tulasi relates that the Seeta seized and carried off by Raavana was not the real Seeta at all but a palpable image of hers left behind by the real Seeta. Thus the story is told in all North India. During the fire ordeal, it is the *maaya*-Seeta that disappears and the real Seeta springs again and returns from the flames.

It was perhaps presumptuous on my part to have begun the task, but it was a joy to re-tell the

Raamaayana. Now, when it is over, I feel like one awaking from a dream of joy. When the Prince left the city, he felt no sorrow; it was only when he lost Seeta that he knew grief. So with me too. When I had to step down from high office and heavy responsibility, I did not feel at a loss or wonder what to do next. But now, when I have come to the end of the tale of the Prince of Ayodhya, the void is like that of a shrine without a God.

Let no one look upon work as a burden. Good work is the secret that keeps life going. While one should not hanker after results, life without work would be unendurable.

GLOSSARY

Aadisesha	.. ..	The primordial Serpent which is Lord Vishnu's bed.
Aagneyaastra	.. ..	A missile charged with an invocation to the God Agni (Fire).
Aaryaputra	.. ..	'Noble prince'; classical form of address by wife to husband, betokening love and respect combined.
Aashrama	.. ..	Hermitage.
Aasuric Yajna	.. ..	Sacrifice pertaining to Asuras. Demoniacal sacrifice and necromancy for gaining power.
Abhisheka	.. ..	Religious rite of pouring or sprinkling sacred waters on the head of one who is installed as King or First Prince.
Adharma	.. ..	Sin, unrighteous action, opposite of *dharma*.
Agni	.. ..	The God of Fire.
Alakaapuri	.. ..	The capital of Kubera, the God of Wealth.
Amaraavati	.. ..	The city in heaven where Indra has his abode.

Aruna	The God of Dawn, first son of Kasyapa Prajaapati and Vinata. He was born lame. Aruna was the elder brother of Garuda. Aruna is the charioteer of the Sun God.
Arundhati	Wife of Sage Vasishtha, a pattern of chastity.
Astras	Miraculous weapons whose power lay in the invocations with which they were charged.
Asuras	Enemies of the Gods.
Aswapati	King of Kekaya, father of Kaikeyi and grandfather of Bharata.
Aswini Devatas	Celestial beings, twin sons of Soorya
Avataar	Incarnation.
Bala, Ati Bala	Two invocations to obviate hunger, thirst and sleep.
Bhaageerathi	Another name of Ganga.
Bhaagyam	Fortune, prosperity.
Bhakta	Devotee.
Bhakti	Devotion to God, loyalty, faith.
Bheda	Diplomacy of playing one against another in the enemy camp.

Bhogavati	The capital of the Serpent King in the nether world.
Braahmana	The first of the four castes devoting their lives to study and teaching and the performance of religious ceremonies.
Brahma	The Creator, one of the Trinity.
Brahmaastra	The most powerful among *Astras*. See *Astras*.
Bhahmachaari	One who is in the first of the four stages in a Brahmin's life, the stage of study and practice of a disciplined life.
Brahmadanda	Holy staff of an austere Brahmin.
Brahmajnaana	The realisation of the Supreme Being, higher wisdom.
Brahmarishi	The highest type of sages.
Brihaspati	The preceptor of the Devas, the planet Jupiter.
Chaitra	The month falling in the second half of April and the first half of May.
Chandaala	Outcaste, untouchable.

Daana	.. ..	Gift, bribing of the enemy.
Daanavaas	.. ..	Sons of Danu and Kasyapa Prajaapati, enemies of Devas.
Daityas	.. ..	Sons of Diti and Kasyapa Prajaapati, enemies of Devas.
Daivam	.. ..	Divine, celestial, fate.
Danda	.. ..	Physical punishment, force used in meeting the enemy's tactics
Darbha	.. ..	A species of sacred grass used for religious rites.
Deva-Loka	.. ..	The celestial regions.
Devarishis	.. ..	Sages of Heaven
Devas	.. ..	Celestial beings, sons of Aditi and Kasyapa.
Dharma	.. ..	Duty as laid down by religion or custom.
Dishtam	.. ..	Indicated.
Gandharvas	.. ..	A class of semi-divine beings. Celestial musicians.
Garuda	.. ..	The bird king who is Vishnu's vehicle.
Govinda	.. ..	One of the names of Krishna.
Guru	.. ..	*Aachaarya*, preceptor.

Hari	One of the names of Vishnu. The second of the Hindu Trinity. Other names are Krishna, Mukunda, Maadhava, Kesava, Naaraayana.
Himavaan	The presiding deity of the Himalaya range.
Ikshvaaku	King of the Solar race from whom the name came for the race of Solar kings.
Indra	The chief and the king of the Gods
Indra-Astra	Missile charged with an invocation to Indra.
Jaambavaan	Leader of bears in the army of Sugreeva.
Jamadagni	A great sage, father of Parasuraama.
Jnaana	Spiritual knowledge, realisation.
Jnaani	A knower of Reality.
Kaama	Desire, usually referred to in relation to sex.
Kaamadhenu	The divine cow of Heaven. It was born of the Ocean when the Devas and Asuras churned it for Nectar.

Kaamavalli	.. ..	A name which Soorpanakha gave to herself.
Kaartaveeryaa-rjuna	.. ..	Son of King Kritaveerya. He had a thousand hands and his golden chariot could go wherever he wished. He was a contemporary of Raavana and had him imprisoned in his city. He was killed by Parasuraama for carrying away Kaamadhenu and killing Jamadagni.
Kailaasa	.. ..	The abode of Siva.
Kalpaka	..	A tree which issued out of the Ocean when it was churned by Devas and Asuras. A celestial tree which grants any wish to people who are under it.
Karma	.. ..	Action, the law that governs all action and its inevitable consequences on the doer.
Karma Yogin	..	One who practices the way of action for salvation.

Kasyapa	.. ..	A celebrated sage, son of Brahma. He had many wives through whom were born the various forms of life on earth.
Kekaya	.. ..	A country north-west of Kosala, the place where Bharata's maternal grandfather ruled. West of modern Punjab.
Kinkaras	.. ..	Soldiers, personal attendants.
Kinnaras	.. ..	Celestial beings like the Gandharvas, who played on musical instruments.
Kodanda	.. ..	Raama's bow
Kokila	.. ..	The cuckoo.
Krodha	.. ..	Anger.
Krouncha	.. ..	A bird
Kshatriya	.. ..	The second of the four castes.
Kubera	.. ..	God of Wealth.
Kurukshetra	.. ..	The battle-field where the Paandavas and Kauravas fought.
Kusa	.. ..	A kind of grass used in religious ceremonies.
Lakshmi	.. ..	The Goddess of Well-being — wife of Vishnu.
Leela	.. ..	Play, the unexplainable ways of Providence.

Maalyavaan	.. ..	The aged Raakshasa grandfather of Raavana.
Maalyavati	.. ..	A steam flowing by the foot of the Chitrakoota Hill.
Maaruti	.. ..	Name of Hanumaan being son of Marut, the Wind-god.
Mahaabali	.. ..	An Asura who became a powerful ruler and a rival to the gods. He was the son of Virochana and grandson of Prahlaada.
Mahaadeva	.. ..	One of the names of Siva.
Maharshi	.. ..	A great Sage.
Manmatha	.. ..	The God of Love
Mantras	.. ..	Scriptural verses, incantations.
Maya	.. ..	The architect of Asuras.
Meru	.. ..	A fabulous mountain around which the Sun is supposed to revolve.
Naaga	.. ..	Semi-divine serpents.
Naaraayana	.. ..	Vishnu.
Naarada	.. ..	The celestial rishi with lute.
Namah	.. ..	Bow, salutation.
Nandigraama	..	A village near Ayodhya where Bharata lived and ruled Ayodhya as a deputy of Raama.

Neeti Saastra	.. ..	Science of government and diplomacy.
Nikumbhila	.. ..	A cave and grove in Lanka where oblations were offered to Kaali.
Niyati	.. ..	Law.
Paaduka	.. ..	Footwear
Paaraayana	.. ..	Reading a Puraana or Epic as a daily devotional exercise.
Paarijaata	.. ..	A celestial flowering tree.
Paarvati	.. ..	Uma, wife of Siva.
Paataala	.. ..	The nether regions
Paayasam	.. ..	A sweet preparation of milk and rice.
Parasuraama	.. ..	The sixth incarnation of Vishnu who curbed the growing arrogance of the Kshatriyas.
Pinaaka	.. ..	Bow of Siva.
Pooja	.. ..	Worship.
Prajaapati	.. ..	The Creator.
Puraanas	.. ..	Sacred legends.
Pushpaka Vimaana	.. ..	Aerial chariot of Raavana which originally belonged to Kubera. Sitting in this chariot, one could obtain anything he or she desired.

Raajagriha	.. ..	The capital of the Kekaya country.
Raajasabha	.. ..	Council of State.
Raajasik	.. ..	Appertaining to the principle of activity, egoism, arrogance.
Raakshasas	.. ..	Evil-minded strong beings similar to Asuras
Raakshasi	.. ..	Feminine of Raakshasa.
Raghu	.. ..	An ancestor of Raama. He was a king of the Solar race.
Raja Rishi	.. ..	An eminent sage, a philosopher-king.
Rishabha	.. ..	A peak in the Himalayas.
Rishi	.. ..	A sage who has undergone severe austerities.
Rudra	.. ..	Siva.
Saama	.. ..	Peaceful approach to the enemy, negotiation.
Saastras	.. ..	Sacred lore.
Saatvik	.. ..	Appertaining to the element of equanimity as distinguished from the principles of activity and inertia.
Sanyaasini	.. ..	A female recluse, feminine of *Sanyaasi*

Sarama	.. ..	Wife of Vibheeshana. She and Trijata were the friends among the *Raakshasis* that Seeta had during her incarceration in the *Asoka Vana*.
Sarayu	.. ..	A tributary of the river Ganges on the North bank.
Satyaparaakr- ama	.. ..	Righteous and strong. Strong in righteousness.
Siddha	.. ..	One who has attained special powers through penance. A class of heavenly beings.
Siva	.. ..	One of the Hindu Trinity.
Sloka	.. ..	Couplet or Quatrain in Sanskrit.
Soorya	.. ..	The Sun God.
Soulabhya	.. ..	Ease of access.
Sri Krishna	.. ..	The eighth incarnation of Vishnu, who gave the *Bhagavad Gita*.
Sruti		Veda, Revelation.
Sukra	.. ..	The Guru or *aachaarya* of the Asuras, the planet Venus.
Swarga	.. ..	Heaven, where the blessed are received after death.

Taamasik	.. ..	Pertaining to the element of inertia.
Tamasaa	.. ..	A river flowing into Ganga.
Tapas	.. ..	Austerities and penances.
Tapasvi	.. ..	One who does *Tapas* or penance.
Tapasvini	.. ..	Feminine of *Tapasvi*
Tapasya	.. ..	Power obtained though *Tapas* or penance.
Tilaka	.. ..	A mark put on the forehead of women.
Trivikrama	.. ..	See Vaamana.
Vaamana	.. ..	The fifth incarnation of Vishnu to curb the power of Mahaabali. Vaamana became Trivikrama of huge stature who measured earth and Heaven in two steps.
Vaanaprastha	..	The third stage of a Brahmin's life retiring with his wife as a preparation for *sanyaasa*.
Vaayu	.. ..	The Wind God who was father of Hanumaan.
Vaidehi	.. ..	Another name of Seeta.
Vaishnava	.. ..	Appertaining to Vishnu or worship of Vishnu.
Vaitarani	.. ..	A terrible river in Hell.

Varuna	.. ..	The Lord of the Ocean.
Veda	.. ..	Scripture. It is in four books — *Rig-Veda, Yajur Veda, Saama Veda* and *Atharva Veda.*
Vidhi	.. ..	Law, decree of fate, that which is ordained.
Vidyut-Jihva	.. ..	'Lightning Tongued', a Raakshasa sorcerer
Vinata	.. ..	Mother of Garuda.
Vishnu	.. ..	See Naaraayana.
Visravas	.. ..	A rishi who was father of Raavana.
Viswakarma	.. ..	The celestial architect.
Vritra	.. ..	An Asura killed by Indra.
Yaaga	.. ..	Sacrifice, a religious ceremony accompanied by oblations.
Yajamaana	.. ..	He who performs a sacrifice, Master of Ceremonies.
Yakshas	.. ..	A class of celestial beings.
Yama	.. ..	God of Death.
Yojana	.. ..	A measure of distance equal probably to nine miles.
Yudhaajit	.. ..	Son of the King of Kekaya. Brother of Kaikeyi.
Yuvaraaja	.. ..	Prince-Regent.

BHAVAN'S BOOK UNIVERSITY
Ramayana Sahitya Series